BLACKLINE MASTERS

Developmental Reading Assessment®

K–3

Second Edition

Joetta M. Beaver

In Collaboration With Primary Classroom Teachers

PEARSON

Author's Acknowledgments

The revision of the *Developmental Reading Assessment K–3* is the result of much feedback, support, and encouragement from teachers, administrators, and other colleagues locally as well as across the United States and parts of Canada. Many thanks to the following people:

The Upper Arlington City Schools' primary classroom and reading teachers for their initial work in the creation of the *DRA* from 1988 to 1996

The 2005 Advisory Committee consisting of Kathy McCulloch, Carol Price, Becky Ruf, Patti Schlaegel, and Kathleen Taps for their expertise, insights, suggestions, and encouragement

All the teachers who field-tested the *DRA K–3* materials and gave us feedback and suggestions for improving the assessment

Beth Sycamore for her assistance with the revision of the teacher forms

Dr. Jane Williams and Dr. Clement Stone for their leadership in the *DRA* pilots and field-tests over the years

Kathleen Taps, Kathy McCulloch, Michelle Bell, Carol Price, and Sue Wilder for their help with the Training DVD.

A special thank you to Kathleen Taps for her help selecting examples of students' written responses for the Handbook.

The following people have contributed to the development of this product:

Art and Design: Dorothea Fox, M. Jane Heelan, Dan Trush, Jennifer Visco, Heather Wendt Kemp
Editorial: Teri Crawford Jones, Jaime Dritt, Donna Garzinsky
Inventory: Yvette Higgins
Marketing: Andreea Cimoca, Ken Clinton
Production/Manufacturing: Jeff Engel, Pam Gallo, Suellen Leavy, Ruth Leine, John Rosta
Publishing Operations: Carolyn Coyle, Jennifer Van Der Heide
Technology: Jeff Wickersty

PEARSON

1-800-321-3106
www.pearsonschool.com

Contents

Name/Date _____   Teacher/Grade _____

Scores: Reading Engagement ___/9   Oral Reading ___/9   Printed Language Concepts ___/6
Independent Range: 8–9   8–9   6

1. READING ENGAGEMENT

T: *Who reads with you or to you at home?* _____

T: *Tell me about one of your favorite books.* _____

2. ORAL READING

INTRODUCTION AND PREVIEW

T: *This book is called* Can You Sing? *Let's read it together and find out who can sing. I'll read some of the story to you. As I read, I will point to each word with my finger. Watch and listen.* Point to each word as you read pages 2–5.

T: Turn to page 6. Say: *Now, I'll point to and read what the bird says. You point to and read what the other animals say.*

Continue to read what the bird says, and have the student point to and read what the other animals say. Note the student's ability to hold/control the book and turn the pages.

RECORD OF ORAL READING

Record the student's oral reading behaviors on the Record of Oral Reading below.

Page 7

"No."

Page 9

"No."

Page 11

"No,   no."

Page 13

"No."   "No."   "No."

Page 15

"Yes!   Yes!   Yes!"

3. TEACHER ANALYSIS

ORAL READING, PERCENT OF ACCURACY

Count the number of miscues that are not self-corrected. Circle the percent of accuracy based on the number of miscues.

Word Count: 10

	EM	DEV	IND	
Number of Miscues	3 or more	2	1	0
Percent of Accuracy	70 or less	80	90	100

- If the student's number of miscues is 1 or less, continue the assessment with a Level 1 text.
- If the student's number of miscues is 2 or more, STOP!
  1. Circle the descriptor in each row of the *DRA2 Continuum* that best describes the student's reading behaviors and responses.
     - Add the circled numbers to obtain a total score for each section.
     - Record the total scores at the top of page 1.
  2. Use the student's profile of reading behaviors to identify instructional needs.
  3. Administer *DRA Word Analysis*, beginning with Task 1, at another time.

DRA2 CONTINUUM	LEVEL A		EMERGENT READERS
	EMERGING	**DEVELOPING**	**INDEPENDENT**
Reading Engagement			
Literacy Support	1 No response or is uncertain	2 Names at least one person who reads with him or her at home	3 Names several people who read with him or her at home
Favorite Book	1 No response or is uncertain	2 Tells something about a favorite book	3 Gives title and shares some specific details about favorite book
Book-Handling Skills	1 Relies on others to hold and turn pages of a book	2 Holds and/or turns pages of a book when prompted	3 Holds and turns pages of a book independently
Score	3 4	5 6 7	8 9
Oral Reading			
Monitoring/Self-Corrections	1 Detects no miscues	2 Self-corrects at least 1 miscue and neglects to self-correct other miscues	3 Self-corrects 2 or more miscues or reads accurately (no miscues or self-corrects all miscues)
Use of Cues	1 Often neglects cues (e.g., pictures, sentence pattern, visual information)	2 Uses cues (e.g., pictures, sentence pattern, visual information) at times	3 Uses cues (e.g., pictures, sentence pattern, visual information) most of the time
Accuracy Rate	1 70% or less	2 80%	3 90%–100%
Score	3 4	5 6 7	8 9
Printed Language Concepts			
Directionality	1 No/little control of directionality	2 Inconsistent control of directionality	3 Controls directionality
One-to-One Correspondence	1 Slides finger; no one-to-one match	2 Points to words; inconsistent one-to-one match	3 Points to words; consistent one-to-one match
Score	2 3	4 5	6

Name/Date _____   Teacher/Grade _____

Scores: Reading Engagement ___/9   Oral Reading ___/9   Printed Language Concepts ___/6
Independent Range: 8–9   8–9   6

Book Selection   Text selected by: ☐ teacher   ☐ student

1. READING ENGAGEMENT

(If the student has recently answered these questions, skip this section.)

T: Who reads with you or to you at home? _____

T: Tell me about one of your favorite books. _____

2. ORAL READING

INTRODUCTION AND PREVIEW

T: In this book, Things That Go, *we will see different things that can go. Look at the pictures, and tell me what can go in this book.*

Note the student's ability to hold/control the book and turn the pages. If the student names less than half of the items, use your best judgment to decide whether you should proceed with this text.

T: Point to and read the title, and then say: *I'll read the first page. As I read, I will point to each word with my finger. Watch and listen.* Read page 2.

T: Point to the first word on page 4, and say: *Now, you point to the words as you read what else can go.*

RECORD OF ORAL READING

Record the student's oral reading behaviors on the Record of Oral Reading below.

Page 4

The   car   can   go.

Page 6

The   bus   can   go.

Page 8

The   boat   can   go.

Page 10

The   plane   can   go.

Things That Go ❶

3. TEACHER ANALYSIS

ORAL READING, PERCENT OF ACCURACY

Count the number of miscues that are not self-corrected. Circle the percent of accuracy based on the number of miscues.

Word Count: 16

	EM	DEV	IND	
Number of Miscues	3 or more	2	1	0
Percent of Accuracy	81 or less	88	94	100

- If the student's number of miscues is 1 or less, continue the assessment with a Level 2 text.
- If the student's number of miscues is 2 or more, STOP!
  1. Circle the descriptor in each row of the *DRA2* Continuum that best describes the student's reading behaviors and responses.
     - Add the circled numbers to obtain a total score for each section.
     - Record the total scores at the top of page 1.
  2. Use the student's profile of reading behaviors to identify instructional needs.
  3. Administer *DRA Word Analysis*, beginning with Task 1, at another time.

DRA2 CONTINUUM	LEVEL 1		EMERGENT READERS
	EMERGING	**DEVELOPING**	**INDEPENDENT**
Reading Engagement			
Literacy Support	1 No response or is uncertain	2 Names at least one person who reads with him or her at home	3 Names several people who read with him or her at home
Favorite Book	1 No response or is uncertain	2 Tells something about a favorite book	3 Gives title and shares some specific details about favorite book
Book-Handling Skills	1 Relies on others to hold and turn pages of a book	2 Holds and/or turns pages of a book when prompted	3 Holds and turns pages of a book independently
Score	3 4	5 6 7	8 9
Oral Reading			
Monitoring/Self-Corrections	1 Detects no miscues	2 Self-corrects at least 1 miscue and neglects to self-correct other miscues	3 Self-corrects 2 or more miscues <u>or</u> reads accurately (no miscues or self-corrects all miscues)
Use of Cues	1 Often neglects cues (e.g., pictures, sentence pattern, visual information)	2 Uses cues (e.g., pictures, sentence pattern, visual information) at times	3 Uses cues (e.g., pictures, sentence pattern, visual information) most of the time
Accuracy Rate	1 81% or less	2 88%	3 94%–100%
Score	3 4	5 6 7	8 9
Printed Language Concepts			
Directionality	1 No/little control of directionality on one line of text	2 Inconsistent control of directionality on one line of text	3 Controls directionality on one line of text
One-to-One Correspondence	1 Slides finger; no one-to-one match	2 Points to words; inconsistent one-to-one match	3 Points to words; consistent one-to-one match
Score	2 3	4 5	6

Name/Date _____ Teacher/Grade _____

Scores: Reading Engagement ___/9   Oral Reading ___/9   Printed Language Concepts ___/6
Independent Range: 8–9   8–9   6

Book Selection   Text selected by: ☐ teacher   ☐ student

1. READING ENGAGEMENT

(If the student has recently answered these questions, skip this section.)

T: Who reads with you or to you at home? _____

T: Tell me about one of your favorite books. _____

2. ORAL READING

INTRODUCTION AND PREVIEW

T: In this book, What Is Red?, *we will see different things that are red. Look at the pictures, and tell me what is red in this book.*

Note the student's ability to hold/control the book and turn the pages. If the student names less than half of the items, use your best judgment to decide whether you should proceed with this text.

T: Point to and read the title, and then say: *I'll read the first page. As I read, I will point to each word with my finger. Watch and listen.* Read page 2.

T: Point to the first word on page 4, and say: *Now, you point to the words as you read what else is red.*

RECORD OF ORAL READING

Record the student's oral reading behaviors on the Record of Oral Reading below.

Page 4

The   car   is   red.

Page 6

The   shirt   is   red.

Page 8

The   ball   is   red.

Page 10

The   ant   is   red.

What Is Red? ❶

3. TEACHER ANALYSIS

ORAL READING, PERCENT OF ACCURACY

Count the number of miscues that are not self-corrected. Circle the percent of accuracy based on the number of miscues.

Word Count: 16

	EM	DEV	IND	
Number of Miscues	3 or more	2	1	0
Percent of Accuracy	81 or less	88	94	100

- If the student's number of miscues is 1 or less, continue the assessment with a Level 2 text.
- If the student's number of miscues is 2 or more, STOP!
  1. Circle the descriptor in each row of the *DRA2 Continuum* that best describes the student's reading behaviors and responses.
     - Add the circled numbers to obtain a total score for each section.
     - Record the total scores at the top of page 1.
  2. Use the student's profile of reading behaviors to identify instructional needs.
  3. Administer *DRA Word Analysis*, beginning with Task 1, at another time.

DRA2 CONTINUUM	LEVEL 1		EMERGENT READERS
	EMERGING	**DEVELOPING**	**INDEPENDENT**
Reading Engagement			
Literacy Support	1 No response or is uncertain	2 Names at least one person who reads with him or her at home	3 Names several people who read with him or her at home
Favorite Book	1 No response or is uncertain	2 Tells something about a favorite book	3 Gives title and shares some specific details about favorite book
Book-Handling Skills	1 Relies on others to hold and turn pages of a book	2 Holds and/or turns pages of a book when prompted	3 Holds and turns pages of a book independently
Score	3 4	5 6 7	8 9
Oral Reading			
Monitoring/Self-Corrections	1 Detects no miscues	2 Self-corrects at least 1 miscue and neglects to self-correct other miscues	3 Self-corrects 2 or more miscues <u>or</u> reads accurately (no miscues or self-corrects all miscues)
Use of Cues	1 Often neglects cues (e.g., pictures, sentence pattern, visual information)	2 Uses cues (e.g., pictures, sentence pattern, visual information) at times	3 Uses cues (e.g., pictures, sentence pattern, visual information) most of the time
Accuracy Rate	1 81% or less	2 88%	3 94%–100%
Score	3 4	5 6 7	8 9
Printed Language Concepts			
Directionality	1 No/little control of directionality on one line of text	2 Inconsistent control of directionality on one line of text	3 Controls directionality
One-to-One Correspondence	1 Slides finger; no one-to-one match	2 Points to words; inconsistent one-to-one match	3 Points to words; consistent one-to-one match
Score	2 3	4 5	6

What Is Red? 1

6

Name/Date _____ Teacher/Grade _____

Scores: Reading Engagement __/9   Oral Reading __/9   Printed Language Concepts __/9
Independent Range: 8–9   8–9   8–9

Book Selection   Text selected by: ☐ teacher   ☐ student

1. READING ENGAGEMENT

(If the student has previously answered these questions, skip this section.)

T: Who reads with you or to you at home? _____

T: Tell me about one of your favorite books. _____

2. ORAL READING

INTRODUCTION AND PREVIEW

T: In this story, Bath Time, *a little girl is taking a bubble bath. She tells her mom what she can see. Each thing is a different color. Look at the pictures, and tell me what the little girl can see.*

Note the student's ability to hold the book and turn pages. If the student names fewer than half of the objects, use your best judgment to decide whether you should proceed with the text.

T: Point to and read the title, and then say: *I'll read the first page. As I read, I will point to each word with my finger. Watch and listen.* Read page 2.

T: Point to the first word on page 4, and say: *Now, you point to the words as you read what else she can see.*

RECORD OF ORAL READING

Record the student's oral reading behaviors on the Record of Oral Reading below and on the following page.

Page 4

I can see a blue fish.

Page 6

I can see a yellow duck.

Page 8

I can see a green frog.

Bath Time 2

Page 10

I   can   see   a   purple   towel.

Page 12

I   can   see   pink   soap . . .

Page 14

and   I   can   see   bubbles.

After the student has read the last page, go back to the following pages and note the student's responses.

T: Turn to page 8. After showing the letter *g* on a card, say: **Find a word that begins with this letter.**

T: Turn to page 12. After showing the letter *p* on a card, say: **Find a word that ends with this letter.**

3. TEACHER ANALYSIS

ORAL READING, PERCENT OF ACCURACY

Count the number of miscues that are not self-corrected. Circle the percent of accuracy based on the number of miscues.

Word Count: 34

	EM	DEV	IND		
Number of Miscues	4 or more	3	2	1	0
Percent of Accuracy	88 or less	91	94	97	100

- If the student's number of miscues is 2 or less, continue the assessment with a Level 3 text.
- If the student's number of miscues is 3 or more, STOP!

*DRA*2 Continuum and Focus for Instruction

1. Circle the descriptors on the *DRA*2 Continuum that best describe the student's reading behaviors and responses.
   - Add the circled numbers to obtain a total score for each section.
   - Record the total scores at the top of page 1.
2. Use the student's profile of reading behaviors to identify instructional needs on the *DRA*2 Focus for Instruction.
3. Administer *DRA Word Analysis*, beginning with Task 1, at another time.

Bath Time 2

DRA2 CONTINUUM	**LEVEL 2**		**EMERGENT READER**
	EMERGING	**DEVELOPING**	**INDEPENDENT**
Reading Engagement			
Literacy Support	1 No response or is uncertain	2 Names at least one person who reads with him or her at home	3 Names several people who read with him or her at home
Favorite Book	1 No response or is uncertain	2 Tells something about a favorite book	3 Gives title and shares some specific details about favorite book
Book-Handling Skills	1 Relies on others to hold and turn pages of a book	2 Holds and/or turns pages of a book when prompted	3 Holds and turns pages of a book independently
Score	3 4	5 6 7	8 9
Oral Reading			
Monitoring/Self-Corrections	1 Detects no miscues	2 Self-corrects at least 1 miscue and neglects to self-correct other miscues	3 Self-corrects 2 or more miscues or reads accurately (no miscues or self-corrects all miscues)
Use of Cues	1 Often neglects cues (e.g., pictures, sentence pattern, visual information)	2 Uses cues (e.g., pictures, sentence pattern, visual information) at times	3 Uses cues (e.g., pictures, sentence pattern, visual information) most of the time
Accuracy	1 88% or less	2 91%	3 94%–100%
Score	3 4	5 6 7	8 9
Printed Language Concepts			
Directionality	1 No/little control of directionality on one line of text	2 Inconsistent control of directionality on one line of text	3 Controls directionality on one line of text
One-to-One Correspondence	1 Slides finger; no one-to-one match	2 Points to words; inconsistent one-to-one match	3 Points to words; consistent one-to-one match
Words/Letters	1 Demonstrates little understanding of the terms *begins*, *ends*, and *letter*; unable to locate either word	2 Demonstrates some understanding of the terms *begins*, *ends*, and *letter* by locating 1 of the words	3 Demonstrates an understanding of the terms *begins*, *ends*, and *letter* by locating both words
Score	3 4	5 6 7	8 9

DRA2 FOCUS FOR INSTRUCTION FOR EMERGENT READERS

Reading Engagement
☐ Create structures and routines to support reading at home
☐ Model and support holding a book while previewing and reading
☐ Model and support turning the pages of a book while previewing and reading

Oral Reading
Teach how to:
☐ Monitor using one-to-one correspondence
☐ Monitor using known words
☐ Problem-solve unknown words by using beginning letter/sound relationships, pictures, and language structures
☐ Confirm word choice by using beginning letter/sound relationships, pictures, and language structures
☐ Self-correct miscues

Printed Language Concepts
Model and support:
☐ Directionality
☐ Concept of a letter and a word
☐ Concept of first and last letter of a word
☐ Concept of the terms *begins* and *ends*
☐ Concept of the terms *letter* and/or *sound*
☐ One-to-one correspondence

OTHER

_____

_____

_____

_____

_____

Bath Time **2**

Name/Date _____   Teacher/Grade _____

Scores: Reading Engagement ___/9   Oral Reading ___/9   Printed Language Concepts ___/9
Independent Range: 8–9   8–9   8–9

Book Selection   Text selected by: ☐ teacher   ☐ student

1. READING ENGAGEMENT

(If the student has recently answered these questions, skip this section.)

T: Who reads with you or to you at home? _____

T: Tell me about one of your favorite books. _____

2. ORAL READING

INTRODUCTION AND PREVIEW

T: This story, I Can See, is about things you can see by a pond. Each thing is a different color. Look at the pictures, and tell me what you can see by the pond.

Note the student's ability to hold the book and turn pages. If the student names fewer than half of the objects, use your best judgment to decide whether you should proceed with the text.

T: Point to and read the title, and then say: *I'll read the first page. As I read, I will point to each word with my finger. Watch and listen.* Read page 2.

T: Point to the first word on page 4, and say: *Now, you point to the words as you read what else can be seen.*

RECORD OF ORAL READING

Record the student's oral reading behaviors on the Record of Oral Reading below and on the following page.

Page 4

I   can   see   a   green   frog.

Page 6

I   can   see   a   red   flower.

Page 8

I   can   see   a   brown   tree.

Page 10

I   can   see   a   black   bird.

Page 12

I   can   see   a   yellow   sun . . .

Page 14

and   I   can   see   a   rainbow.

After the student has read the last page, go back to the following pages and note the student's responses.

T: Turn to page 4. After showing the letter *g* on a card, say: **Find a word that begins with this letter.**

T: Turn to page 6. After showing the letter *r* on a card, say: **Find a word that ends with this letter.**

3. TEACHER ANALYSIS

ORAL READING, PERCENT OF ACCURACY

Count the number of miscues that are not self-corrected. Circle the percent of accuracy based on the number of miscues.

Word Count: 36

	EM	DEV	IND		
Number of Miscues	4 or more	3	2	1	0
Percent of Accuracy	89 or less	92	94	97	100

- If the student's number of miscues is 2 or less, continue the assessment with a Level 3 text.
- If the student's number of miscues is 3 or more, STOP!

*DRA*2 Continuum and Focus for Instruction

1. Circle the descriptors on the *DRA*2 Continuum that best describe the student's reading behaviors and responses.
   - Add the circled numbers to obtain a total score for each section.
   - Record the total scores at the top of page 1.
2. Use the student's profile of reading behaviors to identify instructional needs on the *DRA*2 Focus for Instruction.
3. Administer *DRA Word Analysis*, beginning with Task 1, at another time.

I Can See **2**

DRA2 CONTINUUM	LEVEL 2		EMERGENT READER
	EMERGING	**DEVELOPING**	**INDEPENDENT**
Reading Engagement			
Literacy Support	**1** No response or is uncertain	**2** Names at least one person who reads with him or her at home	**3** Names several people who read with him or her at home
Favorite Book	**1** No response or is uncertain	**2** Tells something about a favorite book	**3** Gives title and shares some specific details about favorite book
Book-Handling Skills	**1** Relies on others to hold and turn pages of a book	**2** Holds and/or turns pages of a book when prompted	**3** Holds and turns pages of a book independently
Score	3 4	5 6 7	8 9
Oral Reading			
Monitoring/Self-Corrections	**1** Detects no miscues	**2** Self-corrects at least 1 miscue and neglects to self-correct other miscues	**3** Self-corrects 2 or more miscues <u>or</u> reads accurately (no miscues or self-corrects all miscues)
Use of Cues	**1** Often neglects cues (e.g., pictures, sentence pattern, visual information)	**2** Uses cues (e.g., pictures, sentence pattern, visual information) at times	**3** Uses cues (e.g., pictures, sentence pattern, visual information) most of the time
Accuracy	**1** 89% or less	**2** 92%	**3** 94%–100%
Score	3 4	5 6 7	8 9
Printed Language Concepts			
Directionality	**1** No/little control of directionality on one line of text	**2** Inconsistent control of directionality on one line of text	**3** Controls directionality on one line of text
One-to-One Correspondence	**1** Slides finger; no one-to-one match	**2** Points to words; inconsistent one-to-one match	**3** Points to words; consistent one-to-one match
Words/Letters	**1** Demonstrates little understanding of the terms *begins*, *ends*, and *letter*; unable to locate either word	**2** Demonstrates some understanding of the terms *begins*, *ends*, and *letter* by locating 1 of the words	**3** Demonstrates an understanding of the terms *begins*, *ends*, and *letter* by locating both words
Score	3 4	5 6 7	8 9

DRA2 FOCUS FOR INSTRUCTION FOR EMERGENT READERS

Reading Engagement
☐ Create structures and routines to support reading at home
☐ Model and support holding a book while previewing and reading
☐ Model and support turning the pages of a book while previewing and reading

Oral Reading
Teach how to:
☐ Monitor using one-to-one correspondence
☐ Monitor using known words
☐ Problem-solve unknown words by using beginning letter/sound relationships, pictures, and language structures
☐ Confirm word choice by using beginning letter/sound relationships, pictures, and language structures
☐ Self-correct miscues

Printed Language Concepts
Model and support:
☐ Directionality
☐ Concept of a letter and a word
☐ Concept of first and last letter of a word
☐ Concept of the terms *begins* and *ends*
☐ Concept of the terms *letter* and/or *sound*
☐ One-to-one correspondence

OTHER

_____

_____

_____

_____

_____

Name/Date _____   Teacher/Grade _____

Scores: Reading Engagement ___/9   Oral Reading ___/9   Printed Language Concepts ___/9
Independent Range: 8–9   8–9   8–9

Book Selection   Text selected by: ☐ teacher   ☐ student

1. READING ENGAGEMENT

(If the student has recently answered these questions, skip this section.)

T: Who reads with you or to you at home? _____

T: Tell me about one of your favorite books. _____

2. ORAL READING

INTRODUCTION AND PREVIEW

T: In this story, **The "I Like" Game,** *two children are playing an "I like" game. They tell each other what foods they like, but they don't seem to like the same things. Look at all of the pictures, and tell me what is happening in this story.*

Note the student's ability to hold the book and turn pages. Also note his or her use of vocabulary relevant to the text. You may use general prompts, such as "Now what is happening?" or "Turn the page," but do <u>not</u> ask specific questions.

T: Point to and read the title, and then say: **The "I Like" Game. *Let's read to see what the girl and boy like. I'll read the first page. As I read, I will point to each word with my finger. Watch and listen.*** Point to and read page 2.

T: Point to the first word on page 4, and say: ***Now, you point to the words as you read the rest of the story.***

RECORD OF ORAL READING

Record the student's oral reading behaviors on the Record of Oral Reading below and on the following page.

Page 4

"No," said the girl.

"I like apples.

 Do you?"

Page 6

"No," said the boy.

"I like bananas.

 Do you?"

The "I Like" Game ③

Page 8

"No," said the girl.

"I like grapes.

Do you?"

Page 10

"No," said the boy.

"I like ice cream.

Do you?"

Page 12

"Yes," said the girl.

"I like ice cream, too!"

After the student has read the last page, turn to page 2, and ask the following questions. Note the student's responses.

T: Say: ***Point to the word*** said.
        What sound does said ***begin with?*** /s/
        What sound does said ***end with?*** /d/
        What letter makes that sound? *d*

3. TEACHER ANALYSIS

ORAL READING, PERCENT OF ACCURACY

Count and circle the number of miscues that are not self-corrected. Circle the percent of accuracy based on the number of miscues.

Word Count: 46

	EM	DEV	IND			
Number of Miscues	5 or more	4	3	2	1	0
Percent of Accuracy	89 or less	91	93	96	98	100

- If the student's number of miscues is 3 or less, continue the assessment with a Level 4 text.
- If the student's number of miscues is 4 or more, STOP!

*DRA*2 Continuum and Focus for Instruction

1. Circle the descriptors on the *DRA*2 Continuum that best describe the student's reading behaviors and responses.
   - Add the circled numbers to obtain a total score for each section.
   - Record the total scores at the top of page 1.

2. Use the student's profile of reading behaviors to identify instructional needs on the *DRA2 Focus for Instruction*.

If the student is reading below the grade-level benchmark, administer *DRA Word Analysis*, beginning with Task 1, at another time.

*DRA*2 CONTINUUM	LEVEL 3		EMERGENT READER
	EMERGING	**DEVELOPING**	**INDEPENDENT**
Reading Engagement			
Literacy Support	1 No response or is uncertain	2 Names at least one person who reads with him or her at home	3 Names several people who read with him or her at home
Favorite Book	1 No response or is uncertain	2 Tells something about a favorite book	3 Gives title and shares some specific details about favorite book
Book-Handling Skills	1 Relies on others to hold and turn pages of a book	2 Holds and/or turns pages of a book when prompted	3 Holds and turns pages of a book independently
Score	3 4	5 6 7	8 9
Oral Reading			
Monitoring/Self-Corrections	1 Detects no miscues	2 Self-corrects at least 1 miscue and neglects to self-correct other miscues	3 Self-corrects 2 or more miscues or reads accurately (no miscues or self-corrects all miscues)
Use of Cues	1 Often neglects cues (e.g., pictures, sentence pattern, visual information)	2 Uses cues (e.g., pictures, sentence pattern, visual information) at times	3 Uses cues (e.g., pictures, sentence pattern, visual information) most of the time
Accuracy	1 89% or less	2 91%	3 93%–100%
Score	3 4	5 6 7	8 9
Printed Language Concepts			
Directionality	1 No/little control of directionality on one line of text	2 Inconsistent control of directionality on one line of text	3 Controls directionality on two or more lines of text
One-to-One Correspondence	1 Slides finger; no one-to-one match	2 Points to words; inconsistent one-to-one match	3 Points to words; consistent one-to-one match
Words/Letters	1 Demonstrates little understanding of the terms: *word*, *begins*, *ends*, *letter*, and/or *sound*	2 Demonstrates some understanding of the terms: *word*, *begins*, *ends*, *letter* and/or *sound* by responding accurately at times	3 Demonstrates an understanding of the following terms: *word*, *begins*, *ends*, *letter* and/or *sound* by responding accurately
Score	3 4	5 6 7	8 9

The "I Like" Game ❸

DRA2 FOCUS FOR INSTRUCTION FOR EMERGENT READERS

READING ENGAGEMENT
- ☐ Create structures and routines to support reading at home
- ☐ Provide guided opportunities to select familiar stories for rereading
- ☐ Model and support holding a book while previewing and reading
- ☐ Model and support turning pages of a book while previewing and reading

ORAL READING
Teach how to:
- ☐ Monitor using one-to-one correspondence
- ☐ Monitor using known words
- ☐ Problem-solve unknown words by using beginning letter/sound relationships, pictures, and language structures
- ☐ Confirm word choice by using beginning letter/sound relationships, pictures, and language structures
- ☐ Self-correct miscues

PRINTED LANGUAGE CONCEPTS
Model and support:
- ☐ Directionality
- ☐ Concept of a letter and a word
- ☐ Concept of first and last letter of a word
- ☐ Concept of the terms *begins* and *ends*
- ☐ Concept of the terms *letter* and/or *sound*
- ☐ One-to-one correspondence

OTHER

_____

_____

_____

_____

_____

_____

Name/Date _____   Teacher/Grade _____

Scores: Reading Engagement ___/9   Oral Reading ___/9   Printed Language Concepts ___/9
Independent Range: 8–9   8–9   8–9

Book Selection   Text selected by: ☐ teacher   ☐ student

1. READING ENGAGEMENT

(If the student has recently answered these questions, skip this section.)

T: Who reads with you or to you at home? _____

T: Tell me about one of your favorite books. _____

2. ORAL READING

INTRODUCTION AND PREVIEW

T: In this story, Look at Me, *two children are at the park with their mothers. They take turns showing their mothers what they can do. Look at all the pictures, and tell me what is happening in this story.*

Note the student's ability to hold the book and turn pages. Also note his or her use of vocabulary relevant to the text. You may use general prompts, such as "Now what is happening?" or "Turn the page," but do <u>not</u> ask specific questions.

T: Point to and read the title, and then say: **Look at Me.** *Let's read to see what the boy and girl can do. I'll read the first page. As I read, I will point to each word with my finger. Watch and listen.* Point to and read page 2.

T: Point to the first word on page 4, and say: *Now, you point to the words as you read the rest of the story.*

RECORD OF ORAL READING

Record the student's oral reading behaviors on the Record of Oral Reading below and on the following page.

Page 4

"Look   at   me,"   said   the   girl.

"I   can   slide."

Page 6

"Look   at   me,"   said   the   boy.

"I   can   swing."

Page 8

"Look   at   me,"   said   the   girl.

"I   can   skate."

Look at Me **3**

Page 10

"Look   at   me,"   said   the   boy.

"I   can   climb."

Page 12

"Look   at   us.

We   can   jump   rope,"

said   the   boy   and   the   girl.

After the student has read the last page, turn to page 2 and ask the following questions. Note the student's responses.

T: Say: **Point to the word** said.
   What sound does said **begin with?** /s/
   What sound does said **end with?**   /d/
   What letter makes that sound?   *d*

3. TEACHER ANALYSIS

ORAL READING, PERCENT OF ACCURACY

Count the number of miscues that are not self-corrected. Circle the percent of accuracy based on the number of miscues.

Word Count: 49

	EM	DEV	IND			
Number of Miscues	5 or more	4	3	2	1	0
Percent of Accuracy	90 or less	92	94	96	98	100

• If the student's number of miscues is 3 or less, continue the assessment with a Level 4 text.
• If the student's number of miscues is 4 or more, STOP!

*DRA*2 Continuum and Focus for Instruction

1. Circle the descriptors on the *DRA*2 Continuum that best describe the student's reading behaviors and responses.
   • Add the circled numbers to obtain a total score for each section.
   • Record the total scores at the top of page 1.
2. Use the student's profile of reading behaviors to identify instructional needs on the *DRA*2 Focus for Instruction.

If the student is reading below the grade-level benchmark, administer *DRA Word Analysis*, beginning with Task 1, at another time.

Look at Me 3

DRA2 CONTINUUM	LEVEL 3		EMERGENT READER
	EMERGING	**DEVELOPING**	**INDEPENDENT**
Reading Engagement			
Literacy Support	**1** No response or is uncertain	**2** Names at least one person who reads with him or her at home	**3** Names several people who read with him or her at home
Favorite Book	**1** No response or is uncertain	**2** Tells something about a favorite book	**3** Gives title and shares some specific details about favorite book
Book-Handling Skills	**1** Relies on others to hold and turn pages of a book	**2** Holds and/or turns pages of a book when prompted	**3** Holds and turns pages of a book independently
Score	3 4	5 6 7	8 9
Oral Reading			
Monitoring/Self-Corrections	**1** Detects no miscues	**2** Self-corrects at least 1 miscue and neglects to self-correct other miscues	**3** Self-corrects 2 or more miscues <u>or</u> reads accurately (no miscues or self-corrects all miscues)
Use of Cues	**1** Often neglects cues (e.g., pictures, sentence pattern, visual information)	**2** Uses cues (e.g., pictures, sentence pattern, visual information) at times	**3** Uses cues (e.g., pictures, sentence pattern, visual information) most of the time
Accuracy	**1** 90% or less	**2** 92%	**3** 94%–100%
Score	3 4	5 6 7	8 9
Printed Language Concepts			
Directionality	**1** No/little control of directionality on one line of text	**2** Inconsistent control of directionality on one line of text	**3** Controls directionality on two or more lines of text
One-to-One Correspondence	**1** Slides finger; no one-to-one match	**2** Points to words; inconsistent one-to-one match	**3** Points to words; consistent one-to-one match
Words/Letters	**1** Demonstrates little understanding of the terms: *word, begins, ends, letter,* and/or *sound*	**2** Demonstrates some understanding of the terms: *word, begins, ends, letter,* and/or *sound* by responding accurately at times	**3** Demonstrates an understanding of the following terms: *word, begins, ends, letter,* and/or *sound* by responding accurately
Score	3 4	5 6 7	8 9

Look at Me **3**

DRA2 FOCUS FOR INSTRUCTION FOR EMERGENT READERS

READING ENGAGEMENT
☐ Create structures and routines to support reading at home
☐ Provide guided opportunities to select familiar stories for rereading
☐ Model and support holding a book while previewing and reading
☐ Model and support turning pages of a book while previewing and reading

ORAL READING
Teach how to:
☐ Monitor using one-to-one correspondence
☐ Monitor using known words
☐ Problem-solve unknown words by using beginning letter/sound relationships, pictures, and language structures
☐ Confirm word choice by using beginning letter/sound relationships, pictures, and language structures
☐ Self-correct miscues

PRINTED LANGUAGE CONCEPTS
Model and support:
☐ Directionality
☐ Concept of a letter and a word
☐ Concept of first and last letter of a word
☐ Concept of the terms *begins* and *ends*
☐ Concept of the terms *letter* and/or *sound*
☐ One-to-one correspondence

OTHER

_____

_____

_____

_____

_____

_____

_____

Look at Me **3**

Name/Date _____ Teacher/Grade _____

Scores: Reading Engagement ___/8   Oral Reading Fluency ___/16   Comprehension ___/28
Independent Range: 6–7   11–14   19–25

Book Selection   Text selected by: ☐ teacher   ☐ student

1. READING ENGAGEMENT

(If the student has recently answered these questions, skip this section.)

T: Who reads with you or to you at home? _____

T: Would you rather listen to a story or read a story to someone? _____

    Why? _____

T: Tell me about one of your favorite books. _____

2. ORAL READING FLUENCY

INTRODUCTION AND PREVIEW
T: In this story, Get Your Umbrella, *Kim and her dad are getting ready to go outside on a rainy day. Dad tells Kim to get her umbrella. Look at all the pictures, and tell me what is happening in this story.*

Note the student's use of connecting words (e.g., *and, then, but*) and vocabulary relevant to the text. You may use general prompts, such as "Now what is happening?" or "Turn the page," but do <u>not</u> ask specific questions. Tally the number of times you prompt.

RECORD OF ORAL READING
Record the student's oral reading behaviors on the Record of Oral Reading below and on the following page.

T: Get Your Umbrella. *Now, read to find out where Kim looks for her umbrella.*

Page 2

"Look at the rain," said Dad.

"Get your umbrella."

Page 3

Kim looked in the closet.

"No umbrella," she said.

Get Your Umbrella 4

Page 4

Kim   looked   under   her   bed.

"No   umbrella,"   she   said.

Page 5

Kim   looked   in   the   kitchen.

"Here   it   is!"   she   said.

Page 6

"Look,   Dad.   I   got   my   umbrella,"

said   Kim.

Page 7

"Look,   Kim.   The   sun   is   out!"

said   Dad.

ORAL READING, PERCENT OF ACCURACY

Count the number of miscues that are not self-corrected. Circle the percent of accuracy based on the number of miscues.

Word Count: 53

	EM	DEV	IND		ADV	
Number of Miscues	5 or more	4	3	2	1	0
Percent of Accuracy	91 or less	92	94	96	98	100

- If the student's score falls in a shaded area, STOP! Reassess with a lower-level text.
- If the student is reading below the grade-level benchmark, administer *DRA Word Analysis*, beginning with Task 8, at another time.

Get Your Umbrella ④

3. COMPREHENSION

RETELLING

As the student retells, underline and record on the Story Overview the information included in the student's retelling. Please note the student does not need to use the exact words.

T: Close the book, and then say: ***Start at the beginning, and tell me what happened in this story.***

Story Overview
Beginning
1. Dad said it was raining and told Kim to get her umbrella.

Middle
2. Kim looked in the closet. No umbrella.

3. Kim looked under her bed. No umbrella.

4. Kim found her umbrella in the kitchen.

End
5. Kim told Dad she got her umbrella.

6. Dad told Kim the sun is out.

If the retelling is limited, use one or more of the following prompts to gain further information. Place a checkmark by a prompt each time it is used.

- ☐ *Tell me more.*
- ☐ *What happened at the beginning?*
- ☐ *What happened before/after* _____ (an event mentioned by the student)*?*
- ☐ *Who else was in the story?*
- ☐ *How did the story end?*

REFLECTION

Record the student's responses to the prompts and questions below.

T: *What part did you like best in this story? Tell me why you liked that part.*

MAKING CONNECTIONS

Note: If the student makes a text-to-self connection in his or her response to the above prompt, skip the following question.

T: *What did this story make you think of?* or *What connection did you make while reading this story?*

4. TEACHER ANALYSIS

ORAL READING

If the student had 4 or more different miscues, use the information recorded on the Record of Oral Reading to complete the chart below.

Student problem-solves words using:	Number of miscues self-corrected: _____
☐ pictures	Number of miscues not self-corrected: _____
☐ beginning letter/sound	Number of words told to the student: _____

Student problem-solves words using:	Miscues interfered with meaning:	Miscues included:
☐ pictures	☐ never	☐ omissions
☐ beginning letter/sound	☐ at times	☐ insertions
☐ letter-sound clusters	☐ often	☐ substitutions that were
☐ onset and rime		☐ visually similar
☐ blending letters/sounds		☐ not visually similar
☐ rereading		
☐ no observable behaviors		

Copy each substitution to help analyze the student's attention to visual information.
e.g., <u>there</u> (substitution)
     here (text)

_DRA_2 Continuum

- Circle the descriptors that best describe the student's reading behaviors and responses.
    1. Use your daily classroom observations and the student's responses to the Reading Engagement questions to select statements that best describe the student's level of Reading Engagement.
    2. Use your recorded observations from this assessment to select the statements that best describe the student's Oral Reading Fluency and Comprehension.
- Add the circled numbers to obtain a total score for each section.
- Record the total scores at the top of page 1.

Note: If the Comprehension score is less than 19, administer _DRA_2 with a lower-level text.

*DRA*2 CONTINUUM	LEVEL 4			EARLY READER
	EMERGING	**DEVELOPING**	**INDEPENDENT**	**ADVANCED**
Reading Engagement				
Book Selection	**1** Selects new texts from identified leveled sets with teacher support; uncertain about a favorite book	**2** Selects new texts from identified leveled sets with moderate support; tells about favorite book in general terms	**3** Selects new texts from identified leveled sets most of the time; identifies favorite book by title and tells about a particular event	**4** Selects a variety of new texts that are "just right"; identifies favorite book by title and gives an overview of the book
Sustained Reading	**1** Sustains independent reading for a short period of time with much encouragement	**2** Sustains independent reading with moderate encouragement	**3** Sustains independent reading for at least 5 minutes at a time	**4** Sustains independent reading for an extended period of time
Score	2 3	4 5	6 7	8
Oral Reading Fluency				
Phrasing	**1** Reads word-by-word	**2** Reads word-by-word with some short phrases	**3** Reads in short phrases most of the time	**4** Reads in longer phrases at times
Monitoring/Self-Corrections	**1** Self-corrects no miscues	**2** Self-corrects at least 1 miscue and neglects to self-correct other miscues	**3** Self-corrects 2 or more miscues or only makes 1 uncorrected miscue	**4** Self-corrects miscues quickly or reads accurately
Problem-Solving Unknown Words	**1** At difficulty stops, relying on support to problem-solve unknown words; 3 or more words told by the teacher	**2** At difficulty, initiates problem-solving of a few unknown words; 1 or 2 words told by the teacher	**3** At difficulty, uses 1 or 2 cues to problem-solve unknown words	**4** At difficulty, uses multiple cues to problem-solve unknown words
Accuracy	**1** 91% or less	**2** 92%	**3** 94%–96%	**4** 98%–100%
Score	4 5 6	7 8 9 10	11 12 13 14	15 16
Comprehension				
Previewing	**1** Comments briefly about each event or action only when prompted or is uncertain	**2** Identifies and comments briefly about each event or action with some prompting	**3** Identifies and connects at least 3 key events without prompting; some relevant vocabulary	**4** Identifies and connects at least 4 key events without prompting; relevant vocabulary
Retelling: Sequence of Events	**1** Includes only 1 or 2 events or details (limited retelling)	**2** Includes at least 3 events, generally in random order (partial retelling)	**3** Includes most of the important events from the beginning, middle, and end, generally in sequence	**4** Includes all important events from the beginning, middle, and end in sequence
Retelling: Characters and Details	**1** Refers to characters using general pronouns; may include incorrect information	**2** Refers to characters using appropriate pronouns; includes at least 1 detail; may include some misinterpretation	**3** Refers to most characters by name and includes some important details	**4** Refers to all characters by name and includes most of the important details
Retelling: Vocabulary	**1** Uses general terms or labels; limited understanding of key words/concepts	**2** Uses some language/vocabulary from the text; some understanding of key words/concepts	**3** Uses language/vocabulary from the text; basic understanding of most key words/concepts	**4** Uses important language/vocabulary from the text; good understanding of key words/concepts
Retelling: Teacher Support	**1** Retells with 5 or more questions or prompts	**2** Retells with 3 or 4 questions or prompts	**3** Retells with 1 or 2 questions or prompts	**4** Retells with no questions or prompts
Reflection	**1** Gives an unrelated response, no reason for opinion, or no response	**2** Gives a limited response and/or a general reason for opinion	**3** Gives a specific story event/action <u>and</u> a relevant reason for response (e.g., personal connection)	**4** Gives a response and reason that reflects higher-level thinking (e.g., synthesis/inference)
Making Connections	**1** Makes an unrelated connection, relates an event in the story, or gives no response	**2** Makes a connection that reflects a limited understanding of the story	**3** Makes a literal connection that reflects a basic understanding of the story	**4** Makes a thoughtful connection that reflects a deeper understanding of the story
Score	7 8 9 10 11 12 13	14 15 16 17 18	19 20 21 22 23 24 25	26 27 28

Choose three to five teaching/learning activities on the *DRA*2 Focus for Instruction on the next page.

Get Your Umbrella **4**

DRA2 FOCUS FOR INSTRUCTION FOR EARLY READERS

READING ENGAGEMENT

Book Selection
☐ Provide guided opportunities to select familiar stories for rereading
☐ Model and support how to select "just right" new texts for independent reading
☐ Model and discuss why readers have favorite books and authors

Sustained Reading
☐ Model and support the use of sustained reading time
☐ Create structures and routines to support buddy reading
☐ Create structures and routines to support reading at home

ORAL READING FLUENCY

Phrasing
☐ Encourage student to read in phrases during shared reading
☐ Show how words are grouped into phrases in big books and poetry charts
☐ Support rereading familiar texts to build fluency

Monitoring/Self-Corrections
☐ Support one-to-one matching as a means to self-monitor
☐ Model and teach how to use known words as a means to self-monitor
☐ Model and support confirming and discounting word choice using meaning, language, and visual information
☐ Demonstrate and teach how to read for meaning, self-correcting when a word doesn't make sense or sound right
☐ Model and teach how to monitor visual information, self-correcting when a word doesn't look right

Problem-Solving Unknown Words
☐ Model and support using beginning letter(s)/sound(s), sentence and/or story structure, as well as meaning (illustrations and background knowledge) to problem-solve unknown words
☐ Teach how to take words apart (onset and rime) to problem-solve unknown words

COMPREHENSION

Previewing
☐ Support creating a story from the illustrations
☐ Model and support previewing a book before reading, during read-aloud and shared reading experiences

Retelling
☐ Model the retelling of familiar stories
☐ Teach the elements in a good retelling
☐ Demonstrate how to create and use story maps to aid retelling
☐ Support retelling a story in sequence
☐ Encourage student to use characters' names when retelling a story
☐ Support using key language/vocabulary from the text in a retelling

Reflection
☐ Support and reinforce student's response to books during read-aloud, and shared and guided reading experiences
☐ Help student identify favorite part of books
☐ Provide opportunities to select a favorite book, toy, TV show, etc., and tell why it is a favorite
☐ Demonstrate how to give reason(s) for one's opinion

Making Connections
☐ Model and teach how to make text-to-self connections
☐ Model and support how to make text-to-text connections

OTHER

_____
_____
_____
_____
_____
_____
_____

Name/Date _____   Teacher/Grade _____

Scores: Reading Engagement ___/8   Oral Reading Fluency ___/16   Comprehension ___/28
Independent Range: 6–7   11–14   19–25

Book Selection   Text selected by: ☐ teacher   ☐ student

1. READING ENGAGEMENT

(If the student has recently answered these questions, skip this section.)

T: Who reads with you or to you at home? _____

T: Would you rather listen to a story or read a story to someone? _____

   *Why?*_____

*T: Tell me about one of your favorite books.*_____

2. ORAL READING FLUENCY

INTRODUCTION AND PREVIEW
T: In this story, Where Is My Hat?, *a little boy named Ben doesn't know where his hat is. Look at all of the pictures, and tell me what is happening in this story.*

Note the student's use of connecting words (e.g., *and, then, but*) and vocabulary relevant to the text. You may use general prompts, such as "Now what is happening?" or "Turn the page," but do <u>not</u> ask specific questions. Tally the number of times you prompt.

RECORD OF ORAL READING
Record the student's oral reading behaviors on the Record of Oral Reading below and on the following page.

T: Where Is My Hat? *Now, read to find out where Ben and his mom look for his hat.*

Page 2
"Where   is   my   hat?"   said   Ben.

Page 3
Ben   looked   under   his   bed.
"It   is   not   here,"   he   said.

Where Is My Hat? 4

Page 4

Mom   looked   in   the   closet.

"It   is   not   here,"   she   said.

Page 5

Ben   looked   in   his   toy   box.

"It   is   not   here,"   he   said.

He   looked   and   looked.

Page 6

Mom   looked   behind   the   chair.

Page 7

"Here   it   is!"   she   said.

ORAL READING, PERCENT OF ACCURACY

Count the number of miscues that are not self-corrected. Circle the percent of accuracy based on the number of miscues.

Word Count: 54

	EM	DEV	IND		ADV	
Number of Miscues	5 or more	4	3	2	1	0
Percent of Accuracy	91 or less	93	94	96	98	100

- If the student's score falls in a shaded area, STOP! Reassess with a lower-level text.
- If the student is reading below the grade-level benchmark, administer *DRA Word Analysis,* beginning with Task 8, at another time.

3. COMPREHENSION

RETELLING

As the student retells, underline and record on the Story Overview the information included in the student's retelling. Please note the student does not need to use the exact words.

T: Close the book, and then say: ***Start at the beginning, and tell me what happened in this story.***

Story Overview
Beginning
1. Ben said, "Where is my hat?"

Middle
2. He looks under the bed, and says, "It is not here."

3. Mom looks in the closet and says, "It is not here."

4. Ben looks in his toy box and says, "It is not here."

5. Mom looks behind a chair and . . .

End
6. Mom finds the hat behind a chair with the dog lying on it.

7. Mom says, "Here it is!" and puts the hat on Ben.

If the retelling is limited, use one or more of the following prompts to gain further information. Place a checkmark by a prompt each time it is used.

- ☐ *Tell me more.*
- ☐ *What happened at the beginning?*
- ☐ *What happened before/after* _____ (an event mentioned by the student)*?*
- ☐ *Who else was in the story?*
- ☐ *How did the story end?*

REFLECTION

Record the student's reponses to the prompts and questions below.

T: *What part did you like best in this story? Tell me why you liked that part.*

MAKING CONNECTIONS

Note: If the student makes a text-to-self connection in his or her response to the above prompt, skip the following question.

T: *What did this story make you think of?* or *What connections did you make while reading this story?*

4. TEACHER ANALYSIS

ORAL READING

If the student had 4 or more different miscues, use the information recorded on the Record of Oral Reading to complete the chart below.

<table>
<tr><td>

Student problem-solves words using:
- ☐ pictures
- ☐ beginning letter/sound
- ☐ letter-sound clusters
- ☐ onset and rime
- ☐ blending letters/sounds
- ☐ rereading
- ☐ no observable behaviors

</td><td colspan="2">

Number of miscues self-corrected: _____
Number of miscues not self-corrected: _____
Number of words told to the student: _____

</td></tr>
<tr><td></td><td>

Miscues interfered with meaning:
- ☐ never
- ☐ at times
- ☐ often

</td><td>

Miscues included:
- ☐ omissions
- ☐ insertions
- ☐ substitutions that were
  - ☐ visually similar
  - ☐ not visually similar

</td></tr>
<tr><td colspan="3">

Copy each substitution to help analyze the student's attention to visual information.
e.g., <u>couch</u> (substitution)
      chair (text)

</td></tr>
</table>

*DRA*2 Continuum

- Circle the descriptors that best describe the student's reading behaviors and responses.
  1. Use your daily classroom observations and the student's responses to the Reading Engagement questions to select statements that best describe the student's level of Reading Engagement.
  2. Use your recorded observations from this assessment to select the statements that best describe the student's Oral Reading Fluency and Comprehension.
- Add the circled numbers to obtain a total score for each section.
- Record the total scores at the top of page 1.

Note: If the Comprehension score is less than 19, administer *DRA*2 with a lower-level text.

DRA2 CONTINUUM	LEVEL 4			EARLY READER
	EMERGING	**DEVELOPING**	**INDEPENDENT**	**ADVANCED**
Reading Engagement				
Book Selection	**1** Selects new texts from identified leveled sets with teacher support; uncertain about a favorite book	**2** Selects new texts from identified leveled sets with moderate support; tells about favorite book in general terms	**3** Selects new texts from identified leveled sets most of the time; identifies favorite book by title and tells about a particular event	**4** Selects a variety of new texts that are "just right"; identifies favorite book by title and gives an overview of the book
Sustained Reading	**1** Sustains independent reading for a short period of time with much encouragement	**2** Sustains independent reading with moderate encouragement	**3** Sustains independent reading for at least 5 minutes at a time	**4** Sustains independent reading for an extended period of time
Score	2 3	4 5	6 7	8
Oral Reading Fluency				
Phrasing	**1** Reads word-by-word	**2** Reads word-by-word with some short phrases	**3** Reads in short phrases most of the time	**4** Reads in longer phrases at times
Monitoring/Self-Corrections	**1** Self-corrects no miscues	**2** Self-corrects at least 1 miscue and neglects to self-correct other miscues	**3** Self-corrects 2 or more miscues or only makes 1 uncorrected miscue	**4** Self-corrects miscues quickly or reads accurately
Problem-Solving Unknown Words	**1** Stops at difficulty, relying on support to problem-solve unknown words; 3 or more words told by the teacher	**2** At difficulty, initiates problem-solving of a few unknown words; 1 or 2 words told by the teacher	**3** At difficulty, uses 1 or 2 cues to problem-solve unknown words	**4** At difficulty, uses multiple cues to problem-solve unknown words
Accuracy	**1** 91% or less	**2** 93%	**3** 94%–96%	**4** 98%–100%
Score	4 5 6	7 8 9 10	11 12 13 14	15 16
Comprehension				
Previewing	**1** Comments briefly about each event or action only when prompted or is uncertain	**2** Identifies and comments briefly about each event or action with some prompting	**3** Identifies and connects at least 3 key events without prompting; some relevant vocabulary	**4** Identifies and connects at least 4 key events without prompting; relevant vocabulary
Retelling: Sequence of Events	**1** Includes only 1 or 2 events or details (limited retelling)	**2** Includes at least 3 events, generally in random order (partial retelling)	**3** Includes most of the important events from the beginning, middle, and end, generally in sequence	**4** Includes all important events from the beginning, middle, and end in sequence
Retelling: Characters and Details	**1** Refers to characters using general pronouns; may include incorrect information	**2** Refers to characters using appropriate pronouns; includes at least 1 detail; may include some misinterpretation	**3** Refers to most characters by name and includes some important details	**4** Refers to all characters by name and includes most of the important details
Retelling: Vocabulary	**1** Uses general terms or labels; limited understanding of key words/concepts	**2** Uses some language/vocabulary from the text; some understanding of key words/concepts	**3** Uses language/vocabulary from the text; basic understanding of most key words/concepts	**4** Uses important language/vocabulary from the text; good understanding of key words/concepts
Retelling: Teacher Support	**1** Retells with 5 or more questions or prompts	**2** Retells with 3 or 4 questions or prompts	**3** Retells with 1 or 2 questions or prompts	**4** Retells with no questions or prompts
Reflection	**1** Gives an unrelated response, no reason for opinion, or no response	**2** Gives a limited response and/or a general reason for opinion	**3** Gives a specific story event/action <u>and</u> a relevant reason for response (e.g., personal connection)	**4** Gives a response and reason that reflects higher-level thinking (e.g., synthesis/inference)
Making Connections	**1** Makes an unrelated connection, relates an event in the story, or gives no response	**2** Makes a connection that reflects a limited understanding of the story	**3** Makes a literal connection that reflects a basic understanding of the story	**4** Makes a thoughtful connection that reflects a deeper understanding of the story
Score	7 8 9 10 11 12 13	14 15 16 17 18	19 20 21 22 23 24 25	26 27 28

Choose three to five teaching/learning activities on the *DRA2* Focus for Instruction on the next page.

DRA2 FOCUS FOR INSTRUCTION FOR EARLY READERS

READING ENGAGEMENT

Book Selection
☐ Provide guided opportunities to select familiar stories for rereading
☐ Model and support how to select "just right" new texts for independent reading
☐ Model and discuss why readers have favorite books and authors

Sustained Reading
☐ Model and support the use of sustained reading time
☐ Create structures and routines to support buddy reading
☐ Create structures and routines to support reading at home

ORAL READING FLUENCY

Phrasing
☐ Encourage student to read in phrases during shared reading
☐ Show how words are grouped into phrases in big books and poetry charts
☐ Support rereading familiar texts to build fluency

Monitoring/Self-Corrections
☐ Support one-to-one matching as a means to self-monitor
☐ Model and teach how to use known words as a means to self-monitor
☐ Model and support confirming and discounting word choice using meaning, language, and visual information
☐ Demonstrate and teach how to read for meaning, self-correcting when a word doesn't make sense or sound right
☐ Model and teach how to monitor visual information, self-correcting when a word doesn't look right

Problem-Solving Unknown Words
☐ Model and support using beginning letter(s)/sound(s), sentence and/or story structure, as well as meaning (illustrations and background knowledge) to problem-solve unknown words
☐ Teach how to take words apart (onset and rime) to problem-solve unknown words

COMPREHENSION

Previewing
☐ Support creating a story from the illustrations
☐ Model and support previewing a book before reading, during read-aloud and shared reading experiences

Retelling
☐ Model the retelling of familiar stories
☐ Teach the elements in a good retelling
☐ Demonstrate how to create and use story maps to aid retelling
☐ Support retelling a story in sequence
☐ Encourage student to use characters' names when retelling a story
☐ Support using key language/vocabulary from the text in a retelling

Reflection
☐ Support and reinforce student's response to books during read-aloud, and shared and guided reading experiences
☐ Help student identify favorite part of books
☐ Provide opportunities to select a favorite book, toy, TV show, etc., and tell why it is a favorite
☐ Demonstrate how to give reason(s) for one's opinion

Making Connections
☐ Model and teach how to make text-to-self connections
☐ Model and support how to make text-to-text connections

OTHER

_____

_____

_____

_____

_____

_____

_____

Name/Date _____   Teacher/Grade _____

Scores: Reading Engagement ___/8   Oral Reading Fluency ___/16   Comprehension ___/28
Independent Range: 6–7   11–14   19–25

Book Selection   Text selected by: ☐ teacher   ☐ student

1. READING ENGAGEMENT

(If the student has recently answered these questions, skip this section.)

T: Who reads with you or to you at home? _____

T: Would you rather listen to a story or read a story to someone? _____

   Why? _____

T: Tell me about one of your favorite books. _____

2. ORAL READING FLUENCY

INTRODUCTION AND PREVIEW

T: In this story, Time to Play, *Lee and Pam like to play after school, but they often have different things to do. Look at all of the pictures, and tell me what is happening in this story.*

Note the student's use of connecting words (e.g., *and*, *then*, *but*) and vocabulary relevant to the text. You may use general prompts, such as "Now what is happening?" or "Turn the page," but do <u>not</u> ask specific questions. Tally the number of times you prompt.

RECORD OF ORAL READING

Record the student's oral reading behaviors on the Record of Oral Reading below and on the following page.

T: Time to Play. Now, read to find out what Lee and Pam did after school on Monday, Tuesday, Wednesday, and Thursday.

Page 2

Lee   and   Pam   liked   to   play   after   school.

Page 3

But   on   Monday   Lee   went   to

art   class   after   school.

"No   time   to   play   with   Pam,"   he   said.

Time to Play 6

Page 4

On Tuesday Pam went to Grandma's house after school.

"No time to play with Lee," she said.

Page 5

On Wednesday Lee went to the store with his mom.

Page 6

On Thursday Pam had a soccer game.

Page 7

On Friday Pam and Lee had time to play. They had fun.

ORAL READING, PERCENT OF ACCURACY

Count the number of miscues that are not self-corrected. Circle the percent of accuracy based on the number of miscues.

Word Count: 72

	EM	DEV	IND			ADV	
Number of Miscues	6 or more	5	4	3	2	1	0
Percent of Accuracy	92 or less	93	94	96	97	99	100

- If the student's score falls in a shaded area, STOP! Reassess with a lower-level text.
- If the student is reading below the grade-level benchmark, administer *DRA Word Analysis*, beginning with Task 8, at another time.

3. COMPREHENSION

RETELLING

As the student retells, underline and record on the Story Overview the information included in the student's retelling. Please note the student does not need to use the exact words.

T: Close the book, and then say: *Start at the beginning, and tell me what happened in this story.*

Story Overview
Beginning
1. Pam and Lee liked to play after school.

Middle
2. On Monday Lee went to art class after school. He had no time to play with Pam.

3. On Tuesday Pam went to Grandma's house after school. She had no time to play with Lee.

4. On Wednesday Lee went to the store with his mom.

5. On Thursday Pam had a soccer game.

End
6. On Friday Lee and Pam played together. They had fun.

If the retelling is limited, use one or more of the following prompts to gain further information. Place a checkmark by a prompt each time it is used.

- ☐ *Tell me more.*
- ☐ *What happened at the beginning?*
- ☐ *What happened before/after* _____ (an event mentioned by the student)*?*
- ☐ *Who else was in the story?*
- ☐ *How did the story end?*

REFLECTION

Record the student's reponses to the prompts and questions below.

T: *What part did you like best in this story? Tell me why you liked that part.*

MAKING CONNECTIONS

Note: If the student makes a text-to-self connection in his or her response to the above prompt, skip the following question.

T: *What did this story make you think of?* or *What connections did you make while reading this story?*

4. TEACHER ANALYSIS

ORAL READING

If the student had 5 or more different miscues, use the information recorded on the Record of Oral Reading to complete the chart below.

Student problem-solves words using:	Number of miscues self-corrected: _____ Number of miscues not self-corrected: _____ Number of words told to the student: _____	

☐ pictures
☐ beginning letter/sound
☐ letter-sound clusters
☐ onset and rime
☐ blending letters/sounds
☐ rereading
☐ no observable behaviors
	Miscues interfered with meaning:
	☐ never
	☐ at times
	☐ often
		Miscues included:
		☐ omissions
		☐ insertions
		☐ substitutions that were
		    ☐ visually similar
		    ☐ not visually similar

Copy each substitution to help analyze the student's attention to visual information.

e.g., <u>Tuesday</u> (substitution)
    Thursday (text)

DRA2 Continuum

- Circle the descriptors that best describe the student's reading behaviors and responses.
    1. Use your daily classroom observations and the student's responses to the Reading Engagement questions to select statements that best describe the student's level of Reading Engagement.
    2. Use your recorded observations from this assessment to select the statements that best describe the student's Oral Reading Fluency and Comprehension.
- Add the circled numbers to obtain a total score for each section.
- Record the total scores at the top of page 1.

Note: If the Comprehension score is less than 19, administer *DRA2* with a lower-level text.

*DRA*2 CONTINUUM	LEVEL 6		EARLY READER	
	EMERGING	**DEVELOPING**	**INDEPENDENT**	**ADVANCED**
Reading Engagement				
Book Selection	**1** Selects new texts from identified leveled sets with teacher support; uncertain about a favorite book	**2** Selects new texts from identified leveled sets with moderate support; tells about favorite book in general terms	**3** Selects new texts from identified leveled sets most of the time; identifies favorite book by title and tells about a particular event	**4** Selects a variety of new texts that are "just right"; identifies favorite book by title and gives an overview of the book
Sustained Reading	**1** Sustains independent reading for a short period of time with much encouragement	**2** Sustains independent reading with moderate encouragement	**3** Sustains independent reading for at least 5 minutes at a time	**4** Sustains independent reading for an extended period of time
Score	2 3	4 5	6 7	8
Oral Reading Fluency				
Phrasing	**1** Reads word-by-word	**2** Reads word-by-word with some short phrases	**3** Reads in short phrases most of the time	**4** Reads in longer phrases at times
Monitoring/Self-Corrections	**1** Self-corrects no miscues	**2** Self-corrects at least 1 miscue and neglects to self-correct other miscues	**3** Self-corrects 2 or more miscues or only makes 1 uncorrected miscue	**4** Self-corrects miscues quickly or reads accurately
Problem-Solving Unknown Words	**1** Stops at difficulty, relying on support to problem-solve unknown words; 3 or more words told by the teacher	**2** At difficulty, initiates problem-solving of a few unknown words; 1 or 2 words told by the teacher	**3** At difficulty, uses 1 or 2 cues to problem-solve unknown words	**4** At difficulty, uses multiple cues to problem-solve unknown words
Accuracy	**1** 92% or less	**2** 93%	**3** 94%–97%	**4** 99%–100%
Score	4 5 6	7 8 9 10	11 12 13 14	15 16
Comprehension				
Previewing	**1** Comments briefly about each event or action only when prompted or is uncertain	**2** Identifies and comments briefly about each event or action with some prompting	**3** Identifies and connects at least 3 key events without prompting; some relevant vocabulary	**4** Identifies and connects at least 4 key events without prompting; relevant vocabulary
Retelling: Sequence of Events	**1** Includes only 1 or 2 events or details (limited retelling)	**2** Includes at least 3 events, generally in random order (partial retelling)	**3** Includes most of the important events from the beginning, middle, and end, generally in sequence	**4** Includes all important events from the beginning, middle, and end in sequence
Retelling: Characters and Details	**1** Refers to characters using general pronouns; may include incorrect information	**2** Refers to characters using appropriate pronouns; includes at least 1 detail; may include some misinterpretation	**3** Refers to most characters by name and includes some important details	**4** Refers to all characters by name and includes most of the important details
Retelling: Vocabulary	**1** Uses general terms or labels; limited understanding of key words/concepts	**2** Uses some language/ vocabulary from the text; some understanding of key words/concepts	**3** Uses language/ vocabulary from the text; basic understanding of most key words/concepts	**4** Uses important language/vocabulary from the text; good understanding of key words/concepts
Retelling: Teacher Support	**1** Retells with 5 or more questions or prompts	**2** Retells with 3 or 4 questions or prompts	**3** Retells with 1 or 2 questions or prompts	**4** Retells with no questions or prompts
Reflection	**1** Gives an unrelated response, no reason for opinion, or no response	**2** Gives a limited response and/or a general reason for opinion	**3** Gives a specific story event/action <u>and</u> a relevant reason for response (e.g., personal connection)	**4** Gives a response and reason that reflects higher-level thinking (e.g., synthesis/inference)
Making Connections	**1** Makes an unrelated connection, relates an event in the story, or gives no response	**2** Makes a connection that reflects a limited understanding of the story	**3** Makes a literal connection that reflects a basic understanding of the story	**4** Makes a thoughtful connection that reflects a deeper understanding of the story
Score	7 8 9 10 11 12 13	14 15 16 17 18	19 20 21 22 23 24 25	26 27 28

Choose three to five teaching/learning activities on the *DRA*2 Focus for Instruction on the next page.

Time to Play **6**

*DRA*2 FOCUS FOR INSTRUCTION FOR EARLY READERS

READING ENGAGEMENT

Book Selection
- ☐ Provide guided opportunities to select familiar stories for rereading
- ☐ Model and support how to select "just right" new texts for independent reading
- ☐ Model and discuss why readers have favorite books and authors

Sustained Reading
- ☐ Model and support the use of sustained reading time
- ☐ Create structures and routines to support buddy reading
- ☐ Create structures and routines to support reading at home

ORAL READING FLUENCY

Phrasing
- ☐ Encourage student to read in phrases during shared reading
- ☐ Show how words are grouped into phrases in big books and poetry charts
- ☐ Support rereading familiar texts to build fluency

Monitoring/Self-Corrections
- ☐ Support one-to-one matching as a means to self-monitor
- ☐ Model and teach how to use known words as a means to self-monitor
- ☐ Model and support confirming and discounting word choice using meaning, language, and visual information
- ☐ Demonstrate and teach how to read for meaning, self-correcting when a word doesn't make sense or sound right
- ☐ Model and teach how to monitor visual information, self-correcting when a word doesn't look right

Problem-Solving Unknown Words
- ☐ Model and support using beginning letter(s)/sound(s), sentence and/or story structure, as well as meaning (illustrations and background knowledge) to problem-solve unknown words
- ☐ Teach how to take words apart (onset and rime) to problem-solve unknown words

COMPREHENSION

Previewing
- ☐ Support creating a story from the illustrations
- ☐ Model and support previewing a book before reading, during read-aloud and shared reading experiences

Retelling
- ☐ Model the retelling of familiar stories
- ☐ Teach the elements in a good retelling
- ☐ Demonstrate how to create and use story maps to aid retelling
- ☐ Support retelling a story in sequence
- ☐ Encourage student to use characters' names when retelling a story
- ☐ Support using key language/vocabulary from the text in a retelling

Reflection
- ☐ Support and reinforce student's response to books during read-aloud, and shared and guided reading experiences
- ☐ Help student identify favorite part of books
- ☐ Provide opportunities to select a favorite book, toy, TV show, etc., and tell why it is a favorite
- ☐ Demonstrate how to give reason(s) for one's opinion

Making Connections
- ☐ Model and teach how to make text-to-self connections
- ☐ Model and support how to make text-to-text connections

OTHER

_____
_____
_____
_____
_____
_____
_____

Time to Play 6

Name/Date _____ Teacher/Grade _____

Scores: Reading Engagement ___/8   Oral Reading Fluency ___/16   Comprehension ___/28
Independent Range: 6–7   11–14   19–25

Book Selection   Text selected by: ☐ teacher   ☐ student

1. READING ENGAGEMENT

(If the student has recently answered these questions, skip this section.)

T: *Who reads with you or to you at home?* _____

T: *Would you rather listen to a story or read a story to someone?* _____

  Why? _____

T: *Tell me about one of your favorite books.* _____

2. ORAL READING FLUENCY

INTRODUCTION AND PREVIEW

T: *In this story,* Why Are We Stopping?, *a police officer stops a bus. A truck and car driver don't know why they are stopping. Look at all the pictures, and tell me what is happening in this story.*

Note the student's use of connecting words (e.g., *and, then, but*) and vocabulary relevant to the text. You may use general prompts, such as "Now what is happening?" or "Turn the page," but do not ask specific questions. Tally the number of times you prompt.

RECORD OF ORAL READING

Record the student's oral reading behaviors on the Record of Oral Reading below and on the following page.

T: Why Are We Stopping? *Now, read to find out who stops.*

Page 2

"Stop!" said the police officer.

The bus stopped.

Page 3

A truck stopped behind the bus.

"Why are we stopping?"

said the truck driver.

Page 4

A car stopped behind the truck.

"Why are we stopping?"

said the car driver.

Page 5

A mother duck and her babies

went across the street.

Page 6

"Go," said the police officer.

The bus went on.

The truck and the car went on.

Page 7

Then the mother duck and her babies

went for a swim.

ORAL READING, PERCENT OF ACCURACY

Count the number of miscues that are not self-corrected. Circle the percent of accuracy based on the number of miscues.

Word Count: 73

	EM	DEV	IND			ADV	
Number of Miscues	6 or more	5	4	3	2	1	0
Percent of Accuracy	92 or less	93	95	96	97	99	100

- If the student's score falls in a shaded area, STOP! Reassess with a lower-level text.
- If the student is reading below the grade-level benchmark, administer *DRA Word Analysis,* beginning with Task 8, at another time.

Why Are We Stopping? ⑥

3. COMPREHENSION

RETELLING

As the student retells, underline and record on the Story Overview the information included in the student's retelling. Please note the student does not need to use the exact words.

T: Close the book, and then say: *Start at the beginning, and tell me what happened in this story.*

Story Overview
Beginning
1. The police officer stopped the bus.

Middle
2. The truck stopped behind the bus, and the driver said, "Why are we stopping?"

3. The car stopped behind the truck, and the driver said, "Why are we stopping?"

4. A mother duck and her babies went across the street.

5. The police officer said, "Go," and the bus, the truck, and the car went on.

End
6. The ducks swam in the pond.

If the retelling is limited, use one or more of the following prompts to gain further information. Place a checkmark by a prompt each time it is used.

- ☐ *Tell me more.*
- ☐ *What happened at the beginning?*
- ☐ *What happened before/after* _____ (an event mentioned by the student)*?*
- ☐ *Who else was in the story?*
- ☐ *How did the story end?*

REFLECTION

Record the student's reponses to the prompts and questions below.

T: What part did you like best in this story? Tell me why you liked that part.

MAKING CONNECTIONS

Note: If the student makes a text-to-self connection in his or her response to the above prompt, skip the following question.

T: What did this story make you think of? or *What connections did you make while reading this story?*

Why Are We Stopping? ❻

Teacher Observation Guide   ***Why Are We Stopping?***   Level 6, Page 4

4. TEACHER ANALYSIS

ORAL READING

If the student had 5 or more different miscues, use the information recorded on the Record of Oral Reading to complete the chart below.

Student problem-solves words using:	Number of miscues self-corrected: _____ Number of miscues not self-corrected: _____ Number of words told to the student: _____	

☐ pictures
 ☐ beginning letter/sound
 ☐ letter-sound clusters
 ☐ onset and rime
 ☐ blending letters/sounds
 ☐ rereading
 ☐ no observable behaviors
	Miscues interfered with meaning:
	 ☐ never
	 ☐ at times
	 ☐ often
		Miscues included:
		 ☐ omissions
		 ☐ insertions
		 ☐ substitutions that were
		  ☐ visually similar
		  ☐ not visually similar

Copy each substitution to help analyze the student's attention to visual information.

e.g., <u>policeman</u> (substitution)
      police officer (text)

*DRA*2 Continuum

- Circle the descriptors that best describe the student's reading behaviors and responses.
  1. Use your daily classroom observations and the student's responses to the Reading Engagement questions to select statements that best describe the student's level of Reading Engagement.
  2. Use your recorded observations from this assessment to select the statements that best describe the student's Oral Reading Fluency and Comprehension.
- Add the circled numbers to obtain a total score for each section.
- Record the total scores at the top of page 1.

Note: If the Comprehension score is less than 19, administer *DRA*2 with a lower-level text.

Why Are We Stopping? ⑥

DRA2 K–3 © Pearson Education, Inc. All rights reserved.

DRA2 CONTINUUM	LEVEL 6			EARLY READER
	EMERGING	**DEVELOPING**	**INDEPENDENT**	**ADVANCED**
Reading Engagement				
Book Selection	**1** Selects new texts from identified leveled sets with teacher support; uncertain about a favorite book	**2** Selects new texts from identified leveled sets with moderate support; tells about favorite book in general terms	**3** Selects new texts from identified leveled sets most of the time; identifies favorite book by title and tells about a particular event	**4** Selects a variety of new texts that are "just right"; identifies favorite book by title and gives an overview of the book
Sustained Reading	**1** Sustains independent reading for a short period of time with much encouragement	**2** Sustains independent reading with moderate encouragement	**3** Sustains independent reading for at least 5 minutes at a time	**4** Sustains independent reading for an extended period of time
Score	2 3	4 5	6 7	8
Oral Reading Fluency				
Phrasing	**1** Reads word-by-word	**2** Reads word-by-word with some short phrases	**3** Reads in short phrases most of the time	**4** Reads in longer phrases at times
Monitoring/Self-Corrections	**1** Self-corrects no miscues	**2** Self-corrects at least 1 miscue and neglects to self-correct other miscues	**3** Self-corrects 2 or more miscues or only makes 1 uncorrected miscue	**4** Self-corrects miscues quickly or reads accurately
Problem-Solving Unknown Words	**1** Stops at difficulty, relying on support to problem-solve unknown words; 3 or more words told by the teacher	**2** At difficulty, initiates problem-solving of a few unknown words; 1 or 2 words told by the teacher	**3** At difficulty, uses 1 or 2 cues to problem-solve unknown words	**4** At difficulty, uses multiple cues to problem-solve unknown words
Accuracy	**1** 92% or less	**2** 93%	**3** 95%–97%	**4** 99%–100%
Score	4 5 6	7 8 9 10	11 12 13 14	15 16
Comprehension				
Previewing	**1** Comments briefly about each event or action only when prompted or is uncertain	**2** Identifies and comments briefly about each event or action with some prompting	**3** Identifies and connects at least 3 key events without prompting; some relevant vocabulary	**4** Identifies and connects at least 4 key events without prompting; relevant vocabulary
Retelling: Sequence of Events	**1** Includes only 1 or 2 events or details (limited retelling)	**2** Includes at least 3 events, generally in random order (partial retelling)	**3** Includes most of the important events from the beginning, middle, and end, generally in sequence	**4** Includes all important events from the beginning, middle, and end in sequence
Retelling: Characters and Details	**1** Refers to characters using general pronouns; may include incorrect information	**2** Refers to characters using appropriate pronouns; includes at least 1 detail; may include some misinterpretation	**3** Refers to most characters by name and includes some important details	**4** Refers to all characters by name and includes most of the important details
Retelling: Vocabulary	**1** Uses general terms or labels; limited understanding of key words/concepts	**2** Uses some language/vocabulary from the text; some understanding of key words/concepts	**3** Uses language/vocabulary from the text; basic understanding of most key words/concepts	**4** Uses important language/vocabulary from the text; good understanding of key words/concepts
Retelling: Teacher Support	**1** Retells with 5 or more questions or prompts	**2** Retells with 3 or 4 questions or prompts	**3** Retells with 1 or 2 questions or prompts	**4** Retells with no questions or prompts
Reflection	**1** Gives an unrelated response, no reason for opinion, or no response	**2** Gives a limited response and/or a general reason for opinion	**3** Gives a specific story event/action <u>and</u> a relevant reason for response (e.g., personal connection)	**4** Gives a response and reason that reflects higher-level thinking (e.g., synthesis/inference)
Making Connections	**1** Makes an unrelated connection, relates an event in the story, or gives no response	**2** Makes a connection that reflects a limited understanding of the story	**3** Makes a literal connection that reflects a basic understanding of the story	**4** Makes a thoughtful connection that reflects a deeper understanding of the story
Score	7 8 9 10 11 12 13	14 15 16 17 18	19 20 21 22 23 24 25	26 27 28

Choose three to five teaching/learning activities on the *DRA2* Focus for Instruction on the next page.

Why Are We Stopping? **6**

DRA2 FOCUS FOR INSTRUCTION FOR EARLY READERS

READING ENGAGEMENT

Book Selection
☐ Provide guided opportunities to select familiar stories for rereading
☐ Model and support how to select "just right" new texts for independent reading
☐ Model and discuss why readers have favorite books and authors

Sustained Reading
☐ Model and support the use of sustained reading time
☐ Create structures and routines to support buddy reading
☐ Create structures and routines to support reading at home

ORAL READING FLUENCY

Phrasing
☐ Encourage student to read in phrases during shared reading
☐ Show how words are grouped into phrases in big books and poetry charts
☐ Support rereading familiar texts to build fluency

Monitoring/Self-Corrections
☐ Support one-to-one matching as a means to self-monitor
☐ Model and teach how to use known words as a means to self-monitor
☐ Model and support confirming and discounting word choice using meaning, language, and visual information
☐ Demonstrate and teach how to read for meaning, self-correcting when a word doesn't make sense or sound right
☐ Model and teach how to monitor visual information, self-correcting when a word doesn't look right

Problem-Solving Unknown Words
☐ Model and support using beginning letter(s)/sound(s), sentence and/or story structure, as well as meaning (illustrations and background knowledge) to problem-solve unknown words
☐ Teach how to take words apart (onset and rime) to problem-solve unknown words

COMPREHENSION

Previewing
☐ Support creating a story from the illustrations
☐ Model and support previewing a book before reading, during read-aloud and shared reading experiences

Retelling
☐ Model the retelling of familiar stories
☐ Teach the elements in a good retelling
☐ Demonstrate how to create and use story maps to aid retelling
☐ Support retelling a story in sequence
☐ Encourage student to use characters' names when retelling a story
☐ Support using key language/vocabulary from the text in a retelling

Reflection
☐ Support and reinforce student's response to books during read-aloud, and shared and guided reading experiences
☐ Help student identify favorite part of books
☐ Provide opportunities to select a favorite book, toy, TV show, etc., and tell why it is a favorite
☐ Demonstrate how to give reason(s) for one's opinion

Making Connections
☐ Model and teach how to make text-to-self connections
☐ Model and support how to make text-to-text connections

OTHER

_____

_____

_____

_____

_____

_____

_____

_____

Why Are We Stopping? ❻

Name/Date _____   Teacher/Grade _____

Scores: Reading Engagement ___/8   Oral Reading Fluency ___/16   Comprehension ___/28
Independent Range: 6–7   11–14   19–25

Book Selection   Text selected by: ☐ teacher   ☐ student

1. READING ENGAGEMENT

(If the student has recently answered these questions, skip this section.)

T: Tell me about one of your favorite books. _____

T: Do you like to read   ☐ *alone,*   ☐ *with a buddy, or*   ☐ *with a group?*

    *Why?*_____

*T: Whom do you read with at home?*_____

2. ORAL READING FLUENCY

INTRODUCTION AND PREVIEW

T: In this story, Duke, *a boy named Jim has a black-and-white dog named Duke. Duke can do lots of tricks. Look at the pictures, and tell me what is happening in this story.*

Note the student's use of connecting words (e.g., *and, then, but*) and vocabulary relevant to the text. You may use general prompts, such as "Now what is happening?" or "Turn the page," but do <u>not</u> ask specific questions. Tally the number of times you prompt.

RECORD OF ORAL READING

Record the student's oral reading behaviors on the Record of Oral Reading below and on the following page.

T: Duke. *Now, read to find out what Duke can do.*

Page 2

Jim   had   a   dog.   The   dog   was

black   and   white.   The   dog's   name

was   Duke.

Page 3

Duke   was   a   big   dog.   He   had

big   feet.   Jim   liked   his   dog.

Page 4

Duke liked to play with Jim.
He could do lots of tricks.
He could sit up and shake
hands. "Good dog!" said Jim.

Page 5

He could jump over a stick.
"Good dog!" said Jim.

Page 6

Jim could throw a ball and
Duke could get it. "Good dog!"
said Jim.

Page 7

Duke liked to lick Jim's face, too.
He was a good dog!

ORAL READING, PERCENT OF ACCURACY

Count the number of miscues that are not self-corrected. Circle the percent of accuracy based on the number of miscues.

Word Count: 87

	EM	DEV	IND			ADV		
Number of Miscues	7 or more	6	5	4	3	2	1	0
Percent of Accuracy	92 or less	93	94	95	97	98	99	100

- If the student's score falls in a shaded area, STOP! Reassess with a lower-level text.
- If the student is reading below the grade-level benchmark, administer *DRA Word Analysis*, beginning with Task 8, at another time.

Duke 8

3. COMPREHENSION

RETELLING

As the student retells, underline and record on the Story Overview the information included in the student's retelling. Please note the student does not need to use the exact words.

T: Close the book, and then say: ***Start at the beginning, and tell me what happened in this story.***

Story Overview
Beginning
1. Jim has a black and white dog with big feet named Duke.

2. Duke likes to play with Jim, and he can do lots of tricks.

Middle
3. Duke sits up and shakes hands, and Jim says, "Good dog!"

4. Duke jumps over a stick, and Jim says, "Good dog!"

5. Duke gets the ball, and Jim says, "Good dog!"

End
6. Duke likes to lick Jim's face. Duke is a good dog.

If the retelling is limited, use one or more of the following prompts to gain further information. Place a checkmark by a prompt each time it is used.

- ☐ *Tell me more.*
- ☐ *What happened at the beginning?*
- ☐ *What happened before/after* _____ (an event mentioned by the student)*?*
- ☐ *Who else was in the story?*
- ☐ *How did the story end?*

REFLECTION

Record the student's responses to the prompts and questions below.

T: ***What part did you like best in this story? Tell me why you liked that part.***

MAKING CONNECTIONS

Note: If the student makes a text-to-self connection in his or her response to the above prompt, skip the following question.

T: ***What did this story make you think of?*** or ***What connections did you make while reading this story?***

4. TEACHER ANALYSIS

ORAL READING

If the student had 5 or more different miscues, use the information recorded on the Record of Oral Reading to complete the chart below.

Student problem-solves words using:	Number of miscues self-corrected: _____	
☐ pictures	Number of miscues not self-corrected: _____	
☐ beginning letter/sound	Number of words told to the student: _____	
☐ letter-sound clusters	**Miscues interfered with meaning:**	**Miscues included:**
☐ onset and rime	☐ never	☐ omissions
☐ blending letters/sounds	☐ at times	☐ insertions
☐ rereading	☐ often	☐ substitutions that were
☐ no observable behaviors		☐ visually similar
		☐ not visually similar

Copy each substitution to help analyze the student's attention to visual information.

e.g., <u>have</u> (substitution)

     had (text)

*DRA*2 Continuum

• Circle the descriptors that best describe the student's reading behaviors and responses.

    1. Use your daily classroom observations and the student's responses to the Reading Engagement questions to select statements that best describe the student's level of Reading Engagement.

    2. Use your recorded observations from this assessment to select the statements that best describe the student's Oral Reading Fluency and Comprehension.

  • Add the circled numbers to obtain a total score for each section.

  • Record the total scores at the top of page 1.

Note: If the Comprehension score is less than 19, administer *DRA*2 with a lower-level text.

*DRA*2 CONTINUUM	LEVEL 8			EARLY READER
	EMERGING	**DEVELOPING**	**INDEPENDENT**	**ADVANCED**
Reading Engagement				
Book Selection	1 Selects new texts from identified leveled sets with teacher support; uncertain about a favorite book	2 Selects new texts from identified leveled sets with moderate support; tells about favorite book in general terms	3 Selects new texts from identified leveled sets most of the time; identifies favorite book by title and tells about a particular event	4 Selects a variety of new texts that are "just right"; identifies favorite book by title and gives an overview of the book
Sustained Reading	1 Sustains independent reading for a short period of time with much encouragement	2 Sustains independent reading with moderate encouragement	3 Sustains independent reading for at least 5 minutes at a time	4 Sustains independent reading for an extended period of time
Score	2 3	4 5	6 7	8
Oral Reading Fluency				
Phrasing	1 Reads word-by-word	2 Reads word-by-word with some short phrases	3 Reads in short phrases most of the time	4 Reads in longer phrases at times
Monitoring/Self-Corrections	1 Self-corrects no miscues	2 Self-corrects at least 1 miscue and neglects to self-correct other miscues	3 Self-corrects 2 or more miscues or only makes 1 uncorrected miscue	4 Self-corrects miscues quickly or reads accurately
Problem-Solving Unknown Words	1 Stops at difficulty, relying on support to problem-solve unknown words; 3 or more words told by the teacher	2 At difficulty, initiates problem-solving of a few unknown words; 1 or 2 words told by the teacher	3 At difficulty, uses 1 or 2 cues to problem-solve unknown words	4 At difficulty, uses multiple cues to problem-solve unknown words
Accuracy	1 92% or less	2 93%	3 94%–97%	4 98%–100%
Score	4 5 6	7 8 9 10	11 12 13 14	15 16
Comprehension				
Previewing	1 Comments briefly about each event or action only when prompted or is uncertain	2 Identifies and comments briefly about each event or action with some prompting	3 Identifies and connects at least 3 key events without prompting; some relevant vocabulary	4 Identifies and connects at least 4 key events without prompting; relevant vocabulary
Retelling: Sequence of Events	1 Includes only 1 or 2 events or details (limited retelling)	2 Includes at least 3 events, generally in random order (partial retelling)	3 Includes most of the important events from the beginning, middle, and end, generally in sequence	4 Includes all important events from the beginning, middle, and end in sequence
Retelling: Characters and Details	1 Refers to characters using general pronouns; may include incorrect information	2 Refers to characters using appropriate pronouns; includes at least 1 detail; may include some misinterpretation	3 Refers to most characters by name and includes some important details	4 Refers to all characters by name and includes most of the important details
Retelling: Vocabulary	1 Uses general terms or labels; limited understanding of key words/concepts	2 Uses some language/vocabulary from the text; some understanding of key words/concepts	3 Uses language/vocabulary from the text; basic understanding of most key words/concepts	4 Uses important language/vocabulary from the text; good understanding of key words/concepts
Retelling: Teacher Support	1 Retells with 5 or more questions or prompts	2 Retells with 3 or 4 questions or prompts	3 Retells with 1 or 2 questions or prompts	4 Retells with no questions or prompts
Reflection	1 Gives an unrelated response, no reason for opinion, or no response	2 Gives a limited response and/or a general reason for opinion	3 Gives a specific story event/action <u>and</u> a relevant reason for response (e.g., personal connection)	4 Gives a response and reason that reflects higher-level thinking (e.g., synthesis/inference)
Making Connections	1 Makes an unrelated connection, relates an event in the story, or gives no response	2 Makes a connection that reflects a limited understanding of the story	3 Makes a literal connection that reflects a basic understanding of the story	4 Makes a thoughtful connection that reflects a deeper understanding of the story
Score	7 8 9 10 11 12 13	14 15 16 17 18	19 20 21 22 23 24 25	26 27 28

Choose three to five teaching/learning activities on the *DRA*2 Focus for Instruction on the next page.

Duke 8

DRA2 FOCUS FOR INSTRUCTION FOR EARLY READERS

READING ENGAGEMENT

Book Selection
☐ Provide guided opportunities to select familiar stories for rereading
☐ Model and support how to select "just right" new texts for independent reading
☐ Model and discuss why readers have favorite books and authors

Sustained Reading
☐ Model and support the use of sustained reading time
☐ Create structures and routines to support buddy reading
☐ Create structures and routines to support reading at home

ORAL READING FLUENCY

Phrasing
☐ Encourage student to read in phrases during shared reading
☐ Show how words are grouped into phrases in big books and poetry charts
☐ Support rereading familiar texts to build fluency

Monitoring/Self-Corrections
☐ Support one-to-one matching as a means to self-monitor
☐ Model and teach how to use known words as a means to self-monitor
☐ Model and support confirming and discounting word choice using meaning, language, and visual information
☐ Demonstrate and teach how to read for meaning, self-correcting when a word doesn't make sense or sound right
☐ Model and teach how to monitor visual information, self-correcting when a word doesn't look right

Problem-Solving Unknown Words
☐ Model and support using beginning letter(s)/sound(s), sentence and/or story structure, as well as meaning (illustrations and background knowledge) to problem-solve unknown words
☐ Model and support how to take words apart (onset and rime) to problem-solve unknown words

COMPREHENSION

Previewing
☐ Support creating a story from the illustrations
☐ Model and support previewing a book before reading, during read-aloud and shared reading experiences

Retelling
☐ Model the retelling of familiar stories
☐ Model and teach the elements in a good retelling
☐ Demonstrate how to create and use story maps to aid retelling
☐ Support retelling a story in sequence
☐ Encourage student to use characters' names when retelling a story
☐ Model and support using key language/vocabulary from the text in a retelling

Reflection
☐ Support and reinforce student's response to books during read-aloud, and shared and guided reading experiences
☐ Help student identify favorite part of books
☐ Provide opportunities to select a favorite book, toy, TV show, etc., and tell why it is a favorite
☐ Demonstrate how to give reason(s) for one's opinion

Making Connections
☐ Model and teach how to make text-to-self connections
☐ Model and support how to make text-to-text connections

OTHER

_____

_____

_____

_____

_____

_____

Duke 8

Name/Date _____   Teacher/Grade _____

Scores: Reading Engagement ___/8   Oral Reading Fluency ___/16   Comprehension ___/28
Independent Range: 6–7   11–14   19–25

Book Selection   Text selected by: ☐ teacher   ☐ student

1. READING ENGAGEMENT

(If the student has recently answered these questions, skip this section.)

T: **Tell me about one of your favorite books.** _____

T: **Do you like to read** ☐ *alone,* ☐ *with a buddy, or* ☐ *with a group?* _____

    Why? _____

T: **Whom do you read with at home?** _____

2. ORAL READING FLUENCY

INTRODUCTION AND PREVIEW

T: **In this story,** The Lost Book, *it is time to take back the library books. One book is missing. The teacher and children need to find the lost book. Look at the pictures, and tell me what is happening in this story.*

Note the student's use of connecting words (e.g., *and, then, but*) and vocabulary relevant to the text. You may use general prompts, such as "Now what is happening?" or "Turn the page," but do not ask specific questions. Tally the number of times you prompt.

T: **The Lost Book.** *Now, read to find out where the children look for the lost book.*

RECORD OF ORAL READING

Record the student's oral reading behaviors on the Record of Oral Reading below and on the following page.

Page 2

It was time to take the
books back to the library.

Page 3

"We had ten books," said the teacher.
"But now we have nine! We must find
the lost book."

Page 4

Two boys looked under the rug. They found one black bug and one penny, but no book.

Page 5

Two girls looked behind a bookcase. They found a yellow ball and some blocks, but no book.

Page 6

A boy and a girl looked in their backpacks. They found no books.

Page 7

The teacher looked under some papers on his desk. "I found it!" he said.

ORAL READING, PERCENT OF ACCURACY

Count the number of miscues that are not self-corrected. Circle the percent of accuracy based on the number of miscues.

Word Count: 90

	EM	DEV	IND			ADV		
Number of Miscues	7 or more	6	5	4	3	2	1	0
Percent of Accuracy	92 or less	93	94	96	97	98	99	100

- If the student's score falls in a shaded area, STOP! Reassess with a lower-level text.
- If the student is reading below the grade-level benchmark, administer *DRA Word Analysis*, beginning with Task 8, at another time.

3. COMPREHENSION

RETELLING

As the student retells, underline and record on the Story Overview the information included in the student's retelling. Please note the student does not need to use the exact words.

T: Close the book, and then say: ***Start at the beginning, and tell me what happened in this story.***

Story Overview
Beginning
1. It was time to take books back to the library, but one book was missing.

2. The teacher told the children, "We must find the lost book."

Middle
3. Two boys looked under a rug and found one black bug and one penny, but no book.

4. Two girls looked behind a bookcase and found a yellow ball and some blocks, but no book.

5. A boy and a girl looked in their backpacks and found no book.

End
6. The teacher looked under some papers on his desk and found the book.

If the retelling is limited, use one or more of the following prompts to gain further information. Place a checkmark by a prompt each time it is used.

☐ *Tell me more.*
☐ *What happened at the beginning?*
☐ *What happened before/after* _____ (an event mentioned by the student)*?*
☐ *Who else was in the story?*
☐ *How did the story end?*

REFLECTION

Record the student's responses to the prompts and questions below.

T: *What part did you like the best in this story? Tell me why you liked that part.*

MAKING CONNECTIONS

Note: If the student makes a text-to-self connection in his or her response to the above prompt, skip the following question.

T: *What did this story make you think of?* or *What connections did you make while reading this story?*

4. TEACHER ANALYSIS

ORAL READING

If the student had 5 or more different miscues, use the information recorded on the Record of Oral Reading to complete the chart below.

<table>
<tr>
<td>

Student problem-solves words using:

☐ pictures

☐ beginning letter/sound

☐ letter-sound clusters

☐ onset and rime

☐ blending letters/sounds

☐ rereading

☐ no observable behaviors

</td>
<td colspan="2">

Number of miscues self-corrected: _____

Number of miscues not self-corrected: _____

Number of words told to the student: _____

</td>
</tr>
<tr>
<td></td>
<td>

Miscues interfered with meaning:

☐ never

☐ at times

☐ often

</td>
<td>

Miscues included:

☐ omissions

☐ insertions

☐ substitutions that were

    ☐ visually similar

    ☐ not visually similar

</td>
</tr>
<tr>
<td colspan="3">

Copy each substitution to help analyze the student's attention to visual information.

e.g., <u>bookbags</u> (substitution)

     backpacks (text)

</td>
</tr>
</table>

DRA2 Continuum

- Circle the descriptors that best describe the student's reading behaviors and responses.
    1. Use your daily classroom observations and the student's responses to the Reading Engagement questions to select statements that best describe the student's level of Reading Engagement.
    2. Use your recorded observations from this assessment to select the statements that best describe the student's Oral Reading Fluency and Comprehension.
- Add the circled numbers to obtain a total score for each section.
- Record the total scores at the top of page 1.

Note: If the Comprehension score is less than 19, administer *DRA2* with a lower-level text.

*DRA*2 CONTINUUM	LEVEL 8			EARLY READER
	EMERGING	**DEVELOPING**	**INDEPENDENT**	**ADVANCED**
Reading Engagement				
Book Selection	1 Selects new texts from identified leveled sets with teacher support; uncertain about a favorite book	2 Selects new texts from identified leveled sets with moderate support; tells about favorite book in general terms	3 Selects new texts from identified leveled sets most of the time; identifies favorite book by title and tells about a particular event	4 Selects a variety of new texts that are "just right"; identifies favorite book by title and gives an overview of the book
Sustained Reading	1 Sustains independent reading for a short period of time with much encouragement	2 Sustains independent reading with moderate encouragement	3 Sustains independent reading for at least 5 minutes at a time	4 Sustains independent reading for an extended period of time
Score	2 3	4 5	6 7	8
Oral Reading Fluency				
Phrasing	1 Reads word-by-word	2 Reads word-by-word with some short phrases	3 Reads in short phrases most of the time	4 Reads in longer phrases at times
Monitoring/Self-Corrections	1 Self-corrects no miscues	2 Self-corrects at least 1 miscue and neglects to self-correct other miscues	3 Self-corrects 2 or more miscues or only makes 1 uncorrected miscue	4 Self-corrects miscues quickly or reads accurately
Problem-Solving Unknown Words	1 Stops at difficulty, relying on support to problem-solve unknown words; 3 or more words told by the teacher	2 At difficulty, initiates problem-solving of a few unknown words; 1 or 2 words told by the teacher	3 At difficulty, uses 1 or 2 cues to problem-solve unknown words	4 At difficulty, uses multiple cues to problem-solve unknown words
Accuracy	1 92% or less	2 93%	3 94%–97%	4 98%–100%
Score	4 5 6	7 8 9 10	11 12 13 14	15 16
Comprehension				
Previewing	1 Comments briefly about each event or action only when prompted or is uncertain	2 Identifies and comments briefly about each event or action with some prompting	3 Identifies and connects at least 3 key events without prompting; some relevant vocabulary	4 Identifies and connects at least 4 key events without prompting; relevant vocabulary
Retelling: Sequence of Events	1 Includes only 1 or 2 events or details (limited retelling)	2 Includes at least 3 events, generally in random order (partial retelling)	3 Includes most of the important events from the beginning, middle, and end, generally in sequence	4 Includes all important events from the beginning, middle, and end in sequence
Retelling: Characters and Details	1 Refers to characters using general pronouns; may include incorrect information	2 Refers to characters using appropriate pronouns; includes at least 1 detail; may include some misinterpretation	3 Refers to most characters by name and includes some important details	4 Refers to all characters by name and includes most of the important details
Retelling: Vocabulary	1 Uses general terms or labels; limited understanding of key words/concepts	2 Uses some language/vocabulary from the text; some understanding of key words/concepts	3 Uses language/vocabulary from the text; basic understanding of most key words/concepts	4 Uses important language/vocabulary from the text; good understanding of key words/concepts
Retelling: Teacher Support	1 Retells with 5 or more questions or prompts	2 Retells with 3 or 4 questions or prompts	3 Retells with 1 or 2 questions or prompts	4 Retells with no questions or prompts
Reflection	1 Gives an unrelated response; no reason for opinion or no response	2 Gives a limited response and/or a general reason for opinion	3 Gives a specific story event/action and a relevant reason for response (e.g., personal connection)	4 Gives a response and reason that reflects higher-level thinking (e.g., synthesis/inference)
Making Connections	1 Makes an unrelated connection, relates an event in the story, or gives no response	2 Makes a connection that reflects a limited understanding of the story	3 Makes a literal connection that reflects a basic understanding of the story	4 Makes a thoughtful connection that reflects a deeper understanding of the story
Score	7 8 9 10 11 12 13	14 15 16 17 18	19 20 21 22 23 24 25	26 27 28

Choose three to five teaching/learning activities on the *DRA*2 Focus for Instruction on the next page.

DRA2 FOCUS FOR INSTRUCTION FOR EARLY READERS

READING ENGAGEMENT

Book Selection
☐ Provide guided opportunities to select familiar stories for rereading
☐ Model and support how to select "just right" new texts for independent reading
☐ Model and discuss why readers have favorite books and authors

Sustained Reading
☐ Model and support the use of sustained reading time
☐ Create structures and routines to support buddy reading
☐ Create structures and routines to support reading at home

ORAL READING FLUENCY

Phrasing
☐ Encourage student to read in phrases during shared reading
☐ Show how words are grouped into phrases in big books and poetry charts
☐ Support rereading familiar texts to build fluency

Monitoring/Self-Corrections
☐ Support one-to-one matching as a means to self-monitor
☐ Model and teach how to use known words as a means to self-monitor
☐ Model and support confirming and discounting word choice using meaning, language, and visual information
☐ Demonstrate how to read for meaning, self-correcting when a word doesn't make sense or sound right
☐ Model and teach how to monitor visual information, self-correcting when a word doesn't look right

Problem-Solving Unknown Words
☐ Model and support using beginning letter(s)/sound(s), sentence and/or story structure, as well as meaning (illustrations and background knowledge) to problem-solve unknown words
☐ Model and support how to take words apart (onset and rime) to problem-solve unknown words

COMPREHENSION

Previewing
☐ Support creating a story from the illustrations
☐ Model and support previewing a book before reading, during read-aloud and shared reading experiences

Retelling
☐ Model the retelling of familiar stories
☐ Model and teach the elements in a good retelling
☐ Demonstrate how to create and use story maps to aid retelling
☐ Support retelling a story in sequence
☐ Encourage student to use characters' names when retelling a story
☐ Model and support using key language/vocabulary from the text in a retelling

Reflection
☐ Support and reinforce student's response to books during read-aloud, and shared and guided reading experiences
☐ Help student identify favorite part of books
☐ Provide opportunities to select a favorite book, toy, TV show, etc., and tell why it is a favorite
☐ Demonstrate how to give reason(s) for one's opinion

Making Connections
☐ Model and teach how to make text-to-self connections
☐ Model and support how to make text-to-text connections

OTHER

_____

_____

_____

_____

_____

_____

_____

Name/Date _____   Teacher/Grade _____

Scores: Reading Engagement ___/8   Oral Reading Fluency ___/16   Comprehension ___/28
Independent Range: 6–7   11–14   19–25

Book Selection   Text selected by: ☐ teacher   ☐ student

1. READING ENGAGEMENT

(If the student has recently answered these questions, skip this section.)

T: Tell me about one of your favorite books. _____

T: Do you like to read   ☐ *alone,*   ☐ *with a buddy, or*   ☐ *with a group?*

   Why? _____

T: Whom do you read with at home? _____

2. ORAL READING FLUENCY

INTRODUCTION AND PREVIEW
T: In this story, Grandma's Surprise, *Mom, Dad, Ben, and Rose decide to make a surprise lunch for Grandma. They each make something for the surprise. Look at the pictures, and tell me what is happening in this story.*

Note the student's use of connecting words (e.g., *and, then, but*) and vocabulary relevant to the text. You may use general prompts, such as "Now what is happening?" or "Turn the page," but do not ask specific questions. Tally the number of times you prompt.

RECORD OF ORAL READING
Record the student's oral reading behaviors on the Record of Oral Reading below and on the following page.

T: Grandma's Surprise. Now, read to see what Mom, Dad, Ben, and Rose make for Grandma's surprise lunch.

Page 2

One   morning   Mom   said,   "Let's   make
lunch   for   Grandma."

"Yes!   Let's   surprise   Grandma!"   said   Ben
and   Rose.

Page 3

Dad   and   Ben   made   some   soup.
"Grandma   loves   soup   and   so   do   I,"
said   Dad.

Page 4

Rose   made   a   picture   of   three   little
kittens   for   Grandma.

"Grandma   and   I   love   kittens,"   said   Rose.

Page 5

Mom   got   some   purple   and   yellow
flowers.   She   put   them   in   a   tall   vase.

"Grandma   loves   flowers,"   said   Mom.

Page 6

Dad,   Mom,   Rose,   and   Ben   went
to   Grandma's   house.

"We   made   a   surprise   lunch   for   you,"
said   Ben.

"I   made   a   picture   for   you,"   said   Rose.

Page 7

Grandma   said,   "I   have   a   surprise   for
you,   too.   I   made   an   apple   pie."

"Apple   pie!   We   love   apple   pie,"   said
Ben   and   Rose.

"We   love   surprises!"   said   Mom   and
Dad.   "Let's   eat!"

ORAL READING, PERCENT OF ACCURACY

Count the number of miscues that are not self-corrected. Circle the percent of accuracy based on the number of miscues.

Word Count: 127

	EM	DEV	IND				ADV		
Number of Miscues	10 or more	9	7–8	6	5	4	2–3	1	0
Percent of Accuracy	92 or less	93	94	95	96	97	98	99	100

- If the student's score falls in a shaded area, STOP! Reassess with a lower-level text.
- If the student is reading below the grade-level benchmark, administer *DRA Word Analysis*, beginning with Task 12, at another time.

3. COMPREHENSION

RETELLING

As the student retells, underline and record on the Story Overview the information included in the student's retelling. Please note the student does not need to use the exact words.

T: Close the book, and then say: ***Start at the beginning, and tell me what happened in this story.***

Story Overview
Beginning
1. One morning Dad, Mom, Ben, and Rose decided to make a surprise lunch for Grandma.

Middle
2. Ben and Dad made soup. Grandma loves soup.

3. Rose made a picture of three little kittens. Grandma loves kittens.

4. Mom put purple and yellow flowers in a tall vase. Grandma loves flowers.

5. They all went to Grandma's house.

6. They gave Grandma the soup, flowers, and picture.

End
7. Grandma surprised Dad, Mom, Ben, and Rose with an apple pie.

If the retelling is limited, use one or more of the following prompts to gain further information. Place a checkmark by a prompt each time it is used.

- ☐ *Tell me more.*
- ☐ *What happened at the beginning?*
- ☐ *What happened before/after* _____ (an event mentioned by the student)*?*
- ☐ *Who else was in the story?*
- ☐ *How did the story end?*

REFLECTION

Record the student's reponses to the prompts and questions below.

T: What part did you like best in this story? Tell me why you liked that part.

MAKING CONNECTIONS

Note: If the student makes a text-to-self connection in his or her response to the above prompt, skip the following question.

T: What did this story make you think of? or *What connections did you make while reading this story?*

4. TEACHER ANALYSIS

ORAL READING

If the student had 5 or more different miscues, use the information recorded on the Record of Oral Reading to complete the chart below.

Student problem-solves words using:	Number of miscues self-corrected: ____	
☐ pictures	Number of miscues not self-corrected: ____	
☐ beginning letter/sound	Number of words told to the student: ____	
☐ letter-sound clusters	**Miscues interfered with meaning:**	**Miscues included:**
☐ onset and rime	☐ never	☐ omissions
☐ blending letters/sounds	☐ at times	☐ insertions
☐ rereading	☐ often	☐ substitutions that were
☐ no observable behaviors		☐ visually similar
		☐ not visually similar

Copy each substitution to help analyze the student's attention to visual information.
e.g., <u>kitties</u> (substitution)
     kittens (text)

DRA2 **Continuum**

- Circle the descriptors that best describe the student's reading behaviors and responses.
  1. Use your daily classroom observations and the student's responses to the Reading Engagement questions to select statements that best describe the student's level of Reading Engagement.
  2. Use your recorded observations from this assessment to select the statements that best describe the student's Oral Reading Fluency and Comprehension.
- Add the circled numbers to obtain a total score for each section.
- Record the total scores at the top of page 1.

Note: If the Comprehension score is less than 19, administer *DRA2* with a lower-level text.

DRA2 CONTINUUM	LEVEL 10		EARLY READER	
	EMERGING	**DEVELOPING**	**INDEPENDENT**	**ADVANCED**
Reading Engagement				
Book Selection	1 Selects new texts from identified leveled sets with teacher support; uncertain about a favorite book	2 Selects new texts from identified leveled sets with moderate support; tells about favorite book in general terms	3 Selects new texts from identified leveled sets most of the time; identifies favorite book by title and tells about a particular event	4 Selects a variety of new texts that are "just right"; identifies favorite book by title and gives an overview of the book
Sustained Reading	1 Sustains independent reading for a short period of time with much encouragement	2 Sustains independent reading with moderate encouragement	3 Sustains independent reading for at least 5 minutes at a time	4 Sustains independent reading for an extended period of time
Score	2 3	4 5	6 7	8
Oral Reading Fluency				
Phrasing	1 Reads word-by-word	2 Reads word-by-word with some short phrases	3 Reads in short phrases most of the time	4 Reads in longer phrases at times
Monitoring/Self-Corrections	1 Self-corrects no miscues	2 Self-corrects at least 1 miscue and neglects to self-correct other miscues	3 Self-corrects 2 or more miscues or only makes 1 uncorrected miscue	4 Self-corrects miscues quickly or reads accurately
Problem-Solving Unknown Words	1 Stops at difficulty, relying on support to problem-solve unknown words; 3 or more words told by the teacher	2 At difficulty, initiates problem-solving of a few unknown words; 1 or 2 words told by the teacher	3 At difficulty, uses 1 or 2 cues to problem-solve unknown words	4 At difficulty, uses multiple cues to problem-solve unknown words
Accuracy	1 92% or less	2 93%	3 94%–97%	4 98%–100%
Score	4 5 6	7 8 9 10	11 12 13 14	15 16
Comprehension				
Previewing	1 Comments briefly about each event or action only when prompted or is uncertain	2 Identifies and comments briefly about each event or action with some prompting	3 Identifies and connects at least 3 key events without prompting; some relevant vocabulary	4 Identifies and connects at least 4 key events without prompting; relevant vocabulary
Retelling: Sequence of Events	1 Includes only 1 or 2 events or details (limited retelling)	2 Includes at least 3 events, generally in random order (partial retelling)	3 Includes most of the important events from the beginning, middle, and end, generally in sequence	4 Includes all important events from the beginning, middle, and end in sequence
Retelling: Characters and Details	1 Refers to characters using general pronouns; may include incorrect information	2 Refers to characters using appropriate pronouns; includes at least 1 detail; may include some misinterpretation	3 Refers to most characters by name and includes some important details	4 Refers to all characters by name and includes most of the important details
Retelling: Vocabulary	1 Uses general terms or labels; limited understanding of key words/concepts	2 Uses some language/vocabulary from the text; some understanding of key words/concepts	3 Uses language/vocabulary from the text; basic understanding of most key words/concepts	4 Uses important language/vocabulary from the text; good understanding of key words/concepts
Retelling: Teacher Support	1 Retells with 5 or more questions or prompts	2 Retells with 3 or 4 questions or prompts	3 Retells with 1 or 2 questions or prompts	4 Retells with no questions or prompts
Reflection	1 Gives an unrelated response, no reason for opinion, or no response	2 Gives a limited response and/or a general reason for opinion	3 Gives a specific story event/action <u>and</u> a relevant reason for response (e.g., personal connection)	4 Gives a response and reason that reflects higher-level thinking (e.g., synthesis/inference)
Making Connections	1 Makes an unrelated connection, relates an event in the story, or gives no response	2 Makes a connection that reflects a limited understanding of the story	3 Makes a literal connection that reflects a basic understanding of the story	4 Makes a thoughtful connection that reflects a deeper understanding of the story
Score	7 8 9 10 11 12 13	14 15 16 17 18	19 20 21 22 23 24 25	26 27 28

Choose three to five teaching/learning activities on the *DRA2* Focus for Instruction on the next page.

Grandma's Surprise 10

DRA2 FOCUS FOR INSTRUCTION FOR EARLY READERS

Grandma's Surprise **10**

READING ENGAGEMENT

Book Selection
- ☐ Provide guided opportunities to select familiar stories for rereading
- ☐ Model and support how to select "just right" new texts for independent reading
- ☐ Model and discuss why readers have favorite books and authors

Sustained Reading
- ☐ Model and support the use of sustained reading time
- ☐ Create structures and routines to support buddy reading
- ☐ Create structures and routines to support reading at home

ORAL READING FLUENCY

Phrasing
- ☐ Encourage student to read in phrases during shared reading
- ☐ Show how words are grouped into phrases in big books and poetry charts
- ☐ Support rereading familiar texts to build fluency

Monitoring/Self-Corrections
- ☐ Support one-to-one matching as a means to self-monitor
- ☐ Model and teach how to use known words as a means to self-monitor
- ☐ Model and support confirming and discounting word choice using meaning, language, and visual information
- ☐ Demonstrate and teach how to read for meaning, self-correcting when a word doesn't make sense or sound right
- ☐ Model and teach how to monitor visual information, self-correcting when a word doesn't look right

Problem-Solving Unknown Words
- ☐ Model and support using beginning letter(s)/sound(s), sentence and/or story structure, as well as meaning (illustrations and background knowledge) to problem-solve unknown words
- ☐ Model and support how to take words apart (onset and rime) to problem-solve unknown words

COMPREHENSION

Previewing
- ☐ Support creating a story from the illustrations
- ☐ Model and support previewing a book before reading, during read-aloud and shared reading experiences

Retelling
- ☐ Model the retelling of familiar stories
- ☐ Model and teach the elements in a good retelling
- ☐ Demonstrate and teach how to create and use story maps to aid retelling
- ☐ Support retelling a story in sequence
- ☐ Encourage student to use characters' names when retelling a story
- ☐ Model and support using key language/vocabulary from the text in a retelling

Reflection
- ☐ Support and reinforce student's response to books during read-aloud, and shared and guided reading experiences
- ☐ Help student identify favorite part of books
- ☐ Provide opportunities to select a favorite book, toy, TV show, etc., and tell why it is a favorite
- ☐ Demonstrate how to give reason(s) for one's opinion

Making Connections
- ☐ Model and teach how to make text-to-self connections
- ☐ Model and support how to make text-to-text connections

OTHER

_____

_____

_____

_____

_____

_____

_____

Name/Date _____   Teacher/Grade _____

Scores: Reading Engagement ___/8   Oral Reading Fluency ___/16   Comprehension ___/28
Independent Range: 6–7   11–14   19–25

Book Selection   Text selected by: ☐ teacher   ☐ student

1. READING ENGAGEMENT

(If the student has recently answered these questions, skip this section.)

T: Tell me about one of your favorite books. _____

T: Do you like to read   ☐ *alone,*   ☐ *with a buddy, or*   ☐ *with a group?*

   *Why?*_____

*T: Whom do you read with at home?*_____

2. ORAL READING FLUENCY

INTRODUCTION AND PREVIEW
T: In this story, Shoe Boxes, *Mandy and her brother and sister each get a new pair of shoes. They do different things with their shoe boxes. Look at the pictures, and tell me what is happening in this story.*

Note the student's use of connecting words (e.g., *and, then, but*) and vocabulary relevant to the text. You may use general prompts, such as "Now what is happening?" or "Turn the page," but do <u>not</u> ask specific questions. Tally the number of times you prompt.

RECORD OF ORAL READING
Record the student's oral reading behaviors on the Record of Oral Reading below and on the following page.

T: Shoe Boxes. *Now, read to see what Mandy, her brother, and her sister do with their shoe boxes.*

Page 2

Mandy and her brother and sister got
new shoes. Her brother got a pair of
shoes for his soccer game. The shoes
came in a red box with white stripes
on it.

Shoe Boxes **10**

Page 3

Mandy's brother took the shoe box home. He put a caterpillar in it. The caterpillar liked his new home.

Page 4

Mandy's sister got new baseball shoes for her baseball game. The shoes came in a blue box with a string.

Page 5

Her sister took the shoe box and the string home. She put her baseball cards and the string in her shoe box.

Page 6

Mandy got a new pair of blue shoes for her birthday. Her shoes came in a green box with flowers on it.

Page 7

Mandy gave her shoe box to her baby sister. She sat on it. Oh, no!

ORAL READING, PERCENT OF ACCURACY

Count the number of miscues that are not self-corrected. Circle the percent of accuracy based on the number of miscues.

Word Count: 130

	EM	DEV	IND				ADV		
Number of Miscues	10 or more	9	8	6–7	5	4	2–3	1	0
Percent of Accuracy	92 or less	93	94	95	96	97	98	99	100

- If the student's score falls in a shaded area, STOP! Reassess with a lower-level text.
- If the student is reading below the grade-level benchmark, administer *DRA Word Analysis*, beginning with Task 12, at another time.

Shoe Boxes **10**

3. COMPREHENSION

RETELLING

As the student retells, underline and record on the Story Overview the information included in the student's retelling. Please note the student does not need to use the exact words.

T: Close the book, and then say: ***Start at the beginning, and tell me what happened in this story.***

Story Overview
Beginning
1. Mandy and her brother and sister got new shoes.

Middle
2. Mandy's brother got new soccer shoes.

3. He put a caterpillar in his red shoe box with white stripes.

4. Mandy's sister got new baseball shoes.

5. She put baseball cards and the string in her blue shoe box.

6. Mandy got new birthday shoes.

End
7. She gave her green shoe box with flowers on it to her baby sister.

8. Her baby sister sat on Mandy's shoe box.

If the retelling is limited, use one or more of the following prompts to gain further information. Place a checkmark by a prompt each time it is used.

☐ *Tell me more.*
☐ *What happened at the beginning?*
☐ *What happened before/after* _____ (an event mentioned by the student)*?*
☐ *Who else was in the story?*
☐ *How did the story end?*

REFLECTION

Record the student's reponses to the prompts and questions below.

T: *What part did you like best in this story? Tell me why you liked that part.*

MAKING CONNECTIONS

Note: If the student makes a text-to-self connection in his or her response to the above prompt, skip the following question.

T: *What did this story make you think of?* or *What connections did you make while reading this story?*

Shoe Boxes ⑩

4. TEACHER ANALYSIS

ORAL READING

If the student had 5 or more different miscues, use the information recorded on the Record of Oral Reading to complete the chart below.

Student problem-solves words using:	Number of miscues self-corrected: _____

☐ pictures
 ☐ beginning letter/sound
 ☐ letter-sound clusters
 ☐ onset and rime
 ☐ blending letters/sounds
 ☐ rereading
 ☐ no observable behaviors
	Number of miscues not self-corrected: _____
	 Number of words told to the student: _____
	
	 Miscues interfered with meaning: **Miscues included:**
	 ☐ never ☐ omissions
	 ☐ at times ☐ insertions
	 ☐ often ☐ substitutions that were
	                  ☐ visually similar
	                  ☐ not visually similar

Copy each substitution to help analyze the student's attention to visual information.

e.g., <u>come</u> (substitution)

      came (text)

*DRA*2 Continuum

- Circle the descriptors that best describe the student's reading behaviors and responses.
    1. Use your daily classroom observations and the student's responses to the Reading Engagement questions to select statements that best describe the student's level of Reading Engagement.
    2. Use your recorded observations from this assessment to select the statements that best describe the student's Oral Reading Fluency and Comprehension.
- Add the circled numbers to obtain a total score for each section.
- Record the total scores at the top of page 1.

Note: If the Comprehension score is less than 19, administer *DRA*2 with a lower-level text.

Shoe Boxes 10

DRA2 CONTINUUM	LEVEL 10			EARLY READER
	EMERGING	**DEVELOPING**	**INDEPENDENT**	**ADVANCED**
Reading Engagement				
Book Selection	1 Selects new texts from identified leveled sets with teacher support; uncertain about a favorite book	2 Selects new texts from identified leveled sets with moderate support; tells about favorite book in general terms	3 Selects new texts from identified leveled sets most of the time; identifies favorite book by title and tells about a particular event	4 Selects a variety of new texts that are "just right"; identifies favorite book by title and gives an overview of the book
Sustained Reading	1 Sustains independent reading for a short period of time with much encouragement	2 Sustains independent reading with moderate encouragement	3 Sustains independent reading for at least 5 minutes at a time	4 Sustains independent reading for an extended period of time
Score	2 3	4 5	6 7	8
Oral Reading Fluency				
Phrasing	1 Reads word-by-word	2 Reads word-by-word with some short phrases	3 Reads in short phrases most of the time	4 Reads in longer phrases at times
Monitoring/Self-Corrections	1 Self-corrects no miscues	2 Self-corrects at least 1 miscue and neglects to self-correct other miscues	3 Self-corrects 2 or more miscues or only makes 1 uncorrected miscue	4 Self-corrects miscues quickly or reads accurately
Problem-Solving Unknown Words	1 Stops at difficulty, relying on support to problem-solve unknown words; 3 or more words told by the teacher	2 At difficulty, initiates problem-solving of a few unknown words; 1 or 2 words told by the teacher	3 At difficulty, uses 1 or 2 cues to problem-solve unknown words	4 At difficulty, uses multiple cues to problem-solve unknown words
Accuracy	1 92% or less	2 93%	3 94%–97%	4 98%–100%
Score	4 5 6	7 8 9 10	11 12 13 14	15 16
Comprehension				
Previewing	1 Comments briefly about each event or action only when prompted or is uncertain	2 Identifies and comments briefly about each event or action with some prompting	3 Identifies and connects at least 3 key events without prompting; some relevant vocabulary	4 Identifies and connects at least 4 key events without prompting; relevant vocabulary
Retelling: Sequence of Events	1 Includes only 1 or 2 events or details (limited retelling)	2 Includes at least 3 events, generally in random order (partial retelling)	3 Includes most of the important events from the beginning, middle, and end, generally in sequence	4 Includes all important events from the beginning, middle, and end in sequence
Retelling: Characters and Details	1 Refers to characters using general pronouns; may include incorrect information	2 Refers to characters using appropriate pronouns; includes at least 1 detail; may include some misinterpretation	3 Refers to most characters by name and includes some important details	4 Refers to all characters by name and includes most of the important details
Retelling: Vocabulary	1 Uses general terms or labels; limited understanding of key words/concepts	2 Uses some language/vocabulary from the text; some understanding of key words/concepts	3 Uses language/vocabulary from the text; basic understanding of most key words/concepts	4 Uses important language/vocabulary from the text; good understanding of key words/concepts
Retelling: Teacher Support	1 Retells with 5 or more questions or prompts	2 Retells with 3 or 4 questions or prompts	3 Retells with 1 or 2 questions or prompts	4 Retells with no questions or prompts
Reflection	1 Gives an unrelated response, no reason for opinion, or no response	2 Gives a limited response; and/or a general reason for opinion	3 Gives a specific story event/action and a relevant reason for response (e.g., personal connection)	4 Gives a response and reason that reflects higher-level thinking (e.g., synthesis/inference)
Making Connections	1 Makes an unrelated connection, relates an event in the story, or gives no response	2 Makes a connection that reflects a limited understanding of the story	3 Makes a literal connection that reflects a basic understanding of the story	4 Makes a thoughtful connection that reflects a deeper understanding of the story
Score	7 8 9 10 11 12 13	14 15 16 17 18	19 20 21 22 23 24 25	26 27 28

Choose three to five teaching/learning activities on the DRA2 Focus for Instruction on the next page.

Shoe Boxes 10

DRA2 FOCUS FOR INSTRUCTION FOR EARLY READERS

READING ENGAGEMENT

Book Selection
☐ Provide guided opportunities to select familiar stories for rereading
☐ Model and support how to select "just right" new texts for independent reading
☐ Model and discuss why readers have favorite books and authors

Sustained Reading
☐ Model and support the use of sustained reading time
☐ Create structures and routines to support buddy reading
☐ Create structures and routines to support reading at home

ORAL READING FLUENCY

Phrasing
☐ Encourage student to read in phrases during shared reading
☐ Show how words are grouped into phrases in big books and poetry charts
☐ Support rereading familiar texts to build fluency

Monitoring/Self-Corrections
☐ Support one-to-one matching as a means to self-monitor
☐ Model and teach how to use known words as a means to self-monitor
☐ Model and support confirming and discounting word choice using meaning, language, and visual information
☐ Demonstrate and teach how to read for meaning, self-correcting when a word doesn't make sense or sound right
☐ Model and teach how to monitor visual information, self-correcting when a word doesn't look right

Problem-Solving Unknown Words
☐ Model and support using beginning letter(s)/sound(s), sentence and/or story structure, as well as meaning (illustrations and background knowledge) to problem-solve unknown words
☐ Model and support how to take words apart (onset and rime) to problem-solve unknown words

COMPREHENSION

Previewing
☐ Support creating a story from the illustrations
☐ Model and support previewing a book before reading, during read-aloud and shared reading experiences

Retelling
☐ Model the retelling of familiar stories
☐ Model and teach the elements in a good retelling
☐ Demonstrate and teach how to create and use story maps to aid retelling
☐ Support retelling a story in sequence
☐ Encourage student to use characters' names when retelling a story
☐ Model and support using key language/vocabulary from the text in a retelling

Reflection
☐ Support and reinforce student's response to books during read-aloud, and shared and guided reading experiences
☐ Help student identify favorite part of books
☐ Provide opportunities to select a favorite book, toy, TV show, etc., and tell why it is a favorite
☐ Demonstrate how to give reason(s) for one's opinion

Making Connections
☐ Model and teach how to make text-to-self connections
☐ Model and support how to make text-to-text connections

OTHER

_____

_____

_____

_____

_____

_____

Shoe Boxes 10

Name/Date _____   Teacher/Grade _____

Scores: Reading Engagement ___/8   Oral Reading Fluency ___/16   Comprehension ___/28
Independent Range: 6–7   11–14   19–25

Book Selection   Text selected by: ☐ teacher   ☐ student

1. READING ENGAGEMENT

(If the student has recently answered these questions, skip this section.)

T: Tell me about one of your favorite books. _____

T: Would you rather read ☐ *alone,* ☐ *with a buddy, or* ☐ *with a group?*

  Why? _____

T: Whom do you read with at home? _____

2. ORAL READING FLUENCY

INTRODUCTION AND PREVIEW

T: In this story, Allie's Wish, *Allie wishes she had a pet. On Monday, Wednesday, and Friday, she helps other people take care of their pets. Look at the pictures, and tell me what is happening in this story.*

Note the student's use of connecting words (e.g., *and, then, but*) and vocabulary relevant to the text. You may use general prompts, such as "Now what is happening?" or "Turn the page," but do not ask specific questions. Tally the number of times you prompt.

RECORD OF ORAL READING

Record the student's oral reading behaviors on the Record of Oral Reading below and on the following page.

T: Allie's Wish. Now, read to see how Allie gets her own pet.

Page 2

Allie   wished   she   had   a   pet.
She   wanted   a   pet   to   play   with
and   to   love.

On   Monday,   Allie   helped   Lee   take   care
of   his   dog.   She   loved   the   dog,
but   he   was   not   her   pet.

Allie's Wish 12

Page 3

On Wednesday, Allie helped Sam.
She loved the bird, but it was not her
pet.

Page 4

On Friday, Allie helped Mrs. May take
care of her cat. She brushed the cat.
Allie wished she had her own pet.

Page 5

One day Allie took her dad to visit
Mrs. May. Allie wanted him to see
Mrs. May's cat.

"Hello," said Mrs. May. "Come in and
see what I have."

Page 6

"My cat had kittens," said Mrs. May.
"Allie, would you like a kitten?"

"Can I, Dad?" Allie asked.

Page 7

Dad smiled and said, "Yes. Now you
can take care of your own pet."

ORAL READING, PERCENT OF ACCURACY

Count the number of miscues that are not self-corrected. Circle the percent of accuracy based on the number of miscues.

Word Count: 134

	EM	DEV	IND				ADV		
Number of Miscues	11 or more	9–10	8	7	5–6	4	3	1–2	0
Percent of Accuracy	92 or less	93	94	95	96	97	98	99	100

- If the student's score falls in a shaded area, STOP! Reassess with a lower-level text.
- If the student is reading below the grade-level benchmark, administer *DRA Word Analysis*, beginning with Task 12, at another time.

3. COMPREHENSION

RETELLING

As the student retells, underline and record on the Story Overview the information included in the student's retelling. Please note the student does not need to use the exact words.

T: Close the book, and then say: ***Start at the beginning, and tell me what happened in this story.***

Story Overview
Beginning
1. Allie wished she had a pet of her own.

Middle
2. On Monday, Allie helped Lee take care of his dog. She loved his dog.

3. On Wednesday, Allie helped Sam take care of his bird. She loved the bird.

4. On Friday, Allie brushed Mrs. May's cat.

5. Allie and her dad went to see Mrs. May's cat.

6. Mrs. May's cat had kittens, and she asked Allie if she'd like to have one.

7. Allie asked her dad if she could have a kitten.

End
8. He said, "Yes." Allie had her own pet to take care of.

If the retelling is limited, use one or more of the following prompts to gain further information. Place a checkmark by a prompt each time it is used.

☐ *Tell me more.*
☐ *What happened at the beginning?*
☐ *What happened before/after* _____ (an event mentioned by the student)*?*
☐ *Who else was in the story?*
☐ *How did the story end?*

Allie's Wish 12

REFLECTION

Record the student's responses to the prompts and questions below.

T: What part did you like best in this story? Tell me why you liked that part.

MAKING CONNECTIONS

Note: If the student makes a text-to-self connection in his or her response to the above prompt, skip the following question.

T: What does this story make you think of? or *What connections did you make while reading this story?*

4. TEACHER ANALYSIS

ORAL READING

If the student had 5 or more different miscues, use the information recorded on the Record of Oral Reading to complete the chart below.

Student problem-solves words using:	
☐ pictures	Number of miscues self-corrected: _____
☐ beginning letter/sound	Number of miscues not self-corrected: _____
☐ letter-sound clusters	Number of words told to the student: _____
☐ onset and rime	**Miscues interfered with meaning:** / **Miscues included:**
☐ blending letters/sounds	☐ never / ☐ omissions
☐ rereading	☐ at times / ☐ insertions
☐ no observable behaviors	☐ often / ☐ substitutions that were
	☐ visually similar
	☐ not visually similar

Copy each substitution to help analyze the student's attention to visual information.

e.g., <u>wished</u> (substitution)
       wanted (text)

DRA2 Continuum

- Circle the descriptors that best describe the student's reading behaviors and responses.
  1. Use your daily classroom observations and the student's responses to the Reading Engagement questions to select statements that best describe the student's level of Reading Engagement.
  2. Use your recorded observations from this assessment to select the statements that best describe the student's Oral Reading Fluency and Comprehension.
- Add the circled numbers to obtain a total score for each section.
- Record the total scores at the top of page 1.

Note: If the Comprehension score is less than 19, administer *DRA2* with a lower-level text.

Allie's Wish **12**

DRA2 CONTINUUM	LEVEL 12			EARLY READER
	EMERGING	**DEVELOPING**	**INDEPENDENT**	**ADVANCED**
Reading Engagement				
Book Selection	1 Selects new texts from identified leveled sets with teacher support; uncertain about a favorite book	2 Selects new texts from identified leveled sets with moderate support; tells about favorite book in general terms	3 Selects new texts from identified leveled sets most of the time; identifies favorite book by title and tells about a particular event	4 Selects a variety of new texts that are "just right"; identifies favorite book by title and gives an overview of the book
Sustained Reading	1 Sustains independent reading for a short period of time with much encouragement	2 Sustains independent reading with moderate encouragement	3 Sustains independent reading for at least 5 minutes at a time	4 Sustains independent reading for an extended period of time
Score	2 3	4 5	6 7	8
Oral Reading Fluency				
Phrasing	1 Reads word-by-word	2 Reads word-by-word with some short phrases	3 Reads in short phrases most of the time	4 Reads in longer phrases at times
Monitoring/Self-Corrections	1 Self-corrects no miscues	2 Self-corrects at least 1 miscue and neglects to self-correct other miscues	3 Self-corrects 2 or more miscues or only makes 1 uncorrected miscue	4 Self-corrects miscues quickly or reads accurately
Problem-Solving Unknown Words	1 Stops at difficulty, relying on support to problem-solve unknown words; 3 or more words told by the teacher	2 At difficulty, initiates problem-solving of a few unknown words; 1 or 2 words told by the teacher	3 At difficulty, uses 1 or 2 cues to problem-solve unknown words	4 At difficulty, uses multiple cues to problem-solve unknown words
Accuracy	1 92% or less	2 93%	3 94%–97%	4 98%–100%
Score	4 5 6	7 8 9 10	11 12 13 14	15 16
Comprehension				
Previewing	1 Comments briefly about each event or action only when prompted or is uncertain	2 Identifies and comments briefly about each event or action with some prompting	3 Identifies and connects at least 3 key events without prompting; some relevant vocabulary	4 Identifies and connects at least 4 key events without prompting; relevant vocabulary
Retelling: Sequence of Events	1 Includes only 1 or 2 events or details (limited retelling)	2 Includes at least 3 events, generally in random order (partial retelling)	3 Includes most of the important events from the beginning, middle, and end, generally in sequence	4 Includes all important events from the beginning, middle, and end in sequence
Retelling: Characters and Details	1 Refers to characters using general pronouns, may include incorrect information	2 Refers to characters using appropriate pronouns; includes at least 1 detail; may include some misinterpretation	3 Refers to most characters by name and includes some important details	4 Refers to all characters by name and includes all important details
Retelling: Vocabulary	1 Uses general terms or labels; limited understanding of key words/concepts	2 Uses some language/vocabulary from the text; some understanding of key words/concepts	3 Uses language/vocabulary from the text; basic understanding of most key words/concepts	4 Uses important language/vocabulary from the text; good understanding of key words/concepts
Retelling: Teacher Support	1 Retells with 5 or more questions or prompts	2 Retells with 3 or 4 questions or prompts	3 Retells with 1 or 2 questions or prompts	4 Retells with no questions or prompts
Reflection	1 Gives an unrelated response, no reason for opinion, or no response	2 Gives a limited response and/or a general reason for opinion	3 Gives a specific story event/action <u>and</u> a relevant reason for a response (e.g., personal connection)	4 Gives a response that reflects higher-level thinking (e.g., synthesis/inference)
Making Connections	1 Makes an unrelated connection, relates an event in the story, or gives no response	2 Makes a connection that reflects a limited understanding of the story	3 Makes a literal connection that relates a basic understanding of the story	4 Makes a thoughtful connection that relates a deeper understanding of the story
Score	7 8 9 10 11 12 13	14 15 16 17 18	19 20 21 22 23 24 25	26 27 28

Choose three to five teaching/learning activities on the *DRA2* Focus for Instruction on the next page.

Allie's Wish 12

DRA2 FOCUS FOR INSTRUCTION FOR EARLY READERS

READING ENGAGEMENT

Book Selection
☐ Provide guided opportunities to select familiar stories for rereading
☐ Model and support how to select "just right" new texts for independent reading
☐ Model and discuss why readers have favorite books and authors

Sustained Reading
☐ Model and support the use of sustained reading time
☐ Create structures and routines to support buddy reading
☐ Create structures to support reading at home

ORAL READING FLUENCY

Phrasing
☐ Encourage student to read in phrases during shared reading
☐ Show how words are grouped into phrases in big books and poetry charts
☐ Support rereading familiar texts to build fluency

Monitoring/Self-Corrections
☐ Support one-to-one matching as a means to self-monitor
☐ Model and teach how to use words as a means to self-monitor
☐ Model and support confirming and discounting word choice using meaning, language, and visual information
☐ Demonstrate and teach how to read for meaning, self-correcting when a word doesn't make sense or sound right
☐ Model and teach how to monitor visual information, self-correcting when a word doesn't look right

Problem-Solving Unknown Words
☐ Model and support using beginning letter(s)/sound(s), sentence and/or story structure, as well as meaning (illustrations and background knowledge) to problem-solve unknown words
☐ Teach how to take words apart (onset and rime) to problem-solve unknown words

COMPREHENSION

Previewing
☐ Support creating a story from the illustrations
☐ Model and support previewing a book before reading, during read-aloud and shared reading experiences

Retelling
☐ Model the retelling of familiar stories
☐ Model and teach the elements in a good retelling
☐ Demonstrate how to create and use story maps to aid retelling
☐ Support retelling a story in sequence
☐ Encourage student to use characters' names when retelling a story
☐ Model and support using key language/vocabulary from the text in a retelling

Reflection
☐ Support and reinforce student's response to books during read-aloud, and shared and guided reading experiences
☐ Help student identify favorite part of books
☐ Provide opportunities to select a favorite book, toy, TV show, etc., and tell why it is a favorite
☐ Demonstrate how to give reason(s) for one's opinion

Making Connections
☐ Model and teach how to make text-to-self connections
☐ Model and support how to make text-to-text connections

OTHER

_____

_____

_____

_____

_____

_____

Allie's Wish 12

Name/Date _____   Teacher/Grade _____

Scores: Reading Engagement ___/8   Oral Reading Fluency ___/16   Comprehension ___/28
Independent Range: 6–7   11–14   19–25

Book Selection   Text selected by: ☐ teacher   ☐ student

1. READING ENGAGEMENT

(If the student has recently answered these questions, skip this section.)

T: Tell me about one of your favorite books. _____

T: Would you rather read ☐ *alone,* ☐ *with a buddy, or* ☐ *with a group?*

    Why? _____

T: Whom do you read with at home? _____

2. ORAL READING FLUENCY

INTRODUCTION AND PREVIEW

T: In this story, Robert's New Friend, *Robert isn't sure he liked his new baby sister, Maria. Mama and Papa are busy taking care of Maria. Look at the pictures, and tell me what is happening in this story.*

Note the student's use of connecting words (e.g., *and, then, but*) and vocabulary relevant to the text. You may use general prompts, such as "Now what is happening?" or "Turn the page," but do not ask specific questions. Tally the number of times you prompt.

RECORD OF ORAL READING

Record the student's oral reading behaviors on the Record of Oral Reading below and on the following page.

T: Robert's New Friend. *Now, read to see how Robert becomes friends with Maria.*

Page 2

Robert   had   a   new   baby   sister.

She   was   very   little.   Her   name

was   Maria.

Page 3

Robert   wasn't   sure   he   liked   Maria.

She   cried   a   lot.

Page 4

Mama was giving Maria a bath.
So Mama was too busy to play with
Robert. Robert felt left out. Mama was
taking care of his baby sister.

Page 5

Papa was feeding Maria.
So Papa was too busy to read to
Robert. Robert felt left out. Papa was
taking care of his baby sister.

Page 6

One day Maria cried and cried.
Mama couldn't make Maria stop crying.

Page 7

Robert went over to his baby sister,
Maria. He put his finger in her hand.
Maria stopped crying and smiled
at Robert.

Page 8

Robert smiled back at Maria.
For the first time he liked his baby
sister. He was happy. Robert told Mama
he would take care of Maria, too.

ORAL READING, PERCENT OF ACCURACY

Count the number of miscues that are not self-corrected. Circle the percent of accuracy based on the number of miscues.

Word Count: 137

	EM	DEV	IND				ADV		
Number of Miscues	11 or more	9–10	8	7	5–6	4	3	1–2	0
Percent of Accuracy	92 or less	93	94	95	96	97	98	99	100

- If the student's score falls in a shaded area, STOP! Reassess with a lower-level text.
- If the student is reading below the grade-level benchmark, administer *DRA Word Analysis*, beginning with Task 12, at another time.

3. COMPREHENSION

RETELLING

As the student retells, underline and record on the Story Overview the information included in the student's retelling. Please note the student does not need to use the exact words.

T: Close the book before the retelling, and then say: ***Start at the beginning, and tell me what happened in this story.***

Story Overview
Beginning
1. Robert isn't sure he likes his new baby sister Maria. She cries a lot.

Middle
2. Mama's giving Maria a bath—she can't play with Robert.

3. Robert feels left out. Mama is busy taking care of Maria.

4. Papa's feeding Maria—he can't read to Robert.

5. Robert feels left out. Papa is busy taking care of Maria.

6. One day, Mama can't stop Maria from crying.

7. Robert puts his finger in Maria's hand, and she stops crying.

End
8. Robert decides he likes Maria and tells Mama he will help take care of Maria, too.

If the retelling is limited, use one or more of the following prompts to gain further information. Place a checkmark by a prompt each time it is used.

- ☐ *Tell me more.*
- ☐ *What happened at the beginning?*
- ☐ *What happened before/after* _____ (an event mentioned by the student)*?*
- ☐ *Who else was in the story?*
- ☐ *How did the story end?*

REFLECTION

Record the student's responses to the prompts and questions below.

T: *What part did you like best in this story? Tell me why you liked that part.*

MAKING CONNECTIONS

Note: If the student makes a text-to-self connection in his or her response to the above prompt, skip the following question.

T: *What did this story make you think of?* or ***What connections did you make while reading this story?***

4. TEACHER ANALYSIS

ORAL READING

If the student had 5 or more different miscues, use the information recorded on the Record of Oral Reading to complete the chart below.

Student problem-solves words using:	Number of miscues self-corrected: _____	
☐ pictures	Number of miscues not self-corrected: _____	
☐ beginning letter/sound	Number of words told to the student: _____	
☐ letter-sound clusters	**Miscues interfered with meaning:**	**Miscues included:**
☐ onset and rime	☐ never	☐ omissions
☐ blending letters/sounds	☐ at times	☐ insertions
☐ rereading	☐ often	☐ substitutions that were
☐ no observable behaviors		☐ visually similar
		☐ not visually similar

Copy each substitution to help analyze the student's attention to visual information.

e.g., <u>feeling</u> (substitution)

     feeding (text)

*DRA*2 Continuum

- Circle the descriptors that best describe the student's reading behaviors and responses.
    1. Use your daily classroom observations and the student's responses to the Reading Engagement questions to select statements that best describe the student's level of Reading Engagement.
    2. Use your recorded observations from this assessment to select the statements that best describe the student's Oral Reading Fluency and Comprehension.
- Add the circled numbers to obtain a total score for each section.
- Record the total scores at the top of page 1.

Note: If the Comprehension score is less than 19, administer *DRA*2 with a lower-level text.

*DRA*2 CONTINUUM	LEVEL 12			EARLY READER
	EMERGING	**DEVELOPING**	**INDEPENDENT**	**ADVANCED**
Reading Engagement				
Book Selection	**1** Selects texts from identified leveled sets with teacher support; uncertain about a favorite book	**2** Selects texts from identified leveled sets with moderate support; tells about favorite book in general terms	**3** Selects new texts from identified leveled sets most of the time; identifies favorite book by title and tells about a particular event	**4** Selects a variety of new texts that are "just right"; identifies favorite book by title and gives an overview of the book
Sustained Reading	**1** Sustains independent reading for a short period of time with much encouragement	**2** Sustains independent reading with moderate encouragement	**3** Sustains independent reading for at least 5 minutes at a time	**4** Sustains independent reading for an extended period of time
Score	2 3	4 5	6 7	8
Oral Reading Fluency				
Phrasing	**1** Reads word-by-word	**2** Reads word-by-word with some short phrases	**3** Reads in short phrases most of the time	**4** Reads in longer phrases at times
Monitoring/Self-Corrections	**1** Self-corrects no miscues	**2** Self-corrects at least 1 miscue and neglects to self-correct other miscues	**3** Self-corrects 2 or more miscues or only makes 1 uncorrected miscue	**4** Self-corrects miscues quickly or reads accurately
Problem-Solving Unknown Words	**1** Stops at difficulty, relying on support to problem-solve unknown words; 3 or more words told by the teacher	**2** At difficulty, initiates problem-solving of a few unknown words; 1 or 2 words told by the teacher	**3** At difficulty, uses 1–2 cues to problem-solve unknown words	**4** At difficulty, uses multiple cues to problem-solve unknown words
Accuracy	**1** 92% or less	**2** 93%	**3** 94%–97%	**4** 98%–100%
Score	4 5 6	7 8 9 10	11 12 13 14	15 16
Comprehension				
Previewing	**1** Comments briefly about each event or action only when prompted or is uncertain	**2** Identifies and comments briefly about each event or action with some prompting	**3** Identifies and connects at least 3 key events without prompting; some relevant vocabulary	**4** Identifies and connects at least 4 key events without prompting; relevant vocabulary
Retelling: Sequence of Events	**1** Includes only 1 or 2 events or details (limited retelling)	**2** Includes at least 3 events, generally in random order (partial retelling)	**3** Includes most of the important events from the beginning, middle, and end, generally in sequence	**4** Includes all important events from the beginning, middle, and end in sequence
Retelling: Characters and Details	**1** Refers to characters using general pronouns; may include incorrect information	**2** Refers to characters using appropriate pronouns; includes at least 1 detail; may include some misinterpretation	**3** Refers to most characters by name and includes some important details	**4** Refers to all characters by name and includes all important details
Retelling: Vocabulary	**1** Uses general terms or labels; limited understanding of key words/concepts	**2** Uses some language/vocabulary from the text; some understanding of key words/concepts	**3** Uses language/vocabulary from the text; basic understanding of most key words/concepts	**4** Uses important language/vocabulary from the text; good understanding of key words/concepts
Retelling: Teacher Support	**1** Retells with 5 or more questions or prompts	**2** Retells with 3 or 4 questions or prompts	**3** Retells with 1 or 2 questions or prompts	**4** Retells with no questions or prompts
Reflection	**1** Gives an unrelated response, no reason for opinion, or no response	**2** Gives a limited response and/or general reason for opinion	**3** Gives a specific story event/action <u>and</u> a relevant reason for response (e.g., personal connection)	**4** Gives a response and reason that reflects higher-level thinking (e.g., synthesis/inference)
Making Connections	**1** Makes an unrelated connection, relates an event in the story, or gives no response	**2** Makes a connection that reflects a limited understanding of the story	**3** Makes a literal connection that reflects a basic understanding of the story	**4** Makes a thoughtful connection that reflects a deeper understanding of the story
Score	7 8 9 10 11 12 13	14 15 16 17 18	19 20 21 22 23 24 25	26 27 28

Choose three to five teaching/learning activities on the *DRA*2 Focus for Instruction on the next page.

Robert's New Friend 12

DRA2 FOCUS FOR INSTRUCTION FOR EARLY READERS

READING ENGAGEMENT

Book Selection
- ☐ Provide guided opportunities to select familiar stories for rereading
- ☐ Model and support how to select "just right" new texts for independent reading
- ☐ Model and discuss why readers have favorite books and authors

Sustained Reading
- ☐ Model and support the use of sustained reading time
- ☐ Create structures and routines to support buddy reading
- ☐ Create structures to support reading at home

ORAL READING FLUENCY

Phrasing
- ☐ Encourage student to read in phrases during shared reading
- ☐ Show how words are grouped into phrases in big books and poetry charts
- ☐ Support rereading familiar texts to build fluency

Monitoring/Self-Corrections
- ☐ Support one-to-one matching as a means to self-monitor
- ☐ Model and teach how to use known words as a means to self-monitor
- ☐ Model and support confirming and discounting word choice using meaning, language, and visual information
- ☐ Demonstrate and teach how to read for meaning, self-correcting when a word doesn't make sense or sound right
- ☐ Model and teach how to monitor visual information, self-correcting when a word doesn't look right

Problem-Solving Unknown Words
- ☐ Model and support using beginning letter(s)/sound(s), sentence and/or story structure, as well as meaning (illustrations and background knowledge) to problem-solve unknown words
- ☐ Teach how to take words apart (onset and rime) to problem-solve unknown words

COMPREHENSION

Previewing
- ☐ Support creating a story from the illustrations
- ☐ Model and support previewing a book before reading, during read-aloud and shared reading experiences

Retelling
- ☐ Model the retelling of familiar stories
- ☐ Model and teach the elements in a good retelling
- ☐ Demonstrate how to create and use story maps to aid retelling
- ☐ Support retelling a story in sequence
- ☐ Encourage student to use characters' names when retelling a story
- ☐ Model and support using key language/vocabulary from the text in a retelling

Reflection
- ☐ Support and reinforce student's response to books during read-aloud, and shared and guided reading experiences
- ☐ Help student identify favorite part of books
- ☐ Provide opportunities to select a favorite book, toy, TV show, etc., and tell why it is a favorite
- ☐ Demonstrate how to give reason(s) for one's opinion

Making Connections
- ☐ Model and teach how to make text-to-self connections
- ☐ Model and support how to make text-to-text connections

OTHER

_____

_____

_____

_____

_____

_____

_____

Name/Date _____   Teacher/Grade _____

Scores: Reading Engagement ___/8   Oral Reading Fluency ___/16   Comprehension ___/28
Independent Range: 6–7   11–14   19–25

Book Selection   Text selected by: ☐ teacher   ☐ student

1. READING ENGAGEMENT

(If the student has recently answered these questions, skip this section.)

T: *Tell me about one of your favorite books.* _____

T: *Would you rather read* ☐ *alone,* ☐ *with a buddy, or* ☐ *with a group?*

    Why? _____

T: *Whom do you read with at home?* _____

2. ORAL READING FLUENCY

INTRODUCTION AND PREVIEW

T: *In this story,* A New School, *Kate and her family have just moved into a new house. Kate isn't sure that she will have any friends at her new school. Look at the pictures, and tell me what is happening in this story.*

Note the student's use of connecting words (e.g., *and, then, but*) and vocabulary relevant to the text. You may use general prompts, such as "Now what is happening?" or "Turn the page," but do <u>not</u> ask specific questions. Tally the number of times you prompt.

RECORD OF ORAL READING

Record the student's oral reading behaviors. Note the student's fluency (expression and phrasing). Be sure to time the student's reading.

T: *A New School.* ***Now, read to find out what happens on Kate's first day at her new school.***

Page 2

Kate   and   her   family   moved   into   a   new   house.

She   would   have   to   go   to   a   new   school   in

the   morning.

Kate   was   sad.   She   wasn't   sure   she   would   like

her   new   school.   She   wasn't   sure   she   would

have   any   friends.

A New School **14**

Page 3

Kate's father took her to her new classroom. The teacher smiled at her and said, "Sit here by me." The teacher read a story to the class.

Kate liked the story, but she still wasn't sure she would like her new school.

Page 4

At reading time, two boys helped Kate find some books. They sat with Kate on the rug to read their books together.

Kate felt a little better, but she still wasn't sure she would like it here.

Page 5

At math time, a boy and a girl helped Kate find a tub of shapes. They made pictures together. Kate made a house. The girl made a dog, and the boy made a bird. They had fun.

Page 6

At lunch time, a girl asked Kate to sit with her. She gave one of her cookies to Kate.

Kate smiled and said, "Thank you." She was starting to like her new school.

Page 7

After school, Kate told her mother about her new friends.

"I like my new school," she said.

Time: _____ minutes:seconds

ORAL READING WORDS PER MINUTE, PERCENT OF ACCURACY
Use the student's oral reading time to circle the WPM range.

Word Count: 207

	INTRVN	INSTR	IND	ADV
Minutes:Seconds	7:02 or more	7:01–5:15	5:14–2:57	2:56 or less
WPM	29 or less	30–39	40–70	71 or more

Count the number of miscues that are not self-corrected. Circle the percent of accuracy based on the number of miscues.

	INTRVN	INSTR	IND				ADV	
Number of Miscues	14 or more	12–13	10–11	8–9	6–7	4–5	1–3	0
Percent of Accuracy	93 or less	94	95	96	97	98	99	100

- If the student's score falls in a shaded area for either WPM or Accuracy, STOP! Reassess with a lower-level text.
- If the student is reading below the grade-level benchmark, administer *DRA Word Analysis*, beginning with Task 16, at another time.

3. COMPREHENSION

RETELLING

As the student retells, underline and record on the Story Overview the information included in the student's retelling. Please note the student does not need to use the exact words.

T: Close the book before the retelling, and then say: **Start at the beginning, and tell me what happened in this story.**

Story Overview

Beginning

1. Kate and her family moved into a new house. She would go to a new school. She wondered if she would like her new school and have any friends.

Middle

2. Kate's father took her to her new classroom.
3. Kate sat next to the teacher as she read a story to the class. Kate liked the story, but she wasn't sure whether she would like the school.
4. At reading time, two boys read with Kate on a rug. Kate felt a little better, but she still wasn't sure whether she would like her new school.
5. At math time, a boy and a girl made pictures out of shapes together with Kate. They had fun.
6. At lunch time, a girl gave a cookie to Kate. Kate was starting to like her new school.

End

7. After school, Kate walked home with her mother. She told her about her new friends.
8. Kate liked her new school.

If the retelling is limited, use one or more of the following prompts to gain further information. Place a checkmark by a prompt each time it is used.

☐ *Tell me more.*
☐ *What happened at the beginning?*
☐ *What happened before/after* _____ (an event mentioned by the student)*?*
☐ *Who else was in the story?*
☐ *How did the story end?*

REFLECTION

Record the student's responses to the prompts and questions below.

T: What part did you like best in this story? Tell me why you liked that part.

MAKING CONNECTIONS

Note: If the student makes a text-to-self connection in his or her response to the above prompt, skip the following question.

T: What did this story make you think of? or **What connections did you make while reading this story?**

4. TEACHER ANALYSIS

ORAL READING

If the student had 5 or more different miscues, use the information recorded on the Record of Oral Reading to complete the chart below.

Student problem-solves words using:	Number of miscues self-corrected: _____
☐ beginning letter(s)/sound(s)	Number of miscues not self-corrected: _____
☐ letter-sound clusters	Number of words told to the student: _____

Student problem-solves words using:	Miscues interfered with meaning:	Miscues included:
☐ onset and rime	☐ never	☐ omissions
☐ blending letters/sounds	☐ at times	☐ insertions
☐ knowledge of spelling patterns (analogies)	☐ often	☐ substitutions that were
☐ syllables		☐ visually similar
☐ rereading		☐ not visually similar
☐ no observable behaviors		

Copy each substitution to help analyze the student's attention to visual information.

e.g., <u>there</u> (substitution)
    here (text)

Oral Reading Rate: (Optional) Use the formula below to determine the student's exact oral reading rate. Convert the student's reading time from minutes:seconds to all seconds.

$$207 \text{ (words)} \div \underline{\hspace{1.5cm}} \text{ total seconds} = \underline{\hspace{1.5cm}} \text{ WPS} \times 60 = \underline{\hspace{1.5cm}} \text{ WPM}$$

DRA2 Continuum

- Circle the descriptors that best describe the student's reading behaviors and responses.
    1. Use your daily classroom observations and the student's responses to the Reading Engagement questions to select statements that best describe the student's level of Reading Engagement.
    2. Use your recorded observations from this assessment to select the statements that best describe the student's Oral Reading Fluency and Comprehension.
- Add the circled numbers to obtain a total score for each section.
- Record the total scores at the top of page 1.

Note: If the Comprehension score is less than 19, administer *DRA2* with a lower-level text.

*DRA*2 CONTINUUM	LEVEL 14		TRANSITIONAL READER	
	INTERVENTION	INSTRUCTIONAL	INDEPENDENT	ADVANCED
Reading Engagement				
Book Selection	**1** Selects texts from identified leveled sets with teacher support; uncertain about a favorite book	**2** Selects texts from identified leveled sets with moderate support; tells about favorite book in general terms	**3** Selects texts from identified leveled sets most of the time; identifies favorite book by title and tells about a particular event	**4** Selects a variety of "just right" texts; identifies favorite book by title and gives an overview of the book
Sustained Reading	**1** Sustains independent reading for a short period of time with much encouragement	**2** Sustains independent reading with moderate encouragement	**3** Sustains independent reading for at least 10–15 minutes at a time	**4** Sustains independent reading for an extended period of time
Score	2 3	4 5	6 7	8
Oral Reading Fluency				
Expression	**1** No expression; monotone	**2** Little expression; rather monotone	**3** Some expression	**4** Expression conveys meaning most of the time
Phrasing	**1** Mostly word-by-word	**2** Short phrases most of the time; inappropriate pauses	**3** Longer word phrases some of the time; heeds most punctuation	**4** Longer, meaningful phrases most of the time; heeds all punctuation
Rate	**1** 29 WPM or less	**2** 30–39 WPM	**3** 40–70 WPM	**4** 71 WPM or more
Accuracy	**1** 93% or less	**2** 94%	**3** 95%–98%	**4** 99%–100%
Score	4 5 6	7 8 9 10	11 12 13 14	15 16
Comprehension				
Previewing	**1** Comments briefly about each event or action only when prompted or is uncertain	**2** Identifies and comments briefly about each event or action with some prompting	**3** Identifies and connects at least 3 key events without prompting; some relevant vocabulary	**4** Identifies and connects at least 4 key events without prompting; relevant vocabulary
Retelling: Sequence of Events	**1** Includes only 1 or 2 events or details (limited retelling)	**2** Includes at least 3 events, generally in random order (partial retelling)	**3** Includes most of the important events from the beginning, middle, and end, generally in sequence	**4** Includes all important events from the beginning, middle, and end in sequence
Retelling: Characters and Details	**1** Refers to characters using general pronouns; may include incorrect information	**2** Refers to characters using appropriate pronouns; includes at least 1 detail; may include some misinterpretation	**3** Refers to most characters by name and includes some important details	**4** Refers to all characters by name and includes all important details
Retelling: Vocabulary	**1** Uses general terms or labels; limited understanding of key words/concepts	**2** Uses some language/vocabulary from the text; some understanding of key words/concepts	**3** Uses language/vocabulary from the text; basic understanding of most key words/concepts	**4** Uses important language/vocabulary from the text; good understanding of key words/concepts
Retelling: Teacher Support	**1** Retells with 5 or more questions or prompts	**2** Retells with 3 or 4 questions or prompts	**3** Retells with 1 or 2 questions or prompts	**4** Retells with no questions or prompts
Reflection	**1** Gives an unrelated response; no reason for opinion or no response	**2** Gives a limited response and/or general reason for opinion	**3** Gives a specific event/action <u>and</u> a relevant reason for response (e.g., personal connection)	**4** Gives a response and reason that reflects higher-level thinking (e.g., synthesis/ inference)
Making Connections	**1** Makes an unrelated connection, relates an event in the story, or gives no response	**2** Makes a connection that reflects a limited understanding of the story	**3** Makes a literal connection that reflects a basic understanding of the story	**4** Makes a thoughtful connection that reflects a deeper understanding of the story
Score	7 8 9 10 11 12 13	14 15 16 17 18	19 20 21 22 23 24 25	26 27 28

Choose three to five teaching/learning activities on the *DRA*2 Focus for Instruction on the next page.

A New School **14**

*DRA*2 FOCUS FOR INSTRUCTION FOR TRANSITIONAL READERS

READING ENGAGEMENT

Book Selection
☐ Teach student strategies to select "just right" texts for independent reading
☐ Introduce student to reading materials from a variety of genres
☐ Model and discuss why readers have favorite books and authors

Sustained Reading
☐ Model and support the use of sustained reading time
☐ Develop clear expectations for amount of independent reading
☐ Provide opportunities for buddy reading
☐ Create structures and routines to support reading at home

ORAL READING FLUENCY

Expression and Phrasing
☐ Have student practice appropriate phrasing and expression with familiar texts
☐ Model and support reading in longer meaningful phrases with appropriate expression
☐ Model and teach how to heed punctuation
☐ Have student participate in choral reading and/or reader's theater

Rate
☐ Provide materials and time for repeated reading to increase reading rate
☐ Teach student to read lower-level and/or familiar texts at an appropriate rate

Accuracy: Word Analysis
☐ Support and reinforce self-corrections of miscues
☐ Model and support how to take words apart (onset and rime, syllables) to problem-solve unknown words
☐ Teach how to use word chunks and analogies to problem-solve unknown words
☐ Provide spelling activities and word sorts to help student recognize patterns in words

COMPREHENSION

Previewing
☐ Support creating a story from the illustrations
☐ Model and support previewing a book during read-aloud and shared reading experiences

Retelling
☐ Model and teach how to retell a story
☐ Model and teach how to identify important events to include in a retelling
☐ Support retelling a story in sequence
☐ Encourage student to use characters' names when retelling a story
☐ Model and teach how to identify important details to include in a retelling
☐ Model and support using key vocabulary/language from the text in a retelling
☐ Model and teach how to create and use story maps to aid retelling

Reflection
☐ Support and reinforce student's responses to books
☐ Provide opportunities to select a favorite book, toy, TV show, etc., and tell why it is a favorite
☐ Help student identify favorite part of books
☐ Demonstrate how to support one's opinion

Making Connections
☐ Model and teach how to make text-to-self connections
☐ Model and teach how to make text-to-text connections

OTHER

_____

_____

_____

_____

_____

_____

_____

A New School 14

Name/Date _____ Teacher/Grade _____

Scores: Reading Engagement ___/8 Oral Reading Fluency ___/16 Comprehension ___/28
Independent Range: 6–7 11–14 19–25

Book Selection Text selected by: ☐ teacher ☐ student

1. READING ENGAGEMENT

(If the student has recently answered these questions, skip this section.)

T: Tell me about one of your favorite books. _____

T: Would you rather read ☐ alone, ☐ with a buddy, or ☐ with a group?

Why? _____

T: Whom do you read with at home? _____

2. ORAL READING FLUENCY

INTRODUCTION AND PREVIEW

T: In this story, The Wagon, *Kevin's two brothers and his sister use the same wagon for different things. Look at the pictures, and tell me what is happening in this story.*

Note the student's use of connecting words (e.g., *and, then, but*) and vocabulary relevant to the text. You may use general prompts, such as "Now what is happening?" or "Turn the page," but do not ask specific questions. Tally the number of times you prompt.

RECORD OF ORAL READING

Record the student's oral reading behaviors. Note the student's fluency (expression and phrasing). Be sure to time the student's reading.

T: The Wagon. Now, read to find out how Kevin's brothers and sister fix the dented, dirty wagon when it is his turn to have it.

Page 2

One day Kevin's big brother got a new wagon. He used it to carry his newspapers.

Kevin liked the wagon, but he never got to ride in it.

The Wagon 14

88

Page 3

Then one day Kevin's brother gave the wagon to their sister. She used the wagon for a sandbox.

Sometimes Kevin got to play in the wagon, but he never got to ride in it.

Page 4

Then one day Kevin's sister gave the wagon to their other brother.
This brother used the wagon for a fort.
He covered it with dirt and sticks.

Kevin never got to ride in the wagon.

Page 5

Then one day Kevin's brother gave the wagon to Kevin. Kevin was happy.

Kevin looked at the wagon.
The wagon looked old and dirty.
It had dents in it.

Page 6

Kevin's big brother said, "We'll fix the wagon.
It will look as good as new."

Kevin's sister got a rag and a bucket of water.
His big brother got a hammer. His other brother got some paint and a brush.

The Wagon 14

Page 7

They   washed   the   wagon   with   the   water.

They   took   out   the   dents   with   the   hammer.

They   painted   the   wagon   a   nice   bright   green.

The   wagon   looked   better   than   new   because

it   had   Kevin's   name   on   it.

Time: _____ minutes:seconds

ORAL READING WORDS PER MINUTE, PERCENT OF ACCURACY

Use the student's oral reading time to circle the WPM range.

Word Count: 202

	INTRVN	INSTR	IND	ADV
Minutes:Seconds	6:51 or more	6:50–5:07	5:06–2:52	2:51 or less
WPM	29 or less	30–39	40–70	71 or more

Count the number of miscues that are not self-corrected. Circle the percent of accuracy based on the number of miscues.

	INTRVN	INSTR	IND					ADV	
Number of Miscues	14 or more	12–13	10–11	8–9	6–7	4–5		1–3	0
Percent of Accuracy	93 or less	94	95	96	97	98		99	100

- If the student's score falls in a shaded area for either WPM or Accuracy, STOP! Reassess with a lower-level text.
- If the student is reading below the grade-level benchmark, administer *DRA Word Analysis,* beginning with Task 16, at another time.

The Wagon 14

3. COMPREHENSION

RETELLING

As the student retells, underline and record on the Story Overview the information included in the student's retelling. Please note the student does not need to use the exact words.

T: Close the book before the retelling, and then say: ***Start at the beginning, and tell me what happened in this story.***

Story Overview

Beginning

1. Kevin's big brother gets a new wagon; he carries newspapers in it—but Kevin never gets to ride in it.

Middle

2. Brother gives the wagon to his sister; she uses it for a sandbox—but Kevin never gets to ride in it.

3. Sister gives the wagon to their other brother; he uses it for a fort—but Kevin never gets to ride in it.

4. Brother gives the wagon to Kevin. Kevin is happy.

5. The wagon is old and dirty and has dents in it.

6. Brothers and sister wash the wagon, take out the dents, and paint it bright green.

End

7. The wagon looks better than new because it has Kevin's name on it.

If the retelling is limited, use one or more of the following prompts to gain further information. Place a checkmark by a prompt each time it is used.

☐ *Tell me more.*
☐ *What happened at the beginning?*
☐ *What happened before/after* _____ (an event mentioned by the student)*?*
☐ *Who else was in the story?*
☐ *How did the story end?*

REFLECTION

Record the student's responses to the prompts and questions below.

T: ***What part did you like best in this story? Tell me why you liked that part.***

MAKING CONNECTIONS

Note: If the student makes a text-to-self connection in his or her response to the above prompt, skip the following question.

T: ***What did this story make you think of?*** or ***What connections did you make while reading this story?***

The Wagon 14

4. TEACHER ANALYSIS

ORAL READING

If the student had 5 or more different miscues, use the information recorded on the Record of Oral Reading to complete the chart below.

Student problem-solves words using:	Number of miscues self-corrected: _____ Number of miscues not self-corrected: _____ Number of words told to the student: _____	

☐ beginning letter(s)/sound(s)
 ☐ letter-sound clusters
 ☐ onset and rime
 ☐ blending letters/sounds
 ☐ knowledge of spelling patterns   (analogies)
 ☐ syllables
 ☐ rereading
 ☐ no observable behaviors
	Miscues interfered with meaning:
	 ☐ never
	 ☐ at times
	 ☐ often
		Miscues included:
		 ☐ omissions
		 ☐ insertions
		 ☐ substitutions that were
		      ☐ visually similar
		      ☐ not visually similar

Copy each substitution to help analyze the student's attention to visual information.

e.g., <u>older</u> (substitution)
     other (text)

Oral Reading Rate: (Optional) Use the formula below to determine the student's exact oral reading rate. Convert the student's reading time to all seconds.

$$202 \text{ (words)} \div \underline{\hspace{2cm}} \text{ total seconds} = \underline{\hspace{2cm}} \text{ WPS} \times 60 = \underline{\hspace{2cm}} \text{ WPM}$$

DRA2 Continuum

- Circle the descriptors that best describe the student's reading behaviors and responses.
  1. Use your daily classroom observations and the student's responses to the Reading Engagement questions to select statements that best describe the student's level of Reading Engagement.
  2. Use your recorded observations from this assessment to select the statements that best describe the student's Oral Reading Fluency and Comprehension.
- Add the circled numbers to obtain a total score for each section.
- Record the total scores at the top of page 1.

Note: If the Comprehension score is less than 19, administer *DRA2* with a lower-level text.

The Wagon 14

DRA2 CONTINUUM	LEVEL 14		TRANSITIONAL READER	
	INTERVENTION	INSTRUCTIONAL	INDEPENDENT	ADVANCED
Reading Engagement				
Book Selection	1 Selects texts from identified leveled sets with teacher support; uncertain about a favorite book	2 Selects texts from identified leveled sets with moderate support; tells about favorite book in general terms	3 Selects texts from identified leveled sets most of the time; identifies favorite book by title and tells about a particular event	4 Selects a variety of "just right" texts; identifies favorite book by title and gives an overview of the book
Sustained Reading	1 Sustains independent reading for a short period of time with much encouragement	2 Sustains independent reading with moderate encouragement	3 Sustains independent reading for at least 10–15 minutes at a time	4 Sustains independent reading for an extended period of time
Score	2 3	4 5	6 7	8
Oral Reading Fluency				
Expression	1 No expression; monotone	2 Little expression; rather monotone	3 Some expression	4 Expression conveys meaning most of the time
Phrasing	1 Mostly word-by-word	2 Short phrases most of the time; inappropriate pauses	3 Longer word phrases some of the time; heeds most punctuation	4 Longer, meaningful phrases most of the time; heeds all punctuation
Rate	1 29 WPM or less	2 30–39 WPM	3 40–70 WPM	4 71 WPM or more
Accuracy	1 93% or less	2 94%	3 95%–98%	4 99%–100%
Score	4 5 6	7 8 9 10	11 12 13 14	15 16
Comprehension				
Previewing	1 Comments briefly about each event or action only when prompted or is uncertain	2 Identifies and comments briefly about each event or action with some prompting	3 Identifies and connects at least 3 key events without prompting; some relevant vocabulary	4 Identifies and connects at least 4 key events without prompting; relevant vocabulary
Retelling: Sequence of Events	1 Includes only 1 or 2 events or details (limited retelling)	2 Includes at least 3 events, generally in random order (partial retelling)	3 Includes most of the important events from the beginnning, middle, and end, generally in sequence	4 Includes all important events from the beginning, middle, and end in sequence
Retelling: Characters and Details	1 Refers to characters using general pronouns; may include incorrect information	2 Refers to characters using appropriate pronouns; includes at least 1 detail; may include some misinterpretation	3 Refers to most characters by name and includes some important details	4 Refers to all characters by name and includes all important details
Retelling: Vocabulary	1 Uses general terms or labels; limited understanding of key words/concepts	2 Uses some language/ vocabulary from the text; some understanding of key words/concepts	3 Uses language/ vocabulary from the text; basic understanding of most key words/concepts	4 Uses important language/vocabulary from the text; good understanding of key words/concepts
Retelling: Teacher Support	1 Retells with 5 or more questions or prompts	2 Retells with 3 or 4 questions or prompts	3 Retells with 1 or 2 questions or prompts	4 Retells with no questions or prompts
Reflection	1 Gives an unrelated response, no reason for opinion, or no response	2 Gives a limited response and/or a general reason for opinion	3 Gives a specific story event/action and a relevant reason for response (e.g., personal connection)	4 Gives a response and reason that reflects higher-level thinking (e.g., synthesis/inference)
Making Connections	1 Makes an unrelated connection, relates an event in the story, or gives no response	2 Makes a connection that reflects a limited understanding of the story	3 Makes a literal connection that reflects a basic understanding of the story	4 Makes a thoughtful connection that reflects a deeper understanding of the story
Score	7 8 9 10 11 12 13	14 15 16 17 18	19 20 21 22 23 24 25	26 27 28

Choose three to five teaching/learning activities on the *DRA*2 Focus for Instruction on the next page.

The Wagon 14

DRA2 FOCUS FOR INSTRUCTION FOR TRANSITIONAL READERS

READING ENGAGEMENT
Book Selection
- ☐ Teach student strategies to select "just right" texts for independent reading
- ☐ Introduce student to reading materials from a variety of genres
- ☐ Model and discuss why readers have favorite books and authors

Sustained Reading
- ☐ Model and support the use of sustained reading time
- ☐ Develop clear expectations for amount of independent reading
- ☐ Provide opportunities for buddy reading
- ☐ Create structures and routines to support reading at home

ORAL READING FLUENCY
Expression and Phrasing
- ☐ Have student practice appropriate phrasing and expression with familiar texts
- ☐ Model and support reading in longer meaningful phrases with appropriate expression
- ☐ Model and teach how to heed punctuation
- ☐ Have student participate in choral reading and/or reader's theater

Rate
- ☐ Provide materials and time for repeated reading to increase reading rate
- ☐ Teach student to read lower-level and/or familiar texts at an appropriate rate

Accuracy: Word Analysis
- ☐ Support and reinforce self-corrections of miscues
- ☐ Model and support how to take words apart (onset and rime, syllables) to problem-solve unknown words
- ☐ Teach how to use word chunks and analogies to problem-solve unknown words
- ☐ Provide spelling activities and word sorts to help student recognize patterns in words

COMPREHENSION
Previewing
- ☐ Support creating a story from the illustrations
- ☐ Model and support previewing a book during read-aloud and shared reading experiences

Retelling
- ☐ Model and teach how to retell a story
- ☐ Model and teach how to identify important events to include in a retelling
- ☐ Support retelling a story in sequence
- ☐ Encourage student to use characters' names when retelling a story
- ☐ Model and teach how to identify important details to include in a retelling
- ☐ Model and support using key vocabulary/language from the text in a retelling
- ☐ Model and teach how to create and use story maps to aid retelling

Reflection
- ☐ Support and reinforce student's responses to books
- ☐ Provide opportunities to select a favorite book, toy, TV show, etc., and tell why it is a favorite
- ☐ Help student identify favorite part of books
- ☐ Demonstrate how to support one's opinion

Making Connections
- ☐ Model and teach how to make text-to-self connections
- ☐ Model and teach how to make text-to-text connections

OTHER

_____

_____

_____

_____

_____

_____

_____

The Wagon 14

Name/Date _____   Teacher/Grade _____

Scores: Reading Engagement ___/8   Oral Reading Fluency ___/16   Comprehension ___/28
Independent Range: 6–7   11–14   19–25

Book Selection   Text selected by: ☐ teacher   ☐ student

1. READING ENGAGEMENT

(If the student has recently answered these questions, skip this section.)

T: What kinds of books do you like to read? _____

T: Tell me about one of your favorite books. _____

T: Whom do you read with at home? _____

2. ORAL READING FLUENCY

INTRODUCTION AND PREVIEW
T: This book is called Animal Homes. *It tells where and how some animals such as squirrels, beavers, and porcupines build their homes. Where have you seen some animals make their homes?*

Student's response reveals   ☐ little,   ☐ some, or   ☐ much background knowledge.

T: Now, look at each picture, and tell me where and how you see animals building their homes.

Note the student's use of connecting words (e.g., *and, then, but*) and vocabulary relevant to the text. You may use general prompts, such as "What else?" or "Turn the page," but do <u>not</u> ask specific questions. Tally the number of times you prompt.

RECORD OF ORAL READING
Record the student's oral reading behaviors. Note the student's fluency (expression and phrasing). Be sure to time the student's reading.

T: Animal Homes. *Now, read to find out what the author says about where and how these animals make their homes.*

Page 2

Animal   homes   are   everywhere.   You   can   find
them   in   trees,   under   the   ground,   and   in   caves.
Animals   build   homes   to   keep   warm   and   safe.

Page 4

Some animals build their homes in trees.

Squirrels build their nests in trees. They use twigs and leaves to make their nests.

Page 5

Other animals build their homes in trees, too.

Page 6

Some animals make their homes under the ground.

Rabbits dig tunnels in the ground. They use their paws to make rooms.

Page 7

Other animals make their homes under the ground, too.

Page 8

Some animals build their homes in the water.

Beavers make dams in the water. They use sticks and mud to make their homes.

Page 9

Other animals build their homes in the water, too.

Page 10

Some animals make their homes in caves.

Bats look for dark places to sleep. They hang upside down from the top of a cave.

Page 11

Other   animals   make   their   homes   in   caves,   too.

Page 12

Some   animals   make   their   homes   in   logs.

Porcupines   put   grass   inside   logs   to   make
homes   for   their   babies.

Page 13

Other   animals   make   their   homes   in   logs,   too.

Time: _____ minutes:seconds

ORAL READING WORDS PER MINUTE, PERCENT OF ACCURACY

Use the student's oral reading time to circle the WPM range.

Word Count: 174

	INTRVN	INSTR	IND	ADV
Minutes:Seconds	5:54 or more	5:53–4:25	4:24–2:29	2:28 or less
WPM	29 or less	30–39	40–70	71 or more

Count the number of miscues that are not self-corrected. Circle the percent of accuracy based on the number of miscues.

	INTRVN	INSTR	IND				ADV	
Number of Miscues	12 or more	10–11	8–9	7	5–6	3–4	1–2	0
Percent of Accuracy	93 or less	94	95	96	97	98	99	100

- If the student's score falls in a shaded area for either WPM or Accuracy, STOP! Reassess with a lower-level text.
- If the student is reading below the grade-level benchmark, administer *DRA Word Analysis*, beginning with Task 16, at another time.

3. COMPREHENSION

RETELLING

As the student retells, underline and record on the Overview the information included in the student's retelling. Please note the student does not need to use the exact words.

T: Close the book before the retelling, and then say: ***Start at the beginning, and tell me what the author said about where and how some animals make their homes.***

Overview

1. Some animals make their homes in trees.
   Squirrels use twigs and leaves to build a nest.

2. Some animals make their homes under the ground.
   Rabbits use their paws to dig tunnels and make rooms in the ground.

3. Some animals build their homes in the water.
   Beavers use sticks and mud to make their homes in the water.

4. Some animals make their homes in caves.
   Bats hang upside down in dark caves to sleep.

5. Some animals make their homes in logs.
   Porcupines put grass inside logs to make homes for their babies.

If necessary, use one or more of the following prompts to gain further information. Place a checkmark by a prompt each time it is used.

☐ *Tell me more.*
☐ *Tell me where other animals make their homes.*
☐ *Tell me how* _____ *(squirrels, rabbits, beavers, bats, or porcupines) make their homes.*

USING NONFICTION TEXT FEATURES

Record the student's responses to the prompts and questions below.

T: Turn to the chart on page 14. ***Use the chart, and tell me what animals make their homes in the water.***

T: ***How is the rabbit's home different from the squirrel's home on this chart?***

MAKING CONNECTIONS

T: ***What did this book make you think of?*** or ***What connections did you make while reading this book?***

4. TEACHER ANALYSIS

ORAL READING

If the student had 5 or more different miscues, use the information recorded on the Record of Oral Reading to complete the chart below.

Student problem-solves words using:	Number of miscues self-corrected: _____	
☐ beginning letter(s)/sound(s)	Number of miscues not self-corrected: _____	
☐ letter-sound clusters	Number of words told to the student: _____	
☐ onset and rime	**Miscues interfered with meaning:**	**Miscues included:**
☐ blending letters/sounds	☐ never	☐ omissions
☐ knowledge of spelling patterns (analogies)	☐ at times	☐ insertions
☐ syllables	☐ often	☐ substitutions that were
☐ rereading		☐ visually similar
☐ no observable behaviors		☐ not visually similar

Copy each substitution to help analyze the student's attention to visual information.
e.g., <u>big</u> (substitution)
 dig (text)

Oral Reading Rate: (Optional). Use the formula below to determine the student's exact oral reading rate. Convert the student's reading time to all seconds.

174 (words) ÷ _____ total seconds = _____ WPS × 60 = _____ WPM

DRA2 Continuum

- Circle the descriptors that best describe the student's reading behaviors and responses.
  1. Use your daily classroom observations and the student's responses to the Reading Engagement questions to select statements that best describe the student's level of Reading Engagement.
  2. Use your recorded observations from this assessment to select the statements that best describe the student's Oral Reading Fluency and Comprehension.
- Add the circled numbers to obtain a total score for each section.
- Record the total scores at the top of page 1.

Note: If the Comprehension score is less than 19, administer *DRA2* with a lower-level text.

Animal Homes **16**

DRA2 CONTINUUM	LEVEL 16		TRANSITIONAL READER	
	INTERVENTION	**INSTRUCTIONAL**	**INDEPENDENT**	**ADVANCED**
Reading Engagement				
Book Selection	1 Selects texts from identified leveled sets with teacher support; uncertain about a favorite book	2 Selects texts from identified leveled sets with moderate support; tells about favorite book in general terms	3 Independently selects texts from identified leveled sets most of the time; identifies favorite book by title and tells about a particular event	4 Independently selects a variety of "just right" texts; identifies favorite book by title and gives an overview of the book
Sustained Reading	1 Sustains independent reading for a short period of time with much encouragement	2 Sustains independent reading with moderate encouragement	3 Sustains independent reading for at least 10–15 minutes at a time	4 Sustains independent reading for an extended period of time
Score	2 3	4 5	6 7	8
Oral Reading Fluency				
Expression	1 No expression; monotone	2 Little expression; rather monotone	3 Some expression	4 Expression conveys meaning most of the time
Phrasing	1 Mostly word-by-word	2 Short phrases most of the time; inappropriate pauses	3 Longer word phrases some of the time; heeds most punctuation	4 Longer, meaningful phrases most of the time; heeds all punctuation
Rate	1 29 WPM or less	2 30–39 WPM	3 40–70 WPM	4 71 WPM or more
Accuracy	1 93% or less	2 94%	3 95%–98%	4 99%–100%
Score	4 5 6	7 8 9 10	11 12 13 14	15 16
Comprehension				
Previewing	1 Comments briefly about ideas only when prompted or is uncertain; may use a few terms or labels relevant to the text	2 Identifies and comments briefly about ideas with some prompting; uses a few terms or labels relevant to the text	3 Identifies and connects at least 3 key ideas (e.g., *and*, *then*, *too*) without prompting; some relevant vocabulary	4 Identifies and connects at least 4 key ideas without prompting; relevant vocabulary
Retelling: Key Ideas and Facts	1 Includes at least 1 idea/fact from the text; limited retelling	2 Includes 2–3 ideas/facts from the text; partial retelling	3 Includes most key ideas/facts, generally in a logical order	4 Includes all key ideas/facts in a logical order
Retelling: Details	1 Includes at least 1 detail; may include incorrect information	2 Includes at least 2 details; may include misinterpretation	3 Includes some important details	4 Includes most important details
Retelling: Vocabulary	1 Uses general terms or labels; limited understanding of key words/concepts	2 Uses some language/vocabulary from the text; some understanding of key words/concepts	3 Uses language/vocabulary from the text; basic understanding of most key words/concepts	4 Uses important language/vocabulary from the text; good understanding of key words/concepts
Retelling: Teacher Support	1 Retells with 5 or more questions or prompts	2 Retells with 3 or 4 questions or prompts	3 Retells with 1 or 2 questions or prompts	4 Retells with no questions or prompts
Using Nonfiction Text Features	1 Locates and uses incorrect information to respond or is uncertain	2 Locates and uses information in the chart to accurately respond to 1 of the prompts; gives a partially correct response	3 Locates and uses information in the chart to accurately respond to both prompts	4 Quickly locates and uses information in the chart to accurately respond with details to both prompts
Making Connections	1 Makes no or an unrelated connection; cites an idea/fact directly from the text	2 Makes a connection that reflects a limited understanding of the text	3 Makes a literal connection that reflects a basic understanding of the text	4 Makes a thoughtful connection that reflects a deeper understanding of the text
Score	7 8 9 10 11 12 13	14 15 16 17 18	19 20 21 22 23 24 25	26 27 28

Choose three to five teaching/learning activities on the *DRA2* Focus for Instruction on the next page.

Animal Homes 16

DRA2 FOCUS FOR INSTRUCTION FOR TRANSITIONAL READERS

READING ENGAGEMENT

Book Selection
☐ Teach student strategies to select "just right" texts for independent reading
☐ Introduce student to reading materials from a variety of genres
☐ Model and discuss why readers have favorite books and authors

Sustained Reading
☐ Model and support the use of sustained reading time
☐ Develop clear expectations for amount of independent reading
☐ Provide opportunities for buddy reading
☐ Create structures and routines to support reading at home

ORAL READING FLUENCY

Expression and Phrasing
☐ Model and teach how to emphasize key words and phrases when reading informational texts
☐ Model and support reading in longer, meaningful phrases with appropriate expression
☐ Model and support how to attend to punctuation
☐ Have student practice appropriate phrasing and expression with familiar texts

Rate
☐ Provide materials and time for repeated reading to increase reading rate
☐ Teach student to read lower-level and/or familiar texts at an appropriate rate

Accuracy: Word Analysis
☐ Support and reinforce self-corrections of miscues
☐ Model and support how to take words apart (e.g., onset and rime, syllables) to problem-solve unknown words
☐ Teach how to use word chunks and analogies to problem-solve unknown words
☐ Provide spelling activities and word sorts to help student recognize patterns in words

COMPREHENSION

Previewing
☐ Model and support previewing informational books during read-aloud and shared reading experiences
☐ Model and teach student how to activate relevant background knowledge before reading an informational text

Retelling
☐ Model and teach how to retell the ideas and facts presented in an informational text
☐ Model and teach how to identify important information (key ideas and facts) to include in a retelling
☐ Support retelling information in a logical order
☐ Model and support using key vocabulary/language from the text in a retelling
☐ Model and support going back into the text for specific information

Using Nonfiction Text Features
☐ Teach student how to read information presented graphically
☐ Teach student how to use graphic organizers to keep track and present facts and ideas

Making Connections
☐ Model and teach how to make text-to-self connections
☐ Model and teach how to make text-to-text connections

OTHER

_____

_____

_____

_____

_____

_____

_____

Animal Homes

16

Baby Birds

Name/Date _____   Teacher/Grade _____

Scores: Reading Engagement ___/8   Oral Reading Fluency ___/16   Comprehension ___/28
Independent Range: 6–7   11–14   19–25

Book Selection   Text selected by: ☐ teacher   ☐ student

1. READING ENGAGEMENT

(If the student has recently answered these questions, skip this section.)

T: What kinds of books do you like to read? _____

T: Tell me about one of your favorite books. _____

T: Whom do you read with at home? _____

2. ORAL READING FLUENCY

INTRODUCTION AND PREVIEW

T: This book is called Baby Birds*. It tells how baby robins hatch and how their parents take care of them. Tell me what you know about baby birds.*

Student's response reveals   ☐ little,   ☐ some, or   ☐ much background knowledge.

T: Now, look at each picture, and tell me what you think you'll learn about baby birds.

Note the student's use of connecting words (e.g., *and, then, but*)) and vocabulary relevant to the text. You may use general prompts, such as "What else?" or "Turn the page," but do <u>not</u> ask specific questions. Tally the number of times you prompt.

RECORD OF ORAL READING

Record the student's oral reading behaviors. Note the student's fluency (expression and phrasing). Be sure to time the student's reading.

T: Baby Birds. Now, read to find out what the author says about baby robins and how their parents take care of them.

Page 2

Birds   make   nests   in   the   spring.

Page 3

Mother   robin   finds   mud   and   twigs   and   leaves.
She   makes   a   round   nest.   She   puts   soft   grass
inside   the   nest.

Page 4

Birds   lay   eggs.

Page 5

Mother   robin   lays   one   egg   each   day   until   she has   about   four   eggs.   Robin   eggs   are   light   blue.

Page 6

Birds   keep   their   eggs   warm.

Page 7

Mother   robin   sits   on   the   nest   to   keep   the   eggs warm.   She   turns   the   eggs   every   day.

Mother   robin   sits   on   the   nest   for   about   13   days. Father   robin   stays   nearby.

Page 8

Baby   birds   hatch   out   of   the   eggs.

Page 9

Baby   robins   crack   their   shells   open   with   their beaks.   They   work   hard   to   get   out   of   their   shells.

Page 10

The   babies   cannot   fly.   They   do   not   have feathers.   They   cannot   see.   Their   eyes   are closed.   Mother   and   father   birds   feed their   babies.

Page 11

Mother   and   father   robin   work   hard   to   feed   their babies.   The   babies   eat   about   35   meals   a   day! They   eat   worms   and   bugs.

Page 12

Baby birds grow.

Page 13

The baby robins grow feathers. Their eyes open. In about 14 days, they leave the nest and learn to fly.

Time: _____ minutes:seconds

ORAL READING WORDS PER MINUTE, PERCENT OF ACCURACY

Use the student's oral reading time to circle the WPM range.

Word Count: 177

	INTRVN	INSTR	IND	ADV
Minutes:Seconds	6:01 or more	6:00–4:29	4:28–2:31	2:30 or less
WPM	29 or less	30–39	40–70	71 or more

Count the number of miscues that are not self-corrected. Circle the percent of accuracy based on the number of miscues.

	INTRVN	INSTR	IND				ADV	
Number of Miscues	12 or more	10–11	8–9	7	5–6	3–4	1–2	0
Percent of Accuracy	93 or less	94	95	96	97	98	99	100

- If the student's score falls in a shaded area for either WPM or Accuracy, STOP! Reassess with a lower-level text.
- If the student is reading below the grade-level benchmark, administer *DRA Word Analysis,* beginning with Task 16, at another time.

3. COMPREHENSION

RETELLING

As the student retells, underline and record on the Overview the information included in the student's retelling. Please note the student does not need to use the exact words.

T: Close the book before the retelling, and then say: **Start at the beginning, and tell me what the author said about baby birds and how their parents take care of them.**

Overview

1. Birds make nests in the spring. Robins make round nests from mud, twigs, leaves, and grass.

2. Birds lay eggs. Mother robins lay one egg each day until they have about four eggs. The eggs are light blue.

3. Birds keep their eggs warm. Mother robin keeps her eggs warm by sitting on the nest for about 13 days. She turns the eggs every day.

4. Baby birds then hatch from the eggs. Baby robins use their beaks to crack open the eggshells.

5. The babies cannot fly. They don't have feathers, and they cannot see.

6. Mother and father birds feed the babies. Robins feed their babies worms and bugs for about 35 meals a day.

7. Baby birds grow. Baby robins grow feathers, and their eyes open.

8. In about 14 days, baby robins leave the nest and learn to fly.

If necessary, use one or more of the following prompts to gain further information. Place a checkmark by a prompt each time it is used.

☐ *Tell me more.*
☐ *Tell me what baby birds are like when they first hatch.*
☐ *Tell me how mother and father birds take care of their babies.*

USING NONFICTION TEXT FEATURES

Record the student's responses to the prompts and questions below.

T: Turn to the timeline on pages 14–15. Say: **Use the timeline, and tell me what happens before the eggs are laid in the nest.**

T: **What happens after the eggs are laid in the nest?**

MAKING CONNECTIONS

T: **What did this book make you think of?** or **What connections did you make while reading this book?**

4. TEACHER ANALYSIS

ORAL READING

If the student had 5 or more different miscues, use the information recorded on the Record of Oral Reading to complete the chart below.

Student problem-solves words using:	Number of miscues self-corrected: _____
☐ beginning letter(s)/sound(s) ☐ letter-sound clusters ☐ onset and rime ☐ blending letters/sounds ☐ knowledge of spelling patterns (analogies) ☐ syllables ☐ rereading ☐ no observable behaviors	Number of miscues not self-corrected: _____ Number of words told to the student: _____

| | Miscues interfered with meaning:
☐ never
☐ at times
☐ often | Miscues included:
☐ omissions
☐ insertions
☐ substitutions that were
  ☐ visually similar
  ☐ not visually similar |

Copy each substitution to help analyze the student's attention to visual information.

e.g., <u>next</u> (substitution)
      nest (text)

Oral Reading Rate: (Optional) Use the formula below to determine the student's exact oral reading rate. Convert the student's reading time to all seconds.

177 (words) ÷ _____ total seconds = _____ WPS × 60 = _____ WPM

*DRA*2 Continuum

- Circle the descriptors that best describe the student's reading behaviors and responses.
    1. Use your daily classroom observations and the student's responses to the Reading Engagement questions to select statements that best describe the student's level of Reading Engagement.
    2. Use your recorded observations from this assessment to select the statements that best describe the student's Oral Reading Fluency and Comprehension.
- Add the circled numbers to obtain a total score for each section.
- Record the total scores at the top of page 1.

Note: If the Comprehension score is less than 19, administer *DRA*2 with a lower-level text.

Baby Birds **16**

DRA2 CONTINUUM	LEVEL 16		TRANSITIONAL READER	
	INTERVENTION	**INSTRUCTIONAL**	**INDEPENDENT**	**ADVANCED**
Reading Engagement				
Book Selection	**1** Selects texts from identified leveled sets with teacher support; uncertain about a favorite book	**2** Selects texts from identified leveled sets with moderate support; tells about favorite book in general terms	**3** Independently selects texts from identified leveled sets most of the time; identifies favorite book by title and tells about a particular event	**4** Independently selects a variety of "just right" texts; identifies favorite book by title and gives an overview of the book
Sustained Reading	**1** Sustains independent reading for a short period of time with much encouragement	**2** Sustains independent reading with moderate encouragement	**3** Sustains independent reading for at least 10–15 minutes at a time	**4** Sustains independent reading for an extended period of time
Score	2 3	4 5	6 7	8
Oral Reading Fluency				
Expression	**1** No expression; monotone	**2** Little expression; rather monotone	**3** Some expression	**4** Expression conveys meaning most of the time
Phrasing	**1** Mostly word-by-word	**2** Short phrases most of the time; inappropriate pauses	**3** Longer word phrases some of the time; heeds most punctuation	**4** Longer, meaningful phrases most of the time; heeds all punctuation
Rate	**1** 29 WPM or less	**2** 30–39 WPM	**3** 40–70 WPM	**4** 71 WPM or more
Accuracy	**1** 93% or less	**2** 94%	**3** 95%–98%	**4** 99%–100%
Score	4 5 6	7 8 9 10	11 12 13 14	15 16
Comprehension				
Previewing	**1** Comments briefly about ideas only when prompted or is uncertain; may use a few terms or labels relevant to the text	**2** Identifies and comments briefly about ideas with some prompting; uses a few terms or labels relevant to the text	**3** Identifies and connects at least 3 key ideas (e.g., *and, then, too*) without prompting; some relevant vocabulary	**4** Identifies and connects at least 4 key ideas without prompting; relevant vocabulary
Retelling: Key Ideas and Facts	**1** Includes at least 1 idea/fact from the text; limited retelling	**2** Includes 2–3 ideas/facts from the text; partial retelling	**3** Includes most key ideas/facts, generally in a logical order	**4** Includes all key ideas/facts in a logical order
Retelling: Details	**1** Includes at least 1 detail; may include incorrect information	**2** Includes at least 2 details; may include misinterpretation	**3** Includes some important details	**4** Includes most important details
Retelling: Vocabulary	**1** Uses general terms or labels; limited understanding of key words/concepts	**2** Uses some language/vocabulary from the text; some understanding of key words/concepts	**3** Uses language/vocabulary from the text; basic understanding of most key words/concepts	**4** Uses important language/vocabulary from the text; good understanding of key words/concepts
Retelling: Teacher Support	**1** Retells with 5 or more questions or prompts	**2** Retells with 3 or 4 questions or prompts	**3** Retells with 1 or 2 questions or prompts	**4** Retells with no questions or prompts
Using Nonfiction Text Features	**1** Locates and uses incorrect information to respond or is uncertain	**2** Locates and uses information in the chart to accurately respond to 1 of the prompts; gives a partially correct response	**3** Locates and uses information in the chart to accurately respond to both prompts	**4** Quickly locates and uses information in the chart to accurately respond with details to both prompts
Making Connections	**1** Makes no or an unrelated connection; cites an idea/fact directly from the text	**2** Makes a connection that reflects a limited understanding of the text	**3** Makes a literal connection that reflects a basic understanding of the text	**4** Makes a thoughtful connection that reflects a deeper understanding of the text
Score	7 8 9 10 11 12 13	14 15 16 17 18	19 20 21 22 23 24 25	26 27 28

Choose three to five teaching/learning activities on the *DRA2* Focus for Instruction on the next page.

Baby Birds **16**

DRA2 FOCUS FOR INSTRUCTION FOR TRANSITIONAL READERS

READING ENGAGEMENT

Book Selection
☐ Teach student strategies to select "just right" texts for independent reading
☐ Introduce student to reading materials from a variety of genres
☐ Model and discuss why readers have favorite books and authors

Sustained Reading
☐ Model and support the use of sustained reading time
☐ Develop clear expectations for amount of independent reading
☐ Provide opportunities for buddy reading
☐ Create structures and routines to support reading at home

ORAL READING FLUENCY

Expression and Phrasing
☐ Model and teach how to emphasize key words and phrases when reading informational texts
☐ Model and support reading in longer, meaningful phrases with appropriate expression
☐ Model and support how to attend to punctuation
☐ Have student practice appropriate phrasing and expression with familiar texts

Rate
☐ Provide materials and time for repeated reading to increase reading rate
☐ Teach student to read lower level and/or familiar texts at an appropriate rate

Accuracy: Word Analysis
☐ Support and reinforce self-corrections of miscues
☐ Model and support how to take words apart (e.g., onset and rime, syllables) to problem-solve unknown words
☐ Teach how to use word chunks and analogies to problem-solve unknown words
☐ Provide spelling activities and word sorts to help student recognize patterns in words

COMPREHENSION

Previewing
☐ Model and support previewing informational books during read-aloud and shared reading experiences
☐ Model and teach student how to activate relevant background knowledge before reading an informational text

Retelling
☐ Model and teach how to retell the ideas and facts presented in an informational text
☐ Model and teach how to identify important information (key ideas and facts) to include in a retelling
☐ Support retelling information in a logical order
☐ Model and support using key vocabulary/language from the text in a retelling
☐ Model and support going back into the text for specific information

Using Nonfiction Text Features
☐ Teach student how to read information presented graphically
☐ Teach student how to use graphic organizers to keep track and present facts and ideas

Making Connections
☐ Model and teach how to make text-to-self connections
☐ Model and teach how to make text-to-text connections

OTHER

_____

_____

_____

_____

_____

_____

_____

Name/Date _____   Teacher/Grade _____

Scores: Reading Engagement ___/8   Oral Reading Fluency ___/16   Comprehension ___/28
Independent Range: 6–7   11–14   19–25

Book Selection   Text selected by: ☐ teacher   ☐ student

1. READING ENGAGEMENT

(If the student has recently answered these questions, skip this section.)

T: What kinds of books do you like to read? _____

T: Tell me about one of your favorite books. _____

T: Whom do you read with at home? _____

2. ORAL READING FLUENCY

INTRODUCTION AND PREVIEW

T: In this story, Chip to the Rescue, *Chip, the mouse, helps Dot and the other giraffes when they go kite flying. Look at the pictures, and tell me what is happening in this story.*

Note the student's use of connecting words (e.g., *and, then, but*) and vocabulary relevant to the text. You may use general prompts, such as "Now what is happening?" or "Turn the page," but do <u>not</u> ask specific questions. Tally the number of times you prompt.

RECORD OF ORAL READING ⏱

Record the student's oral reading behaviors. Note the student's fluency (expression and phrasing). Be sure to time the student's reading.

T: Chip to the Rescue. *Now, read to find out how Chip helps Dot and the other giraffes.*

Page 2

Chip, the mouse, and Dot, the giraffe, were good friends. Dot took Chip out for rides.

"I'm on top of the world!" Chip called out.

Page 3

Some giraffes didn't know why Dot was friends with such a tiny animal.

"Chip is so small," the tallest giraffe told Dot. "He can't do anything."

"Yes, he can," said Dot. "He is a good friend."

Page 4

One day some giraffes wanted to fly kites. They liked flying kites.

Dot asked Chip to go kite flying with her.

"Yes, thank you!" Chip shouted. He was very happy. He skipped all the way up Dot's neck.

Page 5

The giraffes walked to an open field.

Their kites sailed high up into the sky. The giraffes were so tall. Their kites flew higher than the trees.

Just then, the wind blew hard across the field.

Page 6

The kites flew sideways in the wind. The kite strings were very long. The kites got stuck in some trees!

The giraffes were sad. They walked over to the trees. They could not get the kites down. The kite strings were stuck in the branches.

"What can we do now?" asked Dot.

110

Page 7

"I can help!" Chip said. He jumped off Dot onto a branch.

Chip ran in and out of the branches. He carefully pulled on the kite strings and got the kites free.

Page 8

The giraffes cheered for Chip!

"It must be nice to be small," the tallest giraffe told Chip. "You can do things we can't do."

"Yes, that's right," Chip said.

Dot smiled. She knew that.

Time: _____ minutes:seconds

ORAL READING WORDS PER MINUTE, PERCENT OF ACCURACY

Use the student's oral reading time to circle the WPM range.

Word Count: 253

	INTRVN	INSTR	IND	ADV
Minutes:Seconds	7:21 or more	7:20–5:42	5:41–3:22	3:21 or less
WPM	34 or less	35–44	45–75	76 or more

Count the number of miscues that are not self-corrected. Circle the percent of accuracy based on the number of miscues.

	INTRVN	INSTR	IND				ADV	
Number of Miscues	17 or more	14–16	12–13	9–11	7–8	4–6	1–3	0
Percent of Accuracy	93 or less	94	95	96	97	98	99	100

- If the student's score falls in a shaded area for either WPM or Accuracy, STOP! Reassess with a lower-level text.
- If the student is reading below the grade-level benchmark, administer *DRA Word Analysis*, beginning with Task 16, at another time.

3. COMPREHENSION

RETELLING

As the student retells, underline and record on the Story Overview the information included in the student's retelling. Please note the student does not need to use the exact words.

T: Close the book before the retelling, and then say: ***Start at the beginning, and tell me what happened in this story.***

Story Overview
Beginning
1. Chip the mouse and Dot the giraffe were good friends.
2. Some giraffes did not know why Chip and Dot were friends.
3. The giraffes thought Chip couldn't do anything because he was small.

Middle
4. The giraffes went kite flying and Dot asked Chip to go.
5. The kites flew high in the sky.
6. The wind blew so hard that the kites got stuck in some trees.
7. The giraffes were sad. They could not get the kites out of the trees.
8. Chip got the kite strings out of the branches.
9. The giraffes cheered for Chip.

End
10. Chip could do things the giraffes couldn't do because he was small.

If the retelling is limited, use one or more of the following prompts to gain further information. Place a checkmark by a prompt each time it is used.

☐ *Tell me more.*
☐ *What happened at the beginning?*
☐ *What happened before/after* _____ (an event mentioned by the student)*?*
☐ *Who else was in the story?*
☐ *How did the story end?*

REFLECTION

Record the student's responses to the prompts and questions below.

T: *What part did you like best in this story? Tell me why you liked that part.*

MAKING CONNECTIONS

Note: If the student makes a text-to-self connection in his or her response to the above prompt, skip the following question.

T: *What did this story make you think of?* or *What connections did you make while reading this story?*

4. TEACHER ANALYSIS

ORAL READING

If the student had 5 or more different miscues, use the information recorded on the Record of Oral Reading to complete the chart below.

Student problem-solves words using:		
☐ beginning letter(s)/sound(s) ☐ letter-sound clusters ☐ onset and rime ☐ blending letters/sounds ☐ knowledge of spelling patterns (analogies) ☐ syllables ☐ rereading ☐ no observable behaviors	Number of miscues self-corrected: _____ Number of miscues not self-corrected: _____ Number of words told to the student: _____	

	Miscues interfered with meaning:
	☐ never
	☐ at times
	☐ often
		Miscues included:
		☐ omissions
		☐ insertions
		☐ substitutions that were
		    ☐ visually similar
		    ☐ not visually similar

Copy each substitution to help analyze the student's attention to visual information.

e.g., <u>went</u> (substitution)

    wanted (text)

Oral Reading Rate: (Optional) Use the formula below to determine the student's exact oral reading rate. Convert the student's reading time to all seconds.

    253 (words) ÷ _____ total seconds = _____ WPS × 60 = _____ WPM

DRA2 Continuum

- Circle the descriptors that best describe the student's reading behaviors and responses.
    1. Use your daily classroom observations and the student's responses to the Reading Engagement questions to select statements that best describe the student's level of Reading Engagement.
    2. Use your recorded observations from this assessment to select the statements that best describe the student's Oral Reading Fluency and Comprehension.
- Add the circled numbers to obtain a total score for each section.
- Record the total scores at the top of page 1.

Note: If the Comprehension score is less than 19, administer *DRA2* with a lower-level text.

Chip to the Rescue 16

Chip to the Rescue 16

DRA2 CONTINUUM	LEVEL 16		TRANSITIONAL READER	
	INTERVENTION	**INSTRUCTIONAL**	**INDEPENDENT**	**ADVANCED**
Reading Engagement				
Book Selection	1 Selects texts from identified leveled sets with teacher support; uncertain about a favorite book	2 Selects texts from identified leveled sets with moderate support; tells about favorite book in general terms	3 Selects texts from identified leveled sets most of the time; identifies favorite book by title and tells about a particular event	4 Selects a variety of "just right" texts; identifies favorite book by title and gives an overview of the book
Sustained Reading	1 Sustains independent reading for a short period of time with much encouragement	2 Sustains independent reading with moderate encouragement	3 Sustains independent reading for at least 10–15 minutes at a time	4 Sustains independent reading for an extended period of time
Score	2 3	4 5	6 7	8
Oral Reading Fluency				
Expression	1 No expression; monotone	2 Little expression; rather monotone	3 Some expression	4 Expression conveys meaning most of the time
Phrasing	1 Mostly word-by-word	2 Short phrases most of the time; inappropriate pauses	3 Longer word phrases some of the time; heeds most punctuation	4 Longer, meaningful phrases most of the time; heeds all punctuation
Rate	1 34 WPM or less	2 35–44 WPM	3 45–75 WPM	4 76 WPM or more
Accuracy	1 93% or less	2 94%	3 95%–98%	4 99%–100%
Score	4 5 6	7 8 9 10	11 12 13 14	15 16
Comprehension				
Previewing	1 Comments briefly about each event or action only when prompted or is uncertain	2 Identifies and comments briefly about each event or action with some prompting	3 Identifies and connects at least 3 key events without prompting; some relevant vocabulary	4 Identifies and connects at least 4 key events without prompting; relevant vocabulary
Retelling: Sequence of Events	1 Includes 1 or 2 events or details (limited retelling)	2 Includes at least 3 events, generally in random order (partial retelling)	3 Includes most of the important events from the beginning, middle, and end, generally in sequence	4 Includes all important events from the beginning, middle, and end in sequence
Retelling: Characters and Details	1 Refers to characters using general pronouns; may include incorrect information	2 Refers to characters using appropriate pronouns; includes at least 1 detail; may include some misinterpretation	3 Refers to most characters by name and includes some important details	4 Refers to all characters by name and includes all important details
Retelling: Vocabulary	1 Uses general terms or labels; limited understanding of key words/concepts	2 Uses some language/vocabulary from the text; some understanding of key words/concepts	3 Uses language/vocabulary from the text; basic understanding of most key words/concepts	4 Uses important language/vocabulary from the text; good understanding of key words/concepts
Retelling: Teacher Support	1 Retells with 5 or more questions or prompts	2 Retells with 3 or 4 questions or prompts	3 Retells with 1 or 2 questions or prompts	4 Retells with no questions or prompts
Reflection	1 Gives an unrelated response, no reason for opinion, or no response	2 Gives a limited response and/or general reason for opinion	3 Gives a specific event/action; <u>and</u> a relevant reason for response (e.g., personal connection)	4 Gives a response and reason that reflects higher-level thinking (e.g., synthesis/inference)
Making Connections	1 Makes an unrelated connection, relates an event in the story, or gives no response	2 Makes a connection that reflects a limited understanding of the story	3 Makes a literal connection that reflects a basic understanding of the story	4 Makes a thoughtful connection that reflects a deeper understanding of the story
Score	7 8 9 10 11 12 13	14 15 16 17 18	19 20 21 22 23 24 25	26 27 28

Choose three to five teaching/learning activities on the *DRA2* Focus for Instruction on the next page.

DRA2 FOCUS FOR INSTRUCTION FOR TRANSITIONAL READERS

READING ENGAGEMENT

Book Selection
- ☐ Teach student strategies to select "just right" texts for independent reading
- ☐ Introduce student to reading materials from a variety of genres
- ☐ Model and discuss why readers have favorite books and authors

Sustained Reading
- ☐ Model and support the use of sustained reading time
- ☐ Develop clear expectations for amount of independent reading
- ☐ Provide opportunities for buddy reading
- ☐ Create structures and routines to support reading at home

ORAL READING FLUENCY

Expression and Phrasing
- ☐ Have student practice appropriate phrasing and expression with familiar texts
- ☐ Model and support reading in longer, meaningful phrases with appropriate expression
- ☐ Model and teach how to heed punctuation
- ☐ Have student participate in choral reading and/or reader's theater

Rate
- ☐ Provide materials and time for repeated reading to increase reading rate
- ☐ Teach student to read lower-level and/or familiar texts at an appropriate rate

Accuracy: Word Analysis
- ☐ Support and reinforce self-corrections of miscues
- ☐ Model and support how to take words apart (e.g., onset and rime, syllables) to problem-solve unknown words
- ☐ Teach how to use word chunks and analogies to problem-solve unknown words
- ☐ Provide spelling activities and word sorts to help student recognize patterns in words

COMPREHENSION

Previewing
- ☐ Support creating a story from the illustrations
- ☐ Model and support previewing a book during read-aloud and shared reading experiences

Retelling
- ☐ Model and teach how to retell a story
- ☐ Model and teach how to identify important events to include in a retelling
- ☐ Support retelling a story in sequence
- ☐ Encourage student to use characters' names when retelling a story
- ☐ Model and teach how to identify important details to include in a retelling
- ☐ Model and support using key vocabulary/language from the text in a retelling
- ☐ Model and teach how to create and use story maps to aid retelling

Reflection
- ☐ Support and reinforce student's responses to books
- ☐ Provide opportunities to select a favorite book, toy, TV show, etc., and tell why it is a favorite
- ☐ Help student identify favorite part of books
- ☐ Demonstrate how to support one's opinion

Making Connections
- ☐ Model and teach how to make text-to-self connections
- ☐ Model and teach how to make text-to-text connections

OTHER

_____

_____

_____

_____

_____

_____

_____

Chip to the Rescue 16

Name/Date _____   Teacher/Grade _____

Scores: Reading Engagement ___/8   Oral Reading Fluency ___/16   Comprehension ___/28
Independent Range: 6–7   11–14   19–25

Book Selection   Text selected by: ☐ teacher   ☐ student

1. READING ENGAGEMENT

(If the student has recently answered these questions, skip this section.)

T: What kinds of books do you like to read? _____

T: Tell me about one of your favorite books. _____

T: Whom do you read with at home? _____

2. ORAL READING FLUENCY

INTRODUCTION AND PREVIEW

T: In this story, Monkey's Stepping Stones, *Monkey goes for a walk to look for butterflies. He uses the backs of hippos as stepping stones to get across a river. Look at the pictures, and tell me what is happening in this story.*

Note the student's use of connecting words (e.g., *and, then, but*) and vocabulary relevant to the text. You may use general prompts, such as "Now what is happening?" or "Turn the page," but do not ask specific questions. Tally the number of times you prompt.

RECORD OF ORAL READING

Record the student's oral reading behaviors. Note the student's fluency (expression and phrasing). Be sure to time the student's reading.

T: Monkey's Stepping Stones. *Now, read to find out how the hippos help Monkey.*

Page 2

Monkey   and   his   mother   lived   in   the   jungle.
One   day   Monkey   wanted   to   take   a   walk   to
look   for   butterflies.

"Don't   go   too   far,"   said   his   mother.   "There   are
lots   of   animals   who   eat   monkeys."

"Don't   worry,"   said   Monkey.   "I   won't   go
too   far."

Page 3

On his walk Monkey saw lots of birds. Then he saw a purple butterfly. Monkey chased it. He went too far. He was deep in the jungle.

Monkey came to a river. He saw hippos in the water. He could just see the tops of their heads and their backs.

"Those hippos look like stepping stones," said Monkey. So he walked across the river.

Page 4

Monkey walked through some very tall grass. He saw the purple butterfly once again.

All of a sudden Monkey felt something watching him. He turned around. Two big, yellow eyes were looking right at him!

"Oh, no!" said Monkey, as a tiger jumped out of the tall grass.

Page 5

Monkey ran as fast as he could to the river, but the hippos were gone.

"How can I cross the river?" cried Monkey.

"Take my vine," said Bird, who was up in a tree.

Monkey climbed the tree as fast as he could.

Page 6

He grabbed the vine. He swung across the river. But the vine was too short.

"Oh, no!" shouted Monkey.

Page 7

Just then the hippos popped out of the water. Monkey let go of the vine. He used the hippos as stepping stones once more.

Page 8

Soon he was safe on the other side of the river and on his way home.

Time: _____ minutes:seconds

ORAL READING WORDS PER MINUTE, PERCENT OF ACCURACY

Use the student's oral reading time to circle the WPM range.

Word Count: 258

	INTRVN	INSTR	IND	ADV
Minutes:Seconds	7:29 or more	7:28–5:48	5:47–3:26	3:25 or less
WPM	34 or less	35–44	45–75	76 or more

Count the number of miscues that are not self-corrected. Circle the percent of accuracy based on the number of miscues.

	INTRVN	INSTR	IND				ADV	
Number of Miscues	17 or more	15–16	12–14	10–11	7–9	4–6	1–3	0
Percent of Accuracy	93 or less	94	95	96	97	98	99	100

- If the student's score falls in a shaded area for either WPM or Accuracy, STOP! Reassess with a lower-level text.
- If the student is reading below the grade-level benchmark, administer *DRA Word Analysis*, beginning with Task 16, at another time.

Monkey's Stepping Stones 16

3. COMPREHENSION

RETELLING

As the student retells, underline and record on the Story Overview the information included in the student's retelling. Please note the student does not need to use the exact words.

T: Close the book before the retelling, and then say: ***Start at the beginning, and tell me what happened in this story.***

Story Overview
Beginning
1. Monkey took a walk to look for butterflies.
2. Mother told Monkey not to go far. Lots of animals eat monkeys.

Middle
3. Monkey saw a purple butterfly and followed it deep into the jungle.
4. He came to a river and used the hippos as stepping stones to walk across the river.
5. He saw the purple butterfly again.
6. All of a sudden, Monkey saw a tiger!
7. He ran to the river, but the hippos were gone.
8. Bird told Monkey to use the vine, but the vine was too short.
9. Hippos popped out of the water, and Monkey used the hippos as stepping stones.

End
10. Monkey was safe on the other side of the river, and he went home.

If the retelling is limited, use one or more of the following prompts to gain further information. Place a checkmark by a prompt each time it is used.

☐ *Tell me more.*
☐ *What happened at the beginning?*
☐ *What happened before/after* _____ (an event mentioned by the student)*?*
☐ *Who else was in the story?*
☐ *How did the story end?*

REFLECTION

Record the student's responses to the prompts and questions below.

T: *What part did you like best in this story? Tell me why you liked that part.*

MAKING CONNECTIONS

Note: If the student makes a text-to-self connection in his or her response to the above prompt, skip the following question.

T: *What did this story make you think of?* or *What connections did you make while reading this story?*

Monkey's Stepping Stones 16

4. TEACHER ANALYSIS

ORAL READING

If the student had 5 or more different miscues, use the information recorded on the Record of Oral Reading to complete the chart below.

Student problem-solves words using:	Number of miscues self-corrected: _____	
☐ beginning letter(s)/sound(s)	Number of miscues not self-corrected: _____	
☐ letter-sound clusters	Number of words told to the student: _____	
☐ onset and rime	**Miscues interfered with meaning:**	**Miscues included:**
☐ blending letters/sounds	☐ never	☐ omissions
☐ knowledge of spelling patterns (analogies)	☐ at times	☐ insertions
☐ syllables	☐ often	☐ substitutions that were
☐ rereading		☐ visually similar
☐ no observable behaviors		☐ not visually similar

Copy each substitution to help analyze the student's attention to visual information.

e.g., book bags (substitution)

      backpacks (text)

Oral Reading Rate: (Optional) Use the formula below to determine the student's exact oral reading rate. Convert the student's reading time to all seconds.

$$258 \text{ (words)} \div \underline{\hspace{1cm}} \text{ total seconds} = \underline{\hspace{1cm}} \text{ WPS} \times 60 = \underline{\hspace{1cm}} \text{ WPM}$$

*DRA*2 Continuum

- Circle the descriptors that best describe the student's reading behaviors and responses.
    1. Use your daily classroom observations and the student's responses to the Reading Engagement questions to select statements that best describe the student's level of Reading Engagement.
    2. Use your recorded observations from this assessment to select the statements that best describe the student's Oral Reading Fluency and Comprehension.
- Add the circled numbers to obtain a total score for each section.
- Record the total scores at the top of page 1.

Note: If the Comprehension score is less than 19, administer *DRA*2 with a lower-level text.

Monkey's Stepping Stones 16

*DRA*2 CONTINUUM	LEVEL 16		TRANSITIONAL READER	
	INTERVENTION	INSTRUCTIONAL	INDEPENDENT	ADVANCED
Reading Engagement				
Book Selection	1 Selects texts from identified leveled sets with teacher support; uncertain about a favorite book	2 Selects texts from identified leveled sets with moderate support; tells about favorite book in general terms	3 Selects texts from identified leveled sets most of the time; identifies favorite book by title and tells about a particular event	4 Selects a variety of "just right" texts; identifies favorite book by title and gives an overview of the book
Sustained Reading	1 Sustains independent reading for a short period of time with much encouragement	2 Sustains independent reading with moderate encouragement	3 Sustains independent reading for at least 10–15 minutes at a time	4 Sustains independent reading for an extended period of time
Score	2 3	4 5	6 7	8
Oral Reading Fluency				
Expression	1 No expression; monotone	2 Little expression; rather monotone	3 Some expression	4 Expression conveys meaning most of the time
Phrasing	1 Mostly word-by-word	2 Short phrases most of the time; inappropriate pauses	3 Longer word phrases some of the time; heeds most punctuation	4 Longer, meaningful phrases most of the time; heeds all punctuation
Rate	1 34 WPM or less	2 35–44 WPM	3 45–75 WPM	4 76 WPM or more
Accuracy	1 93% or less	2 94%	3 95%–98%	4 99%–100%
Score	4 5 6	7 8 9 10	11 12 13 14	15 16
Comprehension				
Previewing	1 Comments briefly about each event or action only when prompted or is uncertain	2 Identifies and comments briefly about each event or action with some prompting	3 Identifies and connects at least 3 key events without prompting; some relevant vocabulary	4 Identifies and connects at least 4 key events without prompting; relevant vocabulary
Retelling: Sequence of Events	1 Includes only 1 or 2 events or details (limited retelling)	2 Includes at least 3 events, generally in random order (partial retelling)	3 Includes most of the important events from the beginning, middle, and end, generally in sequence	4 Includes all important events from the beginning, middle, and end in sequence
Retelling: Characters and Details	1 Refers to characters using general pronouns; may include incorrect information	2 Refers to characters using appropriate pronouns; includes at least 1 detail; may include some misinterpretation	3 Refers to most characters by name and includes some important details	4 Refers to all characters by name and includes all important details
Retelling: Vocabulary	1 Uses general terms or labels; limited understanding of key words/concepts	2 Uses some language/vocabulary from the text; some understanding of key words/concepts	3 Uses language/vocabulary from the text; basic understanding of most key words/concepts	4 Uses important language/vocabulary from the text; good understanding of key words/concepts
Retelling: Teacher Support	1 Retells with 5 or more questions or prompts	2 Retells with 3 or 4 questions or prompts	3 Retells with 1 or 2 questions or prompts	4 Retells with no questions or prompts
Reflection	1 Gives an unrelated response, no reason for opinion, or no response	2 Gives a limited response and/or general reason for opinion	3 Gives a specific story event/action <u>and</u> a relevant reason for response (e.g., personal connection)	4 Gives a response and reason that reflects higher-level thinking (e.g., synthesis/inference)
Making Connections	1 Makes an unrelated connection, relates an event in the story, or gives no response	2 Makes a connection that reflects a limited understanding of the story	3 Makes a literal connection that reflects a basic understanding of the story	4 Makes a thoughtful connection that reflects a deeper understanding of the story
Score	7 8 9 10 11 12 13	14 15 16 17 18	19 20 21 22 23 24 25	26 27 28

Choose three to five teaching/learning activities on the *DRA*2 Focus for Instruction on the next page.

Monkey's Stepping Stones **16**

DRA2 FOCUS FOR INSTRUCTION FOR TRANSITIONAL READERS

READING ENGAGEMENT

Book Selection
- ☐ Teach student strategies to select "just right" texts for independent reading
- ☐ Introduce student to reading materials from a variety of genres
- ☐ Model and discuss why readers have favorite books and authors

Sustained Reading
- ☐ Model and support the use of sustained reading time
- ☐ Develop clear expectations for amount of independent reading
- ☐ Provide opportunities for buddy reading
- ☐ Create structures and routines to support reading at home

ORAL READING FLUENCY

Expression and Phrasing
- ☐ Have student practice appropriate phrasing and expression with familiar texts
- ☐ Model and support reading in longer, meaningful phrases with appropriate expression
- ☐ Model and teach how to heed punctuation
- ☐ Have student participate in choral reading and/or reader's theater

Rate
- ☐ Provide materials and time for repeated reading to increase reading rate
- ☐ Teach student to read lower-level and/or familiar texts at an appropriate rate

Accuracy: Word Analysis
- ☐ Support and reinforce self-corrections of miscues
- ☐ Model and support how to take words apart (e.g., onset and rime, syllables) to problem-solve unknown words
- ☐ Teach how to use word chunks and analogies to problem-solve unknown words
- ☐ Provide spelling activities and word sorts to help student recognize patterns in words

COMPREHENSION

Previewing
- ☐ Model and support telling a story from the illustrations
- ☐ Model and support previewing a book during read-aloud and shared reading experiences

Retelling
- ☐ Model and teach how to retell a story
- ☐ Model and teach how to identify important events to include in a retelling
- ☐ Support retelling a story in sequence
- ☐ Encourage student to use characters' names when retelling a story
- ☐ Model and teach how to identify important details to include in a retelling
- ☐ Model and support using key vocabulary/language from the text in a retelling
- ☐ Model and teach how to create and use story maps to aid retelling

Reflection
- ☐ Support and reinforce student's responses to books
- ☐ Provide opportunities to select a favorite book, toy, TV show, etc., and tell why it is a favorite
- ☐ Help student identify favorite part of books
- ☐ Demonstrate how to support one's opinion

Making Connections
- ☐ Model and teach how to make text-to-self connections
- ☐ Model and teach how to make text-to-text connections

OTHER

_____

_____

_____

_____

_____

_____

Name/Date _____ Teacher/Grade _____

Scores: Reading Engagement ___/8   Oral Reading Fluency ___/16   Comprehension ___/28
Independent Range: 6–7   11–14   19–25

Book Selection   Text selected by: ☐ teacher   ☐ student

1. READING ENGAGEMENT

(If the student has recently answered these questions, skip this section.)

T: *What kinds of books do you like to read?* _____

T: *Tell me about one of your favorite books.* _____

T: *How do you choose the books you read?* _____

2. ORAL READING FLUENCY

INTRODUCTION

T: *In this story,* Game Day, *Raccoon helps her friends Otter, Rabbit, and Squirrel get ready for the games. Raccoon isn't too sure what she can do. Please read aloud pages 2 through 5.* Show the student where to stop reading at the ✱.

RECORD OF ORAL READING

Record the student's oral reading behaviors. Note the student's fluency (expression and phrasing). Be sure to time the student's reading.

Page 2

One morning Raccoon went to the river to
wash her face. She saw a stopwatch under
some leaves. Raccoon picked up the
stopwatch to look at it.

Page 3

Just then she saw Otter swimming by. He was getting ready for Game Day.

"Raccoon, will you help me?" asked Otter. "I need someone to time me."

"Yes," said Raccoon. She timed Otter with her stopwatch.

"Thanks for helping me," said Otter.

Page 4

Then Raccoon saw Rabbit running around a track.

"Will you help me?" asked Rabbit. "I need someone to tell me when to start."

"Yes," said Raccoon. "Get ready. Get set. Go!"

After Raccoon helped Rabbit, she started to go home.

Page 5

On the way, she saw Squirrel jumping in the grass.

"Will you help me?" asked Squirrel. "I need someone to measure how far I can jump."

So Raccoon stopped to help Squirrel.

Time: _____ minutes:seconds

Game Day 18

ORAL READING WORDS PER MINUTE, PERCENT OF ACCURACY

Use the student's oral reading time to circle the WPM range.

Word Count: 141

	INTRVN	INSTR	IND	ADV
Minutes:Seconds	3:11 or more	3:10–2:36	2:35–1:39	1:38 or less
WPM	44 or less	45–54	55–85	86 or more

Count the number of miscues that are not self-corrected. Circle the percent of accuracy based on the number of miscues.

	INTRVN	INSTR	IND				ADV	
Number of Miscues	10 or more	8–9	7	5–6	4	3	1–2	0
Percent of Accuracy	93 or less	94	95	96	97	98	99	100

- If the student's score falls in a shaded area for either WPM or Accuracy, STOP! Reassess with a lower-level text.
- If the student is reading below the grade-level benchmark, administer *DRA Word Analysis*, beginning with Task 16, at another time.

3. COMPREHENSION

PREDICTION

Students do not use the text when making their predictions. Record the student's responses.

T: Think about the title, the pictures you have seen, and what you have read so far. (Pause) *Tell me three things that you think might happen in the rest of this story.*

SILENT READING

T: Now, it's time to read and enjoy this story by yourself. When you are done, please come to me and I'll ask you to tell me what happened in this story.

RETELLING

As the student retells, underline and record on the Story Overview the information included in the student's retelling. Please note the student does not need to use the exact words.

T: Close the book before retelling, and then say: ***Start at the beginning, and tell me what happened in this story.***

Story Overview
Beginning
1. Raccoon found a stopwatch by the river and picked it up to look at it.

Middle
2. Raccoon helped Otter get ready for Game Day by timing him as he swam.

3. Raccoon helped Rabbit get ready by telling him when to start running.

4. Raccoon helped Squirrel get ready by measuring how far she could jump.

5. On her way home, Raccoon felt sad. She didn't feel she could do anything well.

6. The next day was Game Day. Raccoon's friends all won shiny medals.

7. That night the animals had a party. Raccoon felt sad.

End
8. Then Raccoon's friends gave her a shiny medal for helping them.

9. Raccoon was proud of her new medal. She could be a good friend.

If necessary, use one or more of the following prompts to gain further information after the initial retelling. Place a checkmark by a prompt each time it is used.

☐ *Tell me more.*
☐ *What happened at the beginning?*
☐ *What happened before/after* _____ (an event mentioned by the student)*?*
☐ *Who else was in the story?*
☐ *How did the story end?*

INTERPRETATION

Record the student's responses to the prompts and questions below.

T: *What do you think the author is trying to tell you in this story?*

REFLECTION

T: *What do you think was the most important thing that happened in this story?*

T: *Why do you think that was important?*

4. TEACHER ANALYSIS

ORAL READING

If the student had 5 or more different miscues, use the information recorded on the Record of Oral Reading to complete the chart below.

Student problem-solves words using:	Number of miscues self-corrected: _____
☐ beginning letter(s)/sound(s) ☐ letter-sound clusters	Number of miscues not self-corrected: _____ Number of words told to the student: _____

Student problem-solves words using:	Miscues interfered with meaning:	Miscues included:

☐ onset and rime
☐ blending letters/sounds
☐ knowledge of spelling patterns
   (analogies)
☐ syllables
☐ rereading
☐ no observable behaviors
	☐ never
	☐ at times
	☐ often
		☐ omissions
		☐ insertions
		☐ substitutions that were
		    ☐ visually similar
		    ☐ not visually similar

Copy each substitution to help analyze the student's attention to visual information.
e.g., stoplight (substitution)
     stopwatch (text)

Oral Reading Rate: (Optional) Use the formula below to determine the student's exact oral reading rate. Convert the student's reading time to all seconds.

141 (words) ÷ _____ total seconds = _____ WPS × 60 = _____ WPM

DRA2 Continuum

- Circle the descriptors that best describe the student's reading behaviors and responses.
  1. Use your daily classroom observations and the student's responses to the Reading Engagement questions to select statements that best describe the student's level of Reading Engagement.
  2. Use your recorded observations from this assessment to select the statements that best describe the student's Oral Reading Fluency and Comprehension.
- Add the circled numbers to obtain a total score for each section.
- Record the total scores at the top of page 1.

Note: If the Comprehension score is less than 19, administer DRA2 with a lower-level text.

Game Day 18

*DRA*2 CONTINUUM	LEVEL 18		TRANSITIONAL READER	
	INTERVENTION	**INSTRUCTIONAL**	**INDEPENDENT**	**ADVANCED**
Reading Engagement				
Book Selection	**1** Selects new texts from identified leveled sets with teacher support; uncertain about a favorite book	**2** Selects new texts from identified leveled sets with moderate support; tells about favorite book in general terms	**3** Selects new texts from identified leveled sets most of the time; identifies favorite book by title and tells about a particular event	**4** Selects a variety of new texts that are "just right"; identifies favorite book by title and gives an overview of the book
Sustained Reading	**1** Sustains independent reading for a short period of time with much encouragement	**2** Sustains independent reading with moderate encouragement	**3** Sustains independent reading for at least 15 minutes at a time	**4** Sustains independent reading for an extended period of time
Score	2 3	4 5	6 7	8
Oral Reading Fluency				
Expression	**1** Little expression; monotone	**2** Some expression that conveys meaning	**3** Expression reflects mood, pace, and tension at times	**4** Expression reflects mood, pace, and tension most of the time
Phrasing	**1** Reads mostly word-by-word	**2** Reads in short phrases most of the time; inappropriate pauses	**3** Reads in longer phrases at times; heeds most punctuation	**4** Reads in longer, meaningful phrases most of the time; heeds all punctuation
Rate	**1** 44 WPM or less	**2** 45–54 WPM	**3** 55–85 WPM	**4** 86 WPM or more
Accuracy	**1** 93% or less	**2** 94%	**3** 95%–98%	**4** 99%–100%
Score	4 5 6	7 8 9 10	11 12 13 14	15 16
Comprehension				
Prediction	**1** Makes unrelated or no prediction(s)	**2** Makes at least 1 reasonable prediction related to the text	**3** Makes at least 2 reasonable predictions that go beyond the pages read aloud	**4** Makes at least 3 thoughtful predictions that go beyond the pages read aloud
Retelling: Sequence of Events	**1** Includes only 1 or 2 events or details (limited retelling)	**2** Includes at least 3 events, generally in random order (partial retelling)	**3** Includes most of the important events from the beginning, middle, and end, generally in sequence	**4** Includes all important events from the beginning, middle, and end in sequence
Retelling: Characters and Details	**1** Refers to characters using general pronouns; may include incorrect information	**2** Refers to characters using appropriate pronouns; includes at least 1 detail; may include some misinterpretation	**3** Refers to most characters by name and includes some important details	**4** Refers to all characters by name and includes all important details
Retelling: Vocabulary	**1** Uses general terms or labels; limited understanding of key words/concepts	**2** Uses some language/ vocabulary from the text; some understanding of key words/concepts	**3** Uses language/ vocabulary from the text; basic understanding of most key words/concepts	**4** Uses important language/vocabulary from the text; good understanding of key words/concepts
Retelling: Teacher Support	**1** Retells with 5 or more questions or prompts	**2** Retells with 3 or 4 questions or prompts	**3** Retells with 1 or 2 questions or prompts	**4** Retells with no questions or prompts
Interpretation	**1** Little or no understanding of important text implications	**2** Some understanding of important text implications; no supporting details	**3** Understands important text implications; may include supporting details	**4** Insightful understanding of important text implications with supporting details or rationale
Reflection	**1** Identifies an unrelated event; no reason for opinion or no response	**2** Identifies a less significant event and/or gives a general reason for response	**3** Identifies a significant event _and_ gives relevant reason(s) for opinion	**4** Identifies a significant event _and_ gives reason(s) for opinion that reflects higher-level thinking
Score	7 8 9 10 11 12 13	14 15 16 17 18	19 20 21 22 23 24 25	26 27 28

Choose three to five teaching/learning activities on the *DRA*2 Focus for Instruction on the next page.

Game Day 18

DRA2 FOCUS FOR INSTRUCTION FOR TRANSITIONAL READERS

READING ENGAGEMENT

Book Selection
- ☐ Teach student strategies to select "just right" books for independent reading
- ☐ Introduce student to reading materials from a variety of genres
- ☐ Teach student how to use a reading log to monitor book selection
- ☐ Model/teach how to read for different purposes

Sustained Reading
- ☐ Model and support how to read independently
- ☐ Teach strategies to build reading stamina
- ☐ Develop clear expectations for amount of independent reading
- ☐ Create structures to support reading at home

ORAL READING FLUENCY

Expression and Phrasing
- ☐ Model and support reading in longer, meaningful phrases with appropriate expression
- ☐ Have student practice appropriate expression with familiar texts
- ☐ Have student participate in choral reading and/or reader's theater
- ☐ Teach student to heed punctuation

Rate
- ☐ Provide materials and time for repeated reading to increase reading rate
- ☐ Teach student to read lower-level and/or familiar texts at an appropriate rate

Accuracy: Word Analysis
- ☐ Support and reinforce self-corrections of miscues
- ☐ Model and support how to take words apart (e.g., onset and rime, syllables) to problem-solve unknown words
- ☐ Teach how to use word chunks and analogies to problem-solve unknown words
- ☐ Provide spelling activities and word sorts to help student recognize patterns in words

COMPREHENSION

Prediction
- ☐ Teach student how to make predictions based on title and book cover, as well as opening paragraphs and illustrations of texts read aloud
- ☐ Model and support how to use background knowledge to make meaningful predictions

Retelling
- ☐ Model and teach how to retell a story
- ☐ Model and teach how to identify important events to include in a retelling
- ☐ Support retelling a story in sequence
- ☐ Encourage student to use characters' names when retelling a story
- ☐ Model and teach how to identify important details to include in a retelling
- ☐ Model and support using key language and vocabulary from the text in a retelling
- ☐ Model and teach how to create and use story maps to aid retelling

Interpretation
- ☐ Model how to infer during shared reading and read-alouds
- ☐ Teach and share examples of inferences
- ☐ Model and teach student how to think about *Why?* questions while and after reading a text
- ☐ Model and teach how to support inferences with information or examples from the text

Reflection
- ☐ Help student identify important information and/or message in a story
- ☐ Provide opportunities to identify and discuss the important event in a story
- ☐ Demonstrate and teach student how to support opinion with details from the text

OTHER

_____

_____

_____

_____

_____

A Giant in the Forest **18**

Name/Date _____   Teacher/Grade _____

Scores: Reading Engagement ___/8   Oral Reading Fluency ___/16   Comprehension ___/28
Independent Range: 6–7   11–14   19–25

Book Selection   Text selected by: ☐ teacher   ☐ student

1. READING ENGAGEMENT

(If the student has recently answered these questions, skip this section.)

T: *What kinds of books do you like to read?*_____

T: *Tell me about one of your favorite books.* _____

T: *How do you choose the books you read?* _____

2. ORAL READING FLUENCY

INTRODUCTION

T: *In this story,* A Giant in the Forest, *an ugly giant sleeps all day and then walks through the forest at night looking for things to eat. One day a little boy stays too long in the forest. Please read aloud pages 2 through 4.* Show the student where to stop reading at the **✳**.

RECORD OF ORAL READING

Record the student's oral reading behaviors. Note the student's fluency (expression and phrasing). Be sure to time the student's reading.

Page 2

Once upon a time there was a little boy
who lived next to a cool, green forest.
There was a lake in the forest.

A big, ugly giant lived in the forest. The
giant liked to sleep all day. But at night
he walked in the forest, looking for things
to eat.

Page 3

Every week the little boy's mother gave him a big bar of soap. Then she sent him to the lake to take a bath.

"You'll be safe in the lake because the giant can't swim," she always said. "But don't forget to be home before dark."

Page 4

One day when the little boy was going to take his bath, he saw a baby bird on the ground. It had fallen out of its nest. The boy put the bird back in its nest.

Time: _____ minutes:seconds

ORAL READING WORDS PER MINUTE, PERCENT OF ACCURACY

Use the student's oral reading time to circle the WPM range.

Word Count: 134

	INTRVN	INSTR	IND	ADV
Minutes:Seconds	3:01 or more	3:00–2:28	2:27–1:35	1:34 or less
WPM	44 or less	45–54	55–85	86 or more

Count the number of miscues that are not self-corrected. Circle the percent of accuracy based on the number of miscues.

	INTRVN	INSTR	IND				ADV	
Number of Miscues	9 or more	8	7	5–6	4	3	1–2	0
Percent of Accuracy	93 or less	94	95	96	97	98	99	100

- If the student's score falls in a shaded area for either WPM or Accuracy, STOP! Reassess with a lower-level text.
- If the student is reading below the grade-level benchmark, administer *DRA Word Analysis*, beginning with Task 16, at another time.

3. COMPREHENSION

PREDICTION

Students do not use the text when making their predictions. Record the student's responses.

T: *Think about the title, the pictures you have seen, and what you have read so far.* (Pause) *Tell me three things that you think might happen in the rest of this story.*

SILENT READING

T: *Now, it's time to read and enjoy this story by yourself. When you are done, please come to me and I'll ask you to tell me what happened in this story.*

RETELLING

As the student retells, underline and record on the Story Overview the information included in the student's retelling. Please note the student does not need to use the exact words.

T: Close the book before the retelling, and then say: *Start at the beginning, and tell me what happened in this story.*

Story Overview

Beginning

1. A little boy lived next to a forest with a lake.

2. A big, ugly giant lived in the forest. He slept all day but walked in the forest at night looking for things to eat.

3. Mother sent the boy to the lake to take a bath.

4. She told the boy, "You'll be safe in the lake because the giant can't swim. Be home before dark."

Middle

5. On his way to the lake to take a bath, the boy found a baby bird on the ground and put it back in its nest.

6. Mother bird sang—and the boy sat down and listened.

7. It was getting dark when he got to the lake. He took a bath as fast as he could.

8. The boy started home after dark. He saw the giant.

9. The boy ran back to the lake, dropped his soap and . . .

End

10. The giant slipped on the soap and fell into the lake.

If necessary, use one or more of the following prompts to gain further information after the initial retelling. Place a checkmark by a prompt each time it is used.

☐ *Tell me more.*
☐ *What happened at the beginning?*
☐ *What happened before/after* _____ (an event mentioned by the student)*?*
☐ *Who else was in the story?*
☐ *How did the story end?*

INTERPRETATION

Record the student's responses to the prompts and questions below.

T: What do you think the author is trying to tell you in this story?

REFLECTION

T: What do you think was the most important thing that happened in this story?

T: Why do you think that was important?

4. TEACHER ANALYSIS

ORAL READING

If the student had 5 or more different miscues, use the information recorded on the Record of Oral Reading to complete the chart below.

Student problem-solves words using:	Number of miscues self-corrected: _____	
☐ beginning letter(s)/sound(s)	Number of miscues not self-corrected: _____	
☐ letter-sound clusters	Number of words told to the student: _____	
☐ onset and rime	**Miscues interfered with meaning:**	**Miscues included:**
☐ blending letters/sounds	☐ never	☐ omissions
☐ knowledge of spelling patterns (analogies)	☐ at times	☐ insertions
☐ syllables	☐ often	☐ substitutions that were
☐ rereading		☐ visually similar
☐ no observable behaviors		☐ not visually similar

Copy each substitution to help analyze the student's attention to visual information.
e.g., <u>sing</u> (substitution)
     sang (text)

Oral Reading Rate: (Optional) Use the formula below to determine the student's exact oral reading rate. Convert the student's reading time to all seconds.

$$134 \text{ (words)} \div \underline{\hspace{1cm}} \text{ total seconds} = \underline{\hspace{1cm}} \text{ WPS} \times 60 = \underline{\hspace{1cm}} \text{ WPM}$$

DRA2 Continuum

- Circle the descriptors that best describe the student's reading behaviors and responses.
  1. Use your daily classroom observations and the student's responses to the Reading Engagement questions to select statements that best describe the student's level of Reading Engagement.
  2. Use your recorded observations from this assessment to select the statements that best describe the student's Oral Reading Fluency and Comprehension.
- Add the circled numbers to obtain a total score for each section.
- Record the total scores at the top of page 1.

Note: If the Comprehension score is less than 19, administer DRA2 with a lower-level text.

A Giant in the Forest 18

DRA2 CONTINUUM	LEVEL 18		TRANSITIONAL READER	
	INTERVENTION	**INSTRUCTIONAL**	**INDEPENDENT**	**ADVANCED**
Reading Engagement				
Book Selection	**1** Selects new texts from identified leveled sets with teacher support; uncertain about a favorite book	**2** Selects new texts from identified leveled sets with moderate support; tells about favorite book in general terms	**3** Selects new texts from identified leveled sets most of the time; identifies favorite book by title and tells about a particular event	**4** Selects a variety of new texts that are "just right"; identifies favorite book by title and gives an overview of the book
Sustained Reading	**1** Sustains independent reading for a short period of time with much encouragement	**2** Sustains independent reading with moderate encouragement	**3** Sustains independent reading for at least 15 minutes at a time	**4** Sustains independent reading for an extended period of time
Score	2 3	4 5	6 7	8
Oral Reading Fluency				
Expression	**1** Little expression; monotone	**2** Some expression that conveys meaning	**3** Expression reflects mood, pace, and tension at times	**4** Expression reflects mood, pace, and tension most of the time
Phrasing	**1** Reads mostly word-by-word	**2** Reads in short phrases most of the time; inappropriate pauses	**3** Reads in longer phrases at times; heeds most punctuation	**4** Reads in longer, meaningful phrases most of the time; heeds all punctuation
Rate	**1** 44 WPM or less	**2** 45–54 WPM	**3** 55–85 WPM	**4** 86 WPM or more
Accuracy	**1** 93% or less	**2** 94%	**3** 95%–98%	**4** 99%–100%
Score	4 5 6	7 8 9 10	11 12 13 14	15 16
Comprehension				
Prediction	**1** Makes unrelated or no prediction(s)	**2** Makes at least 1 reasonable prediction related to the text	**3** Makes at least 2 reasonable predictions that go beyond the pages read aloud	**4** Makes at least 3 thoughtful predictions that go beyond the pages read aloud
Retelling: Sequence of Events	**1** Includes only 1 or 2 events or details (limited retelling)	**2** Includes at least 3 events, generally in random order (partial retelling)	**3** Includes most of the important events from the beginning, middle, and end, generally in sequence	**4** Includes all important events from the beginning, middle, and end in sequence
Retelling: Characters and Detail	**1** Refers to characters using general pronouns; may include incorrect information	**2** Refers to characters using appropriate pronouns; includes at least 1 detail; may include some misinterpretation	**3** Refers to most characters by name and includes some important details	**4** Refers to all characters by name and includes all important details
Retelling: Vocabulary	**1** Uses general terms or labels; limited understanding of key words/concepts	**2** Uses some language/vocabulary from the text; some understanding of key words/concepts	**3** Uses language/vocabulary from the text; basic understanding of most key words/concepts	**4** Uses important language/vocabulary from the text; good understanding of key words/concepts
Retelling: Teacher Support	**1** Retells with 5 or more questions or prompts	**2** Retells with 3 or 4 questions or prompts	**3** Retells with 1 or 2 questions or prompts	**4** Retells with no questions or prompts
Interpretation	**1** Little or no understanding of important text implications	**2** Some understanding of important text implications; no supporting details	**3** Understands important text implications; may include supporting details	**4** Insightful understanding of important text implications with supporting details or rationale
Reflection	**1** Identifies an unrelated event; no reason for opinion or no response	**2** Identifies a less significant event and/or gives a general reason for response	**3** Identifies a significant event <u>and</u> gives relevant reason(s) for opinion	**4** Identifies a significant event <u>and</u> gives reason(s) for opinion that reflects higher-level thinking
Score	7 8 9 10 11 12 13	14 15 16 17 18	19 20 21 22 23 24 25	26 27 28

Choose three to five teaching/learning activities on the *DRA2* Focus for Instruction on the next page.

A Giant in the Forest

DRA2 FOCUS FOR INSTRUCTION FOR TRANSITIONAL READERS

READING ENGAGEMENT

Book Selection
- ☐ Teach student strategies to select "just right" books for independent reading
- ☐ Introduce student to reading materials from a variety of genres
- ☐ Teach student how to use a reading log to monitor book selection
- ☐ Model/teach how to read for different purposes

Sustained Reading
- ☐ Model and support how to read independently
- ☐ Teach strategies to build reading stamina
- ☐ Develop clear expectations for amount of independent reading
- ☐ Create structures to support reading at home

ORAL READING FLUENCY

Expression and Phrasing
- ☐ Model and support reading in longer, meaningful phrases with appropriate expression
- ☐ Have student practice appropriate expression with familiar texts
- ☐ Have student participate in choral reading and/or reader's theater
- ☐ Teach student to heed punctuation

Rate
- ☐ Provide materials and time for repeated reading to increase reading rate
- ☐ Teach student to read lower-level and/or familiar texts at an appropriate rate

Accuracy: Word Analysis
- ☐ Support and reinforce self-corrections of miscues
- ☐ Model and support how to take words apart (e.g., onset and rime, syllables) to problem-solve unknown words
- ☐ Teach how to use word chunks and analogies to problem-solve unknown words
- ☐ Provide spelling activities and word sorts to help student recognize patterns in words

COMPREHENSION

Prediction
- ☐ Teach student how to make predictions based on title and book cover, as well as opening paragraphs and illustrations of texts read aloud
- ☐ Model and support how to use background knowledge to make meaningful predictions

Retelling
- ☐ Model and teach how to retell a story
- ☐ Model and teach how to identify important events to include in a retelling
- ☐ Support retelling a story in sequence
- ☐ Encourage student to use characters' names when retelling a story
- ☐ Model and teach how to identify important details to include in a retelling
- ☐ Model and support using key language and vocabulary from the text in a retelling
- ☐ Model and teach how to create and use story maps to aid retelling

Interpretation
- ☐ Model how to infer during shared reading and read-alouds
- ☐ Teach and share examples of inferences
- ☐ Model and teach student how to think about *Why?* questions while and after reading a text
- ☐ Model and teach how to support inferences with information or examples from the text

Reflection
- ☐ Help student identify important information and/or message in a story
- ☐ Provide opportunities to identify and discuss the important event in a story
- ☐ Demonstrate and teach student how to support opinion with details from the text

OTHER

_____

_____

_____

_____

_____

Name/Date _____   Teacher/Grade _____

Scores: Reading Engagement ___/8   Oral Reading Fluency ___/16   Comprehension ___/28
Independent Range: 6–7   11–14   19–25

Book Selection   Text selected by: ☐ teacher   ☐ student

1. READING ENGAGEMENT

(If the student has recently answered these questions, skip this section.)

T: What kinds of books do you like to read? _____

T: Tell me about one of your favorite books. _____

T: How do you choose the books you read? _____

2. ORAL READING FLUENCY

INTRODUCTION

T: In this story, Green Freddie, *Freddie is a frog who lives by a pond. He meets two friends who make him feel sad. Please read aloud pages 2 through 4.* Show the student where to stop reading at the ✱.

RECORD OF ORAL READING

Record the student's oral reading behaviors. Note the student's fluency (expression and phrasing). Be sure to time the student's reading.

Page 2

Freddie the Frog was sitting on a log. He wasn't doing anything. He was not eating or drinking. He was just sitting there.

A squirrel came hopping along. He looked at himself in the water. He smiled. Then he patted his silver-gray fur with his paw.

The squirrel looked at Freddie and said, "My fur looks pretty, doesn't it?"

Freddie smiled at the squirrel. "Yes, it looks very pretty."

Page 3

"Don't you wish you looked like me?" asked the squirrel.

"No," said Freddie. "I look okay."

"But look at you," said the squirrel. "You're all green."

Then the squirrel hopped away, all shining and silver in the sunshine.

Freddie sat on his log thinking. He was thinking that what the squirrel had said was true. He was all green.

Page 4

A chipmunk came skipping along. She looked at herself in the water. She smiled. Then she patted her golden-brown fur with her paw.

Time: _____ minutes:seconds

ORAL READING WORDS PER MINUTE, PERCENT OF ACCURACY

Use the student's oral reading time to circle the WPM range.

Word Count: 153

	INTRVN	INSTR	IND	ADV
Minutes:Seconds	2:49 or more	2:48–2:23	2:22–1:37	1:36 or less
WPM	54 or less	55–64	65–95	96 or more

Count the number of miscues that are not self-corrected. Circle the percent of accuracy based on the number of miscues.

	INTRVN	INSTR	IND				ADV	
Number of Miscues	10 or more	9	7–8	6	4–5	3	1–2	0
Percent of Accuracy	93 or less	94	95	96	97	98	99	100

- If the student's score falls in a shaded area for either WPM or Accuracy, STOP! Reassess with a lower-level text.
- If the student is reading below the grade-level benchmark, administer *DRA Word Analysis,* beginning with Task 22, at another time.

3. COMPREHENSION

PREDICTION

Students do not use the text when making their predictions. Record the student's responses.

T: Think about the title, the pictures you have seen, and what you have read so far. (Pause) *Tell me three things that you think might happen in the rest of this story.*

SILENT READING

T: Now, it's time to read and enjoy this story by yourself. When you are done, please come to me and I'll ask you to tell me what happened in this story.

RETELLING

As the student retells, underline and record on the Story Overview the information included in the student's retelling. Please note the student does not need to use the exact words.

T: Close the book before the retelling, and then say: *Start at the beginning, and tell me what happened in this story.*

Story Overview
Beginning
1. Freddie sat on a log. He wasn't eating or drinking. He was just sitting there.

Middle
2. Squirrel came along and asked Freddie, "My fur is pretty. Don't you wish you looked like me? You're all green."
3. Freddie said he looked okay, but he thought what Squirrel said was true.
4. Chipmunk came along and asked Freddie, "My fur is pretty. Don't you wish you looked like me? You're all green."
5. Freddie sat on his log and cried.
6. A wise old owl came flying by and asked Freddie why he was crying.
7. When Freddie told him, the owl told him that things all around him were green—that green is a great color to be.

End
8. Freddie croaked loudly so that everyone could hear that green is a great color to be.

If necessary, use one or more of the following prompts to gain further information after the initial retelling. Place a checkmark by a prompt each time it is used.

☐ *Tell me more.*
☐ *What happened at the beginning?*
☐ *What happened before/after* _____ (an event mentioned by the student)*?*
☐ *Who else was in the story?*
☐ *How did the story end?*

INTERPRETATION

Record student's responses to the prompts and questions below.

T: What do you think the author is trying to tell you in this story?

REFLECTION

T: What do you think was the most important thing that happened in this story?

T: Why do you think that was important?

4. TEACHER ANALYSIS

ORAL READING

If the student had 5 or more different miscues, use the information recorded on the Record of Oral Reading to complete the chart below.

Student problem-solves words using:	Number of miscues self-corrected: _____
☐ beginning letter(s)/sound(s)	Number of miscues not self-corrected: _____
☐ letter-sound clusters	Number of words told to the student: _____

Student problem-solves words using:	Miscues interfered with meaning:	Miscues included:
☐ onset and rime	☐ never	☐ omissions
☐ blending letters/sounds	☐ at times	☐ insertions
☐ knowledge of spelling patterns (analogies)	☐ often	☐ substitutions that were
☐ syllables		☐ visually similar
☐ rereading		☐ not visually similar
☐ no observable behaviors		

Copy each substitution to help analyze the student's attention to visual information.
e.g., <u>sliver</u> (substitution)
    silver (text)

Oral Reading Rate: (Optional) Use the formula below to determine the student's exact oral reading rate. Convert the student's reading time to all seconds.

$$153 \text{ (words)} \div \underline{\hspace{1cm}} \text{ total seconds} = \underline{\hspace{1cm}} \text{ WPS} \times 60 = \underline{\hspace{1cm}} \text{ WPM}$$

DRA2 Continuum

- Circle the descriptors that best describe the student's reading behaviors and responses.
    1. Use your daily classroom observations and the student's responses to the Reading Engagement questions to select statements that best describe the student's level of Reading Engagement.
    2. Use your recorded observations from this assessment to select the statements that best describe the student's Oral Reading Fluency and Comprehension.
- Add the circled numbers to obtain a total score for each section.
- Record the total scores at the top of page 1.

Note: If the Comprehension score is less than 19, administer *DRA2* with a lower-level text.

Green Freddie 20

DRA2 CONTINUUM	LEVEL 20			TRANSITIONAL READER
	INTERVENTION	INSTRUCTIONAL	INDEPENDENT	ADVANCED
Reading Engagement				
Book Selection	1 Selects texts from identified leveled sets with teacher support; uncertain about a favorite book	2 Selects texts from identified leveled sets with moderate support; tells about favorite book in general terms	3 Independently selects texts from identified leveled sets most of the time; identifies favorite book by title and tells about a particular event	4 Independently selects a variety of "just right" texts; identifies favorite book by title and gives an overview of the book
Sustained Reading	1 Sustains independent reading for a short period of time with much encouragement	2 Sustains independent reading with moderate encouragement	3 Sustains independent reading for at least 15 minutes at a time	4 Sustains independent reading for an extended period of time
Score	2 3	4 5	6 7	8
Oral Reading Fluency				
Expression	1 Little expression; monotone	2 Some expression that conveys meaning	3 Expression reflects mood, pace, and tension at times	4 Expression reflects mood, pace, and tension most of the time
Phrasing	1 Reads mostly word-by-word	2 Reads in short phrases most of the time; inappropriate pauses	3 Reads in longer phrases at times; heeds most punctuation	4 Reads in longer, meaningful phrases most of the time; heeds all punctuation
Rate	1 54 WPM or less	2 55–64 WPM	3 65–95 WPM	4 96 WPM or more
Accuracy	1 93% or less	2 94%	3 95%–98%	4 99%–100%
Score	4 5 6	7 8 9 10	11 12 13 14	15 16
Comprehension				
Prediction	1 Makes unrelated or no prediction(s)	2 Makes at least 1 reasonable prediction related to the text	3 Makes at least 2 reasonable predictions that go beyond the pages read aloud	4 Makes at least 3 thoughtful predictions that go beyond the pages read aloud
Retelling: Sequence of Events	1 Includes only 1 or 2 events or details (limited retelling)	2 Includes at least 3 events, generally in random order (partial retelling)	3 Includes most of the important events from the beginning, middle, and end, generally in sequence	4 Includes all important events from the beginning, middle, and end in sequence
Retelling: Characters and Details	1 Refers to characters using general pronouns; may include incorrect information	2 Refers to characters using appropriate pronouns; includes at least 1 detail; may include some misinterpretation	3 Refers to most characters by name and includes some important details	4 Refers to all characters by name and includes all important details
Retelling: Vocabulary	1 Uses general terms or labels; limited understanding of key words/concepts	2 Uses some language/vocabulary from the text; some understanding of key words/concepts	3 Uses language/vocabulary from the text; basic understanding of most key words/concepts	4 Uses important language/vocabulary from the text; good understanding of key words/concepts
Retelling: Teacher Support	1 Retells with 5 or more questions or prompts	2 Retells with 3 or 4 questions or prompts	3 Retells with 1 or 2 questions or prompts	4 Retells with no questions or prompts
Interpretation	1 Little or no understanding of important text implications	2 Some understanding of important text implications; no supporting details	3 Understands important text implications; may include supporting details	4 Insightful understanding of important text implications with supporting details or rationale
Reflection	1 Identifies an unrelated event; no reason for opinion or no response	2 Identifies a less significant event and/or gives a general reason for response	3 Identifies a significant event <u>and</u> gives relevant reason(s) for opinion	4 Identifies a significant event <u>and</u> gives reason(s) for opinion that reflects higher-level thinking
Score	7 8 9 10 11 12 13	14 15 16 17 18	19 20 21 22 23 24 25	26 27 28

Choose three to five teaching/learning activities on the *DRA2* Focus for Instruction on the next page.

*DRA*2 FOCUS FOR INSTRUCTION FOR TRANSITIONAL READERS

READING ENGAGEMENT
Book Selection
- ☐ Teach student strategies to select "just right" books for independent reading
- ☐ Introduce student to reading materials from a variety of genres
- ☐ Teach student how to use a reading log to monitor book selection
- ☐ Model/teach how to read for different purposes

Sustained Reading
- ☐ Model and support how to read independently
- ☐ Teach strategies to build reading stamina
- ☐ Develop clear expectations for amount of independent reading
- ☐ Create structures to support reading at home

ORAL READING FLEUNCY
Expression and Phrasing
- ☐ Model and support reading in longer, meaningful phrases with appropriate expression
- ☐ Have student practice appropriate expression with familiar texts
- ☐ Have student participate in choral reading and/or reader's theater
- ☐ Teach student to heed punctuation

Rate
- ☐ Provide materials and time for repeated reading to increase reading rate
- ☐ Teach student to read lower-level and/or familiar texts at an appropriate rate

Accuracy: Word Analysis
- ☐ Support and reinforce self-corrections of miscues
- ☐ Model and support how to take words apart (e.g., onset and rime, syllables) to problem-solve unknown words
- ☐ Teach how to use word chunks and analogies to problem-solve unknown words
- ☐ Provide spelling activities and word sorts to help student recognize patterns in words

COMPREHENSION
Prediction
- ☐ Teach student how to make predictions based on title and book cover, as well as opening paragraphs and illustrations of texts read aloud
- ☐ Model and support how to use background knowledge to make meaningful predictions

Retelling
- ☐ Model and teach how to retell a story
- ☐ Model and teach how to identify important events to include in a retelling
- ☐ Support retelling a story in sequence
- ☐ Encourage student to use characters' names when retelling a story
- ☐ Model and teach how to identify important details to include in a retelling
- ☐ Model and support using key language and vocabulary from the text in a retelling
- ☐ Model and teach how to create and use story maps to aid retelling

Interpretation
- ☐ Model how to infer during shared reading and read-alouds
- ☐ Teach and share examples of inferences
- ☐ Model and teach student how to think about *Why?* questions while and after reading a text
- ☐ Model and teach how to support inferences with information or examples from the text

Reflection
- ☐ Help student identify important information and/or message in a story
- ☐ Provide opportunities to identify and discuss the important event in a story
- ☐ Demonstrate and teach student how to support opinion with details from the text

OTHER

_____

_____

_____

_____

_____

_____

Green Freddie 20

Name/Date _____   Teacher/Grade _____

Scores: Reading Engagement ___/8   Oral Reading Fluency ___/16   Comprehension ___/28
Independent Range: 6–7   11–14   19–25

Book Selection   Text selected by: ☐ teacher   ☐ student

1. READING ENGAGEMENT

(If the student has recently answered these questions, skip this section.)

T: What kinds of books do you like to read? _____

T: Tell me about one of your favorite books. _____

T: How do you choose the books you read? _____

2. ORAL READING FLUENCY

INTRODUCTION

T: In this Native American folktale, Turtle's Big Race, *Turtle really likes his home in a pond. One day he finds he might have to leave his pond. Please read aloud pages 2 through 4.* Show the student where to stop reading at the ✱.

RECORD OF ORAL READING

Record the student's oral reading behaviors. Note the student's fluency (expression and phrasing). Be sure to time the student's reading.

Page 2

Turtle   liked   the   little   pond   he   called   home.
It   had   lots   of   green   grass   around   it.   There
were   little   fish   for   him   to   catch   and   eat.

"This   is   a   good   place   to   live,"   said   Turtle.

Page 3

During   the   cold   days   of   winter,   Turtle   slept
in   the   mud   at   the   bottom   of   the   pond.   He
dreamed   of   sunny   spring   days.

Turtle's Big Race **20**

Page 4

In the spring, when the days were nice again, Turtle woke up. The pond was different. The water was much deeper. Some trees had been cut down, and there was a wood dam at one end.

An animal with a long, flat tail and very big teeth sat on top of the dam.

"Who are you?" asked Turtle.

"I am Beaver!" said the animal. "You are in my pond, and you must leave now!"

"No! This is my pond, too!" said Turtle.

"Then let's fight for it," said Beaver.

Time: _____ minutes:seconds

ORAL READING WORDS PER MINUTE, PERCENT OF ACCURACY

Use the student's oral reading time to circle the WPM range.

Word Count: 147

	INTRVN	INSTR	IND	ADV
Minutes:Seconds	2:42 or more	2:41–2:17	2:16–1:33	1:32 or less
WPM	54 or less	55–64	65–95	96 or more

Count the number of miscues that are not self-corrected. Circle the percent of accuracy based on the number of miscues.

	INTRVN	INSTR	IND				ADV	
Number of Miscues	10 or more	9	7–8	6	4–5	3	1–2	0
Percent of Accuracy	93 or less	94	95	96	97	98	99	100

- If the student's score falls in a shaded area for either WPM or Accuracy, STOP! Reassess with a lower-level text.

- If the student is reading below the grade-level benchmark, administer *DRA Word Analysis,* beginning with Task 22, at another time.

Turtle's Big Race **20**

3. COMPREHENSION

PREDICTION

Students do not use the text when making their predictions. Record the student's responses.

T: *Think about the title, the pictures you have seen, and what you have read so far.* (Pause) ***Tell me three things that you think might happen in the rest of this story.***

SILENT READING

T: *Now, it's time to read and enjoy this story by yourself. When you are done, please come to me and I'll ask you to tell me what happened in this story.*

RETELLING

As the student retells, underline and record on the Story Overview the information included in the student's retelling. Please note the student does not need to use the exact words.

T: Close the book before the retelling, and then say: ***Start at the beginning, and tell me what happened in this story.***

Story Overview

Beginning

1. Turtle thought the pond he lived in was a good place, with lots of grass around it and with little fish to eat.
2. During the winter, Turtle slept at the bottom of the pond and dreamed of spring, but the pond was different in the spring.

Middle

3. Beaver wanted to fight Turtle for the pond, but Turtle knew he couldn't win a fight because Beaver had a very big tail and sharp teeth. Turtle said he would race.
4. Beaver knew he could win because Turtle had short legs and a heavy shell. The loser must leave the pond.
5. As they raced across the pond, Beaver was ahead of Turtle. But Turtle had a plan. He bit Beaver's tail with his jaws.
6. When Beaver flipped his tail over his head, Turtle popped out of the pond and flew over Beaver's head. Turtle landed on the other side of the pond and won the race.

End

7. Beaver lost the race and would have to leave the pond, but Turtle asked Beaver to share the pond because it was big enough for two.
8. Turtle sat on the bank and said, "This is a good place to live!"

If necessary, use one or more of the following prompts to gain further information after the initial retelling. Place a checkmark by a prompt each time it is used.

☐ *Tell me more.*
☐ *What happened at the beginning?*
☐ *What happened before/after* _____ (an event mentioned by the student)*?*
☐ *Who else was in the story?*
☐ *How did the story end?*

Turtle's Big Race 20

INTERPRETATION

Record the student's reponses to the prompts and questions below.

T: What do you think the author is trying to tell you in this story?

REFLECTION

T: What do you think was the most important thing that happened in this story?

T: Why do you think that was important?

---

4. TEACHER ANALYSIS

ORAL READING

If the student had 5 or more different miscues, use the information recorded on the Record of Oral Reading to complete the chart below.

Student problem-solves words using:	Number of miscues self-corrected: _____	
☐ beginning letter(s)/sound(s)	Number of miscues not self-corrected: _____	
☐ letter-sound clusters	Number of words told to the student: _____	
☐ onset and rime	**Miscues interfered with meaning:**	**Miscues included:**
☐ blending letters/sounds	☐ never	☐ omissions
☐ knowledge of spelling patterns (analogies)	☐ at times	☐ insertions
☐ syllables	☐ often	☐ substitutions that were
☐ rereading		☐ visually similar
☐ no observable behaviors		☐ not visually similar

Copy each substitution to help analyze the student's attention to visual information.
e.g., <u>were</u> (substitution)
     was (text)

Oral Reading Rate: (Optional) Use the formula below to determine the student's exact oral reading rate. Convert the student's reading time to all seconds.

$$147 \text{ (words)} \div \rule{1.5cm}{0.15mm} \text{ total seconds} = \rule{1.5cm}{0.15mm} \text{ WPS} \times 60 = \rule{1.5cm}{0.15mm} \text{ WPM}$$

DRA2 Continuum

- Circle the descriptors that best describe the student's reading behaviors and responses.
  1. Use your daily classroom observations and the student's responses to the Reading Engagement questions to select statements that best describe the student's level of Reading Engagement.
  2. Use your recorded observations from this assessment to select the statements that best describe the student's Oral Reading Fluency and Comprehension.
- Add the circled numbers to obtain a total score for each section.
- Record the total scores at the top of page 1.

Note: If the Comprehension score is less than 19, administer *DRA2* with a lower-level text.

Turtle's Big Race **20**

DRA2 CONTINUUM	LEVEL 20		TRANSITIONAL READER	
	INTERVENTION	INSTRUCTIONAL	INDEPENDENT	ADVANCED
Reading Engagement				
Book Selection	1 Selects texts from identified leveled sets with teacher support; uncertain about a favorite book	2 Selects texts from identified leveled sets with moderate support; tells about favorite book in general terms	3 Selects texts from identified leveled sets most of the time; identifies favorite book by title and tells about a particular event	4 Selects a variety of "just right" texts; identifies favorite book by title and gives an overview of the book
Sustained Reading	1 Sustains independent reading for a short period of time with much encouragement	2 Sustains independent reading with moderate encouragement	3 Sustains independent reading for at least 15 minutes at a time	4 Sustains independent reading for an extended period of time
Score	2 3	4 5	6 7	8
Oral Reading Fluency				
Expression	1 Little expression; monotone	2 Some expression that conveys meaning	3 Expression reflects mood, pace, and tension at times	4 Expression relects mood, pace, and tension most of the time
Phrasing	1 Reads mostly word-by-word	2 Reads in short phrases most of the time; inappropriate pauses	3 Reads in longer phrases at times; heeds most punctuation	4 Reads in longer, meaningful phrases most of the time; heeds all punctuation
Rate	1 54 WPM or less	2 55–64 WPM	3 65–95 WPM	4 96 WPM or more
Accuracy	1 93% or less	2 94%	3 95%–98%	4 99%–100%
Score	4 5 6	7 8 9 10	11 12 13 14	15 16
Comprehension				
Prediction	1 Makes unrelated or no prediction(s)	2 Makes at least 1 reasonable prediction related to the text	3 Makes at least 2 reasonable predictions that go beyond the pages read aloud	4 Makes at least 3 thoughtful predictions that go beyond the pages read aloud
Retelling: Sequence of Events	1 Includes only 1 or 2 events or details (limited retelling)	2 Includes at least 3 events, generally in random order (partial retelling)	3 Includes most of the important events from the beginning, middle, and end, generally in sequence	4 Includes all important events from the beginning, middle, and end in sequence
Retelling: Characters and Details	1 Refers to characters using general pronouns; may include incorrect information	2 Refers to characters using appropriate pronouns; includes at least 1 detail; may include some misinterpretation	3 Refers to most characters by name and includes some important details	4 Refers to all characters by name and includes all important details
Retelling: Vocabulary	1 Uses general terms or labels; limited understanding of key words/concepts	2 Uses some language/vocabulary from the text; some understanding of key words/concepts	3 Uses language/vocabulary from the text; basic understanding of most key words/concepts	4 Uses important language/vocabulary from the text; good understanding of key words/concepts
Retelling: Teacher Support	1 Retells with 5 or more questions or prompts	2 Retells with 3 or 4 questions or prompts	3 Retells with 1 or 2 questions or prompts	4 Retells with no questions or prompts
Interpretation	1 Little or no understanding of important text implications	2 Some understanding of important text implications; no supporting details	3 Understands important text implications; may include supporting details	4 Insightful understanding of important text implications with supporting details or rationale
Reflection	1 Identifies an unrelated event; no reason for opinion or no response	2 Identifies a less significant event and/or gives a general reason for response	3 Identifies a significant event and gives relevant reason(s) for opinion	4 Identifies a significant event and gives reason(s) for opinion that reflects higher-level thinking
Score	7 8 9 10 11 12 13	14 15 16 17 18	19 20 21 22 23 24 25	26 27 28

Choose three to five teaching/learning activities on the DRA2 Focus for Instruction on the next page.

Turtle's Big Race 20

*DRA*2 FOCUS FOR INSTRUCTION FOR TRANSITIONAL READERS

READING ENGAGEMENT
Book Selection
- ☐ Teach student strategies to select "just right" books for independent reading
- ☐ Introduce student to reading materials from a variety of genres
- ☐ Teach student how to use a reading log to monitor book selection
- ☐ Model/teach how to read for different purposes

Sustained Reading
- ☐ Model and support how to read independently
- ☐ Teach strategies to build reading stamina
- ☐ Develop clear expectations for amount of independent reading
- ☐ Create structures to support reading at home

ORAL READING FLUENCY
Expression and Phrasing
- ☐ Model and support reading in longer, meaningful phrases with appropriate expression
- ☐ Have student practice appropriate expression with familiar texts
- ☐ Have student participate in choral reading and/or reader's theater
- ☐ Teach student to heed punctuation

Rate
- ☐ Provide materials and time for repeated reading to increase reading rate
- ☐ Teach student to read lower-level and/or familiar texts at an appropriate rate

Accuracy: Word Analysis
- ☐ Support and reinforce self-corrections of miscues
- ☐ Model and support how to take words apart (e.g., onset and rime, syllables) to problem-solve unknown words
- ☐ Teach how to use word chunks and analogies to problem-solve unknown words
- ☐ Provide spelling activities and word sorts to help student recognize patterns in words

COMPREHENSION
Prediction
- ☐ Teach student how to make predictions based on title and book cover, as well as opening paragraphs and illustrations of texts read aloud
- ☐ Model and support how to use background knowledge to make meaningful predictions

Retelling
- ☐ Model and teach how to retell a story
- ☐ Model and teach how to identify important events to include in a retelling
- ☐ Support retelling a story in sequence
- ☐ Encourage student to use characters' names when retelling a story
- ☐ Model and teach how to identify important details to include in a retelling
- ☐ Model and support using key language and vocabulary from the text in a retelling
- ☐ Model and teach how to create and use story maps to aid retelling

Interpretation
- ☐ Model how to infer during shared reading and read-alouds
- ☐ Teach and share examples of inferences
- ☐ Model and teach student how to think about *Why?* questions while and after reading a text
- ☐ Model and teach how to support inferences with examples from the text

Reflection
- ☐ Help student identify important message in a story
- ☐ Provide opportunities to identify and discuss the important event in a story
- ☐ Demonstrate and teach student how to support opinion with details from the text

OTHER

_____

_____

_____

_____

_____

_____

Turtle's Big Race **20**

Name/Date _____   Teacher/Grade _____

Scores: Reading Engagement ___/8   Oral Reading Fluency ___/16   Comprehension ___/28
Independent Range: 6–7   11–14   19–25

Book Selection   Text selected by: ☐ teacher   ☐ student

1. READING ENGAGEMENT

(If the student has recently answered these questions, skip this section.)

T: What kinds of books do you like to read? _____

T: Tell me about one of your favorite books. _____

T: How do you choose the books you read? _____

2. ORAL READING FLUENCY

INTRODUCTION

T: In this folktale, Thin as a Stick, *Lizard is a very fat fellow. Lizard changes after he meets Prairie Dog. Please read aloud pages 2 through 4.* Show the student where to stop reading at the ✱.

RECORD OF ORAL READING

Record the student's oral reading behaviors. Note the student's fluency (expression and phrasing). Be sure to time the student's reading.

Page 2

A   long   time   ago,   Lizard   was   a   very   fat   fellow.
Each   day   he   would   sit   in   the   sun   and   sleep.
When   he   was   hungry,   he   would   tip   his   head
and   zap   ants   with   his   long   tongue.   He   didn't
even   move   to   get   his   food.   He   would   just
wait   until   the   ants   walked   by.

Page 3

One day, Lizard slowly climbed up on a large rock. He slept most of the day in the warm sun. Under the ground, Prairie Dog was making a tunnel. By lunch time he was hot and tired. As Prairie Dog came up through the ground, he bumped his head on Lizard's rock.

"Ouch!" he cried, popping out of the ground. "Who put this rock here?"

"Not me," said Lizard, as he laid down once again on top of his rock. "Maybe you should watch where you're going."

Page 4

Prairie Dog was in a bad mood. "Oh, yeah?" he shouted. "Well, maybe you should watch where you're going!" With that, Prairie Dog gave the rock a great big shove.

Time: _____ minutes:seconds

ORAL READING WORDS PER MINUTE, PERCENT OF ACCURACY

Use the student's oral reading time to circle the WPM range.

Word Count: 170

	INTRVN	INSTR	IND	ADV
Minutes:Seconds	2:52 or more	2:51–2:27	2:26–1:42	1:41 or less
WPM	59 or less	60–69	70–100	101 or more

Count the number of miscues that are not self-corrected. Circle the percent of accuracy based on the number of miscues.

	INTRVN	INSTR	IND				ADV	
Number of Miscues	12 or more	10–11	8–9	6–7	5	3–4	1–2	0
Percent of Accuracy	93 or less	94	95	96	97	98	99	100

- If the student's score falls in a shaded area for either WPM or Accuracy, STOP! Reassess with a lower-level text.
- If the student is reading below the grade-level benchmark, administer *DRA Word Analysis*, beginning with Task 22, at another time.

3. COMPREHENSION

PREDICTION

Students do not use the text when making their predictions. Record the student's responses.

T: Think about the title, the pictures you have seen, and what you have read so far. (Pause) *Tell me three things that you think might happen in the rest of this story.*

SILENT READING

T: Now, it's time to read and enjoy this story by yourself. When you are done, please come to me and I'll ask you to tell me what happened in this story.

RETELLING

As the student retells, underline and record on the Story Overview the information included in the student's retelling. Please note the student does not need to use the exact words.

T: Close the book before the retelling, and then say: *Start at the beginning, and tell me what happened in this story.*

Story Overview
Beginning
1. A long time ago Lizard was a fat fellow. He didn't even move to get his food.
2. Prairie Dog was working hard, making a tunnel.
3. When Prairie Dog came up, he bumped his head on the rock where Lizard was sitting and asked, "Who put this rock here?"
4. Lizard said, "Not me. Maybe you should watch where you're going."
Middle
5. Prairie Dog said, "Maybe you should watch where you're going." Then he gave the rock a big shove.
6. Lizard held on tight to the rock as it rolled down the hill and stopped at the bottom, not far from a river.
7. He was too big and heavy to wiggle out from under the rock. No one heard Lizard's cries for help.
8. As the days passed, lizard lost weight and was able to slither out from under the rock.
9. Lizard was very thirsty, so he dashed to the river. He looked at his reflection and was sad because he was as thin as a stick and not a fine fat fellow.
End
10. Hawk flew over Lizard, looking for dinner. He flew down toward Lizard.
11. Lizard darted between two rocks out of Hawk's sight and said, "I'm glad I'm thin as a stick because I'm also as fast as lightning!"
12. From that day on, Lizard was quite happy to be as thin as a stick.

Thin as a Stick 24

If necessary, use one or more of the following prompts to gain further information after the initial retelling. Place a checkmark by a prompt each time it is used.

- ☐ *Tell me more.*
- ☐ *What happened at the beginning?*
- ☐ *What happened before/after* _____ (an event mentioned by the student)*?*
- ☐ *Who else was in the story?*
- ☐ *How did the story end?*

INTERPRETATION

Record the student's reponses to the prompts and questions below.

T: What do you think the author is trying to tell you in this story?

REFLECTION

T: What do you think was the most important thing that happened in this story?

T: Why do you think that was important?

4. TEACHER ANALYSIS

ORAL READING

If the student had 5 or more different miscues, use the information recorded on the Record of Oral Reading to complete the chart below.

Student problem-solves words using:	Number of miscues self-corrected: _____ Number of miscues not self-corrected: _____ Number of words told to the student: _____	

☐ beginning letter(s)/sound(s)
 ☐ letter-sound clusters
 ☐ onset and rime
 ☐ blending letters/sounds
 ☐ knowledge of spelling patterns (analogies)
 ☐ syllables
 ☐ rereading
 ☐ no observable behaviors
	Miscues interfered with meaning:
	 ☐ never
	 ☐ at times
	 ☐ often
		Miscues included:
		 ☐ omissions
		 ☐ insertions
		 ☐ substitutions that were
		   ☐ visually similar
		   ☐ not visually similar

Copy each substitution to help analyze the student's attention to visual information. e.g., <u>scratched</u> (substitution) stretched (text)		

Oral Reading Rate: (Optional) Use the formula below to determine the student's exact oral reading rate. Convert the student's reading time to all seconds.

170 (words) ÷ _____ total seconds = _____ WPS × 60 = _____ WPM

DRA2 Continuum

- Circle the descriptors that best describe the student's reading behaviors and responses.

  1. Use your daily classroom observations and the student's responses to the Reading Engagement questions to select statements that best describe the student's level of Reading Engagement.

  2. Use your recorded observations from this assessment to select the statements that best describe the student's Oral Reading Fluency and Comprehension.

- Add the circled numbers to obtain a total score for each section.

- Record the total scores at the top of page 1.

Note: If the Comprehension score is less than 19, administer *DRA2* with a lower-level text.

Thin as a Stick 24

DRA2 CONTINUUM	LEVEL 24		TRANSITIONAL READER	
	INTERVENTION	INSTRUCTIONAL	INDEPENDENT	ADVANCED
Reading Engagement				
Book Selection	1 Selects texts from identified leveled sets with teacher support; uncertain about a favorite book	2 Selects texts from identified leveled sets with moderate support; tells about favorite book in general terms	3 Selects texts from identified leveled sets most of the time; identifies favorite book by title and tells about a particular event	4 Selects a variety of "just right" texts; identifies favorite book by title and gives an overview of the book
Sustained Reading	1 Sustains independent reading for a short period of time with much encouragement	2 Sustains independent reading with moderate encouragement	3 Sustains independent reading for at least 15 minutes at a time	4 Sustains independent reading for an extended period of time
Score	2 3	4 5	6 7	8
Oral Reading Fluency				
Expression	1 Little expression; monotone	2 Some expression that conveys meaning	3 Expression reflects mood, pace, and tension at times	4 Expression reflects mood, pace, and tension most of the time
Phrasing	1 Reads mostly word-by-word	2 Reads in short phrases most of the time; inappropriate pauses	3 Reads in longer phrases at times; heeds most punctuation	4 Reads in longer, meaningful phrases most of the time; heeds all punctuation
Rate	1 59 WPM or less	2 60–69 WPM	3 70–100 WPM	4 101 WPM or more
Accuracy	1 93% or less	2 94%	3 95%–98%	4 99%–100%
Score	4 5 6	7 8 9 10	11 12 13 14	15 16
Comprehension				
Prediction	1 Makes unrelated or no prediction(s)	2 Makes at least 1 reasonable prediction related to the text	3 Makes at least 2 reasonable predictions that go beyond the pages read aloud	4 Makes at least 3 thoughtful predictions that go beyond the pages read aloud
Retelling: Sequence of Events	1 Includes only 1 or 2 events or details (limited retelling)	2 Includes at least 3 events, generally in random order (partial retelling)	3 Includes most of the important events from the beginning, middle, and end, generally in sequence	4 Includes all important events from the beginning, middle, and end in sequence
Retelling: Characters and Details	1 Refers to characters using general pronouns; may include incorrect information	2 Refers to characters using appropriate pronouns; includes at least 1 detail; may include some misinterpretation	3 Refers to most characters by name and includes some important details	4 Refers to all characters by name and includes all important details
Retelling: Vocabulary	1 Uses general terms or labels; limited understanding of key words/concepts	2 Uses some language/vocabulary from the text; some understanding of key words/concepts	3 Uses language/vocabulary from the text; basic understanding of most key words/concepts	4 Uses important language/vocabulary from the text; good understanding of key words/concepts
Retelling: Teacher Support	1 Retells with 5 or more questions or prompts	2 Retells with 3 or 4 questions or prompts	3 Retells with 1 or 2 questions or prompts	4 Retells with no questions or prompts
Interpretation	1 Little or no understanding of important text implications	2 Some understanding of important text implications; no supporting details	3 Understands important text implications; may include supporting details	4 Insightful understanding of important text implications with supporting details or rationale
Reflection	1 Identifies an unrelated event; no reason for opinion or no response	2 Identifies a less significant event and/or gives a general reason for response	3 Identifies a significant event <u>and</u> gives relevant reason(s) for opinion	4 Identifies a significant event <u>and</u> gives reason(s) for opinion that reflects higher-level thinking
Score	7 8 9 10 11 12 13	14 15 16 17 18	19 20 21 22 23 24 25	26 27 28

Choose three to five teaching/learning activities on the *DRA2* Focus for Instruction on the next page.

Thin as a Stick **24**

DRA2 FOCUS FOR INSTRUCTION FOR TRANSITIONAL READERS

READING ENGAGEMENT

Book Selection
- ☐ Teach student strategies to select "just right" books for independent reading
- ☐ Introduce student to reading materials from a variety of genres
- ☐ Teach student how to use a reading log to monitor book selection
- ☐ Model/teach how to read for different purposes

Sustained Reading
- ☐ Model and support how to read independently
- ☐ Teach strategies to build reading stamina
- ☐ Develop clear expectations for amount of independent reading
- ☐ Create structures to support reading at home

ORAL READING FLUENCY

Expression and Phrasing
- ☐ Model and support reading in longer, meaningful phrases with appropriate expression
- ☐ Have student practice appropriate expression with familiar texts
- ☐ Have student participate in choral reading and/or reader's theater
- ☐ Teach student to heed punctuation

Rate
- ☐ Provide materials and time for repeated reading to increase reading rate
- ☐ Teach student to read lower-level and/or familiar texts at an appropriate rate

Accuracy: Word Analysis
- ☐ Support and reinforce self-corrections of miscues
- ☐ Model and support how to take words apart (e.g., onset and rime, syllables) to problem-solve unknown words
- ☐ Teach how to use word chunks and analogies to problem-solve unknown words
- ☐ Provide spelling activities and word sorts to help student recognize patterns in words

COMPREHENSION

Prediction
- ☐ Teach student how to make predictions based on title and book cover, as well as opening paragraphs and illustrations of texts read aloud
- ☐ Model and support how to use background knowledge to make meaningful predictions

Retelling
- ☐ Model and teach how to retell a story
- ☐ Model and teach how to identify important events to include in a retelling
- ☐ Support retelling a story in sequence
- ☐ Encourage student to use characters' names when retelling a story
- ☐ Model and teach how to identify important details to include in a retelling
- ☐ Model and support using key language and vocabulary from the text in a retelling
- ☐ Model and teach how to create and use story maps to aid retelling

Interpretation
- ☐ Model how to infer during shared reading and read-alouds
- ☐ Teach and share examples of inferences
- ☐ Model and teach student how to think about *Why?* questions while and after reading a text
- ☐ Model and teach how to support inferences with examples from the text

Reflection
- ☐ Help student identify important message in a story
- ☐ Provide opportunities to identify and discuss the important event in a story
- ☐ Demonstrate and teach student how to support opinion with details from the text

OTHER

_____

_____

_____

_____

_____

_____

_____

Thin as a Stick **24**

154

Name/Date _____   Teacher/Grade _____

Scores: Reading Engagement ___/8   Oral Reading Fluency ___/16   Comprehension ___/28
Independent Range: 6–7   11–14   19–25

Book Selection   Text selected by: ☐ teacher   ☐ student

1. READING ENGAGEMENT

(If the student has recently answered these questions, skip this section.)

T: What kinds of books do you like to read? _____

T: Tell me about one of your favorite books. _____

T: How do you choose the books you read? _____

2. ORAL READING FLUENCY

INTRODUCTION

T: In this story, The Wonderful Day, *a rabbit named Roger finds a giant cabbage. He likes cabbage so much that he decides to take it home. Please read aloud pages 2 through 4.* Show the student where to stop reading at the ✱.

RECORD OF ORAL READING

Record the student's oral reading behaviors. Note the student's fluency (expression and phrasing). Be sure to time the student's reading.

Page 2

Roger Rabbit could not believe his eyes.

He stood still in the middle of the road.

He stared, and he stared, and he stared.

Then he just had to believe his eyes.

That really was a giant cabbage sitting

there in the road.

"I never saw a cabbage like that," Roger

told himself. "This is the most wonderful

day I've ever had! A giant cabbage all

crisp and green, just for me!"

The Wonderful Day 24

Page 3

He began to roll the cabbage home. It was a big cabbage. Roger was a small rabbit. Every once in a while he had to stop and rest. But at last he rolled the giant cabbage right up to the door of his house. He pushed, and he pushed, and he pushed.

"Something's wrong," he thought. "This cabbage is too big, or my door is too small. I can't get the cabbage into my house. This isn't such a wonderful day after all."

Page 4

Because Roger could not help himself, he began to cry. Big splashy tears bounced off the cabbage.

Time: _____ minutes:seconds

ORAL READING WORDS PER MINUTE, PERCENT OF ACCURACY

Use the student's oral reading time to circle the WPM range.

Word Count: 172

	INTRVN	INSTR	IND	ADV
Minutes:Seconds	2:54 or more	2:53–2:29	2:28–1:43	1:42 or less
WPM	59 or less	60–69	70–100	101 or more

Count the number of miscues that are not self-corrected. Circle the percent of accuracy based on the number of miscues.

	INTRVN	INSTR	IND				ADV	
Number of Miscues	12 or more	10–11	8–9	7	5–6	3–4	1–2	0
Percent of Accuracy	93 or less	94	95	96	97	98	99	100

- If the student's score falls in a shaded area for either WPM or Accuracy, STOP! Reassess with a lower-level text.
- If the student is reading below the grade-level benchmark, administer *DRA Word Analysis*, beginning with Task 22, at another time.

3. COMPREHENSION

PREDICTION

Students do not use the text when making their predictions. Record the student's responses.

T: Think about the title, the pictures you have seen, and what you have read so far. (Pause) *Tell me three things that you think might happen in the rest of this story.*

SILENT READING

T: Now, it's time to read and enjoy this story by yourself. When you are done, please come to me and I'll ask you to tell me what happened in this story.

RETELLING

As the student retells, underline and record on the Story Overview the information included in the student's retelling. Please note the student does not need to use the exact words.

T: Close the book before the retelling, and then say: *Start at the beginning, and tell me what happened in this story.*

Story Overview
Beginning
1. Roger, a small rabbit, found a giant cabbage in the road.
2. At first, he couldn't believe there was a cabbage in the road.
3. Then he decided the cabbage was real, and it was all his.
Middle
4. Roger rolled the cabbage home. He had to stop and rest from time to time.
5. He finally rolled the cabbage to the front door of his house, but the cabbage was too big to go through the door.
6. Roger cried, and then said, "Crying never helps anything. Thinking helps. I'll do some good thinking."
7. He called rabbits of all kinds to a cabbage party.
8. The rabbits ate until they were full.
9. Now the cabbage was small enough to go through the door.
End
10. Roger rolled the small cabbage inside and put it on his table.
11. Roger laughed and said it was a wonderful day.

If necessary, use one or more of the following prompts to gain further information after the initial retelling. Place a checkmark by a prompt each time it is used.

☐ *Tell me more.*
☐ *What happened at the beginning?*
☐ *What happened before/after* _____ (an event mentioned by the student)*?*
☐ *Who else was in the story?*
☐ *How did the story end?*

INTERPRETATION

Record the student's reponses to the prompts and questions below.

T: What do you think the author is trying to tell you in this story?

REFLECTION

T: What do you think was the most important thing that happened in this story?

T: Why do you think that was important?

4. TEACHER ANALYSIS

ORAL READING

If the student had 5 or more different miscues, use the information recorded on the Record of Oral Reading to complete the chart below.

Student problem-solves words using:	Number of miscues self-corrected: _____
☐ beginning letter(s)/sound(s) ☐ letter-sound clusters ☐ onset and rime ☐ blending letters/sounds ☐ knowledge of spelling patterns (analogies) ☐ syllables ☐ rereading ☐ no observable behaviors	Number of miscues not self-corrected: _____ Number of words told to the student: _____

	Miscues interfered with meaning:	**Miscues included:**

	☐ never
	 ☐ at times
	 ☐ often
		☐ omissions
		 ☐ insertions
		 ☐ substitutions that were
		      ☐ visually similar
		      ☐ not visually similar

Copy each substitution to help analyze the student's attention to visual information.
e.g., <u>stood</u> (substitution)
     stared (text)

Oral Reading Rate: (Optional) Use the formula below to determine the student's exact oral reading rate. Convert the student's reading time to all seconds.

$$172 \text{ (words)} \div \underline{\hspace{1.5cm}} \text{ total seconds} = \underline{\hspace{1.5cm}} \text{ WPS} \times 60 = \underline{\hspace{1.5cm}} \text{ WPM}$$

*DRA*2 Continuum

- Circle the descriptors that best describe the student's reading behaviors and responses.
    1. Use your daily classroom observations and the student's responses to the Reading Engagement questions to select statements that best describe the student's level of Reading Engagement.
    2. Use your recorded observations from this assessment to select the statements that best describe the student's Oral Reading Fluency and Comprehension.
- Add the circled numbers to obtain a total score for each section.
- Record the total scores at the top of page 1.

Note: If the Comprehension score is less than 19, administer *DRA*2 with a lower-level text.

*DRA*2 CONTINUUM	LEVEL 24		TRANSITIONAL READER	
	INTERVENTION	**INSTRUCTIONAL**	**INDEPENDENT**	**ADVANCED**
Reading Engagement				
Book Selection	**1** Selects texts from identified leveled sets with teacher support; uncertain about a favorite book	**2** Selects texts from identified leveled sets with moderate support; tells about favorite book in general terms	**3** Selects texts from identified leveled sets most of the time; identifies favorite book by title and tells about a particular event	**4** Selects a variety of "just right" texts; identifies favorite book by title and gives an overview of the book
Sustained Reading	**1** Sustains independent reading for a short period of time with much encouragement	**2** Sustains independent reading with moderate encouragement	**3** Sustains independent reading for at least 15 minutes at a time	**4** Sustains independent reading for an extended period of time
Score	2 3	4 5	6 7	8
Oral Reading Fluency				
Expression	**1** Little expression; monotone	**2** Some expression that conveys meaning	**3** Expression reflects mood, pace, and tension at times	**4** Expression reflects mood, pace, and tension most of the time
Phrasing	**1** Reads mostly word-by-word	**2** Reads in short phrases most of the time; inappropriate pauses	**3** Reads in longer phrases at times; heeds most punctuation	**4** Reads in longer, meaningful phrases most of the time; heeds all punctuation
Rate	**1** 59 WPM or less	**2** 60–69 WPM	**3** 70–100 WPM	**4** 101 WPM or more
Accuracy	**1** 93% or less	**2** 94%	**3** 95%–98%	**4** 99%–100%
Score	4 5 6	7 8 9 10	11 12 13 14	15 16
Comprehension				
Prediction	**1** Makes unrelated or no prediction(s)	**2** Makes at least 1 reasonable prediction related to the text	**3** Makes at least 2 reasonable predictions that go beyond the pages read aloud	**4** Makes at least 3 thoughtful predictions that go beyond the pages read aloud
Retelling: Sequence of Events	**1** Includes only 1 or 2 events or details (limited retelling)	**2** Includes at least 3 events, generally in random order (partial retelling)	**3** Includes most of the important events from the beginning, middle, and end, generally in sequence	**4** Includes all important events from the beginning, middle, and end in sequence
Retelling: Characters and Details	**1** Refers to characters using general pronouns; may include incorrect information	**2** Refers to characters using appropriate pronouns; includes at least 1 detail; may include some misinterpretation	**3** Refers to most characters by name and includes some important details	**4** Refers to all characters by name and includes all important details
Retelling: Vocabulary	**1** Uses general terms or labels; limited understanding of key words/concepts	**2** Uses some language/ vocabulary from the text; some understanding of key words/concepts	**3** Uses language/vocabulary from the text; basic understanding of most key words/concepts	**4** Uses important language/vocabulary from the text; good understanding of key words/concepts
Retelling: Teacher Support	**1** Retells with 5 or more questions or prompts	**2** Retells with 3 or 4 questions or prompts	**3** Retells with 1 or 2 questions or prompts	**4** Retells with no questions or prompts
Interpretation	**1** Little or no understanding of important text implications	**2** Some understanding of important text implications; no supporting details	**3** Understands important text implications; may include supporting details	**4** Insightful understanding of important text implications with supporting details or rationale
Reflection	**1** Identifies an unrelated event; no reason for opinion or no response	**2** Identifies a less significant event and/or gives a general reason for response	**3** Identifies a significant event <u>and</u> gives relevant reason(s) for opinion	**4** Identifies a significant event <u>and</u> gives reason(s) for opinion that reflects higher-level thinking
Score	7 8 9 10 11 12 13	14 15 16 17 18	19 20 21 22 23 24 25	26 27 28

Choose three to five teaching/learning activities on the *DRA*2 Focus for Instruction on the next page.

DRA2 FOCUS FOR INSTRUCTION FOR TRANSITIONAL READERS

READING ENGAGEMENT

Book Selection
☐ Teach student strategies to select "just right" books for independent reading
☐ Introduce student to reading materials from a variety of genres
☐ Teach student how to use a reading log to monitor book selection
☐ Model/teach how to read for different purposes

Sustained Reading
☐ Model and support how to read independently
☐ Teach strategies to build reading stamina
☐ Develop clear expectations for amount of independent reading
☐ Create structures to support reading at home

ORAL READING FLUENCY

Expression and Phrasing
☐ Model and support reading in longer, meaningful phrases with appropriate expression
☐ Have student practice appropriate expression with familiar texts
☐ Have student participate in choral reading and/or reader's theater
☐ Teach student to heed punctuation

Rate
☐ Provide materials and time for repeated reading to increase reading rate
☐ Teach student to read lower-level and/or familiar texts at an appropriate rate

Accuracy: Word Analysis
☐ Support and reinforce self-corrections of miscues
☐ Model and support how to take words apart (e.g., onset and rime, syllables) to problem-solve unknown words
☐ Teach how to use word chunks and analogies to problem-solve unknown words
☐ Provide spelling activities and word sorts to help student recognize patterns in words

COMPREHENSION

Prediction
☐ Teach student how to make predictions based on title and book cover, as well as opening paragraphs and illustrations of texts read aloud
☐ Model and support how to use background knowledge to make meaningful predictions

Retelling
☐ Model and teach how to retell a story
☐ Model and teach how to identify important events to include in a retelling
☐ Support retelling a story in sequence
☐ Encourage student to use characters' names when retelling a story
☐ Model and teach how to identify important details to include in a retelling
☐ Model and support using key language and vocabulary from the text in a retelling
☐ Model and teach how to create and use story maps to aid retelling

Interpretation
☐ Model how to infer during shared reading and read-alouds
☐ Teach and share examples of inferences
☐ Model and teach student how to think about *Why?* questions while and after reading a text
☐ Model and teach how to support inferences with examples from the text

Reflection
☐ Help student identify important message in a story
☐ Provide opportunities to identify and discuss the important event in a story
☐ Demonstrate and teach student how to support opinion with details from the text

OTHER

_____

_____

_____

_____

_____

_____

_____

Name/Date _____   Teacher/Grade _____

Scores: Reading Engagement ___/8   Oral Reading Fluency ___/16   Comprehension ___/28
Independent Range: 6–7   11–14   19–25

Book Selection   Text selected by: ☐ teacher   ☐ student

1. READING ENGAGEMENT

Ask the student to bring his or her reading record to the conference. If the Student Reading Survey was not completed prior to the assessment conference, read aloud the questions on the survey and record the student's responses.

2. ORAL READING FLUENCY

INTRODUCTION

T: This book is called Animals Can Help. *It is about animals that help people in different ways. Please read aloud pages 2 through 6.* Show the student where to stop reading at the ✱.

RECORD OF ORAL READING

Record the student's oral reading behaviors. Note the student's fluency (expression and phrasing). Be sure to time the student's reading.

Page 2

Animal Helpers

Animals that are a part of the family are called pets. Some people have pets like dogs, cats, birds, or rabbits. Other people have animals that are more than just pets.

Page 3

These animals are trained to help people. Some help people feel better. Some help people move and get stronger. Others help people who cannot see, hear, or move.

Page 4

Animals in Hospitals

People go to hospitals when they are sick. People may feel sad when they stay in a hospital for a long time. A trained dog can help.

Page 5

It is strange to see a dog in a hospital. The dog makes sick people smile. People talk to the dog and pet it. They laugh when the dog does funny tricks.

Page 6

Animals in Nursing Homes

Animals are trained to visit people in nursing homes. They help people feel more at home.

Time: _____ minutes:seconds

ORAL READING WORDS PER MINUTE, PERCENT OF ACCURACY

Use the student's oral reading time to circle the WPM range.

Word Count: 143

	INTRVN	INSTR	IND	ADV
Minutes:Seconds	2:14 or more	2:13–1:56	1:55–1:22	1:21 or less
WPM	64 or less	65–74	75–105	106 or more

Count the number of miscues that are not self-corrected. Circle the percent of accuracy based on the number of miscues.

	INTRVN	INSTR	IND				ADV	
Number of Miscues	10 or more	8–9	7	6	4–5	3	1–2	0
Percent of Accuracy	93 or less	94	95	96	97	98	99	100

- If the student's score falls in a shaded area for either WPM or Accuracy, STOP! Reassess with a lower-level text.
- If the student is reading below the grade-level benchmark, administer *DRA Word Analysis*, beginning with Task 28, at another time.

3. COMPREHENSION

TEXT FEATURES and STUDENT PREDICTION

Read aloud the questions/prompts on page 1 in the Student Booklet, and record the student's responses on the same page. Do not give additional prompts. Students may use the indicated book pages when responding to the Prediction and Nonfiction Text Features questions/prompts.

Note: Continue with the assessment if time permits. Otherwise, have the student read the book and complete the Student Booklet at another time.

Animals Can Help 28

STUDENT READS AND RESPONDS

All students may use the text to complete pages 2–3 of the Student Booklet.

T: Read the book. When you are finished, write a summary of what you have read and answer the remaining questions in the Student Booklet. If you have questions, please come to me (or raise your hand).

Note: For students who have an Individual Education Plan in place for reading and/or written communication, follow the directions in their plan. You may read aloud the prompts on pages 2 and 3 of the Student Booklet and/or scribe their responses if required. Give <u>no</u> additional prompts.

While the student reads the text independently, complete the Teacher Analysis of Oral Reading below and circle the descriptors on the *DRA*2 Continuum that best describe the student's oral reading fluency.

4. TEACHER ANALYSIS

ORAL READING

If the student had 5 or more different miscues, use the information recorded on the Record of Oral Reading to complete the chart below.

<table>
<tr>
<td colspan="2">Student problem-solves words using:
☐ beginning letter(s)/sound(s)
☐ letter-sound clusters
☐ blending letters/sounds
☐ onset and rime
☐ knowledge of spelling patterns
   (analogies)
☐ syllables
☐ rereading
☐ no observable behaviors</td>
<td colspan="2">Number of miscues self-corrected: _____
Number of miscues not self-corrected: _____
Number of words told to the student: _____</td>
</tr>
<tr>
<td colspan="2"></td>
<td>Miscues interfered with meaning:
☐ never
☐ at times
☐ often</td>
<td>Miscues included:
☐ omissions
☐ insertions
☐ reversals
☐ substitutions that were
    ☐ visually similar
    ☐ not visually similar</td>
</tr>
<tr>
<td colspan="4">Copy each substitution to help analyze the student's attention to visual information.
e.g., <u>nursery</u> (substitution)
      nursing (text)</td>
</tr>
</table>

Oral Reading Rate: (Optional) Use the formula below to determine the student's exact oral reading rate. Convert the student's reading time to all seconds.

143 (words) ÷ _____ total seconds = _____ WPS × 60 = _____ WPM

*DRA*2 Continuum

- Use the information from the Student Reading Survey and the Student Booklet to circle the descriptors that best describe the student's responses for Reading Engagement and Comprehension.
- Add the circled numbers to obtain a total score for each section.
- Record the total scores at the top of page 1. Record the Comprehension score at the top of page 4 after the colon.

Note: If the Comprehension score is less than 14, administer *DRA*2 with a lower-level text.   **163**

Name/Date _____ Teacher/Grade _____

DRA2 CONTINUUM	LEVEL 28		EXTENDING READER	
	INTERVENTION	**INSTRUCTIONAL**	**INDEPENDENT**	**ADVANCED**
Reading Engagement				
Wide Reading	1 Title(s) below grade level; limited reading experiences and book knowledge	2 Titles slightly below grade level; rather limited reading experiences	3 Titles within 2 genres or multiple books within a genre; generally on-grade-level texts	4 Titles across 3 or more genres; many on- and above-grade-level texts
Self-Assessment/ Goal Setting	1 No strengths and/or goals	2 General strength(s) and goal(s) related to the reading process	3 2 specific strengths and 2 specific goals related to the reading process	4 3 specific strengths and 3 specific goals that reflect a higher level of thinking
Score	2 3	4 5	6 7	8
Oral Reading Fluency				
Expression	1 Little expression; monotone	2 Some expression that conveys meaning	3 Expression emphasizing key phrases and words at times	4 Expression emphasizing key phrases and words most of the time
Phrasing	1 Mostly word-by-word	2 Short phrases most of the time; inappropriate pauses	3 Longer phrases most of the time; heeds most punctuation	4 Consistently longer, meaningful phrases; heeds all punctuation
Rate	1 64 WPM or less	2 65–74 WPM	3 75–105 WPM	4 106 WPM or more
Accuracy	1 93% or less	2 94%	3 95%–98%	4 99%–100%
Score	4 5 6	7 8 9 10	11 12 13 14	15 16
Comprehension				
Prediction	1 Unrelated question(s) or no response	2 At least 1 reasonable question related to the text	3 At least 2 reasonable questions that go beyond page(s) read aloud	4 3 thoughtful questions that go beyond page(s) read aloud
Nonfiction Text Features	1 Limited information accessed from text features or no response	2 Partial information accessed from text features	3 Accurate information accessed from text features	4 Detailed information accessed from text features
Scaffolded Summary	1 1–2 ideas/facts in own language and/or copied text; may include incorrect information	2 Partial summary; generally in own language; some important ideas/facts; may include misinterpretations	3 Summary in own language; includes important ideas and a few supporting facts from each section	4 Summary in own language; includes the most important ideas and some supporting facts from each section
Scaffolded Summary: Vocabulary	1 General terms or labels; limited understanding of key words/concepts	2 Some language/ vocabulary from the text; some understanding of key words/concepts	3 Most language/ vocabulary from the text; basic understanding of most key words/concepts	4 All important language/vocabulary from the text; good understanding of key words/concepts
Literal Comprehension	1 Incorrect response or no response	2 Partial response; may include misinterpretation	3 Accurate response	4 Accurate response with specific details
Interpretation	1 Little or no understanding of important text implications	2 Some understanding of important text implications; no supporting details	3 Understands important text implications; may include supporting details	4 Insightful understanding of important text implications with supporting details or rationale
Reflection	1 Insignificant message; no reason for opinion or no response	2 Less significant message and/or a general reason for opinion	3 Significant message and a relevant reason for opinion	4 Significant message and reason for opinion that reflects higher-level thinking
Score	7 8 9 10 11 12 13	14 15 16 17 18	19 20 21 22 23 24 25	26 27 28

Choose three to five teaching/learning activities on the *DRA2* Focus for Instruction on the next page

Animals Can Help 28

DRA2 FOCUS FOR INSTRUCTION FOR EXTENDING READERS

READING ENGAGEMENT
Wide Reading
- ☐ Teach student strategies to select appropriately leveled texts for independent reading
- ☐ Introduce student to reading materials from a variety of genres
- ☐ Teach strategies to build reading stamina
- ☐ Create structures and/or routines to support reading at home
- ☐ Develop clear expectations for amount of independent reading
- ☐ Teach student how to use a reading log to monitor book selection and set reading goals
- ☐ Model/teach how to read for different purposes

Self-Assessment/Goal Setting
- ☐ Model and discuss strategies good readers use
- ☐ Help student identify 1–2 reading goals and a plan of action to improve reading
- ☐ Support revision of ongoing reading goals

ORAL READING FLUENCY
Expression and Phrasing
- ☐ Model and support reading in longer, meaningful phrases with appropriate expression
- ☐ Have student practice appropriate expression with familiar texts
- ☐ Teach student to recognize and emphasize key phrases and words in nonfiction texts
- ☐ Teach student to heed punctuation

Rate
- ☐ Provide materials and time for repeated reading to increase reading rate
- ☐ Teach student to read lower-level and/or familiar texts at an appropriate rate

Accuracy: Word Analysis
- ☐ Support and reinforce self-corrections of miscues
- ☐ Model and support how to take words apart (e.g., onset and rime, syllables) to problem-solve unknown words
- ☐ Teach how to use word chunks and analogies to problem-solve unknown words
- ☐ Provide spelling activities and word sorts to help student recognize patterns in words

COMPREHENSION
Prediction
- ☐ Provide opportunities for student to make predictions based on title, table of contents, and headings
- ☐ Model and support using background information to make meaningful predictions
- ☐ Model and teach student how to pose questions as a basis for predictions

Nonfiction Text Features
- ☐ Model and support how to read and interpret charts, graphs, maps, tables, etc.
- ☐ Model and teach how to use table of contents, headings, glossary, etc.

Summary
- ☐ Share and identify characteristics of good summaries
- ☐ Model and co-construct written summaries of texts read aloud
- ☐ Model and support how to distinguish between more important and less important ideas and facts
- ☐ Model and support how to write a summary in one's own words
- ☐ Model and support how to use examples from the text
- ☐ Teach student how to use headings to organize a summary of an informational/nonfiction text

Literal Comprehension
- ☐ Show student how to use key words to identify specific information from the text
- ☐ Provide opportunities for student to answer and construct literal questions
- ☐ Teach student how to use graphic organizers to keep track of key ideas and facts

Interpretation
- ☐ Teach and share examples of inferences
- ☐ Provide opportunities for student to support inferences with information or examples from the text
- ☐ Give student opportunities to respond to inference questions orally and in writing
- ☐ Model and support how to interpret nonfiction text features (e.g., how to read a chart or diagram)

Reflection
- ☐ Help student identify important information and key vocabulary
- ☐ Demonstrate how to support opinion with details from the text

Name _____   Date _____

Teacher _____   Grade _____

The teacher reads aloud the prompts/questions and records the student's responses on this Before Reading page only.

BEFORE READING

PREDICTION

Open the book to the title and table of contents page. What are 3 questions you think may be answered as you read this book?

1. _____

_____

2. _____

_____

3. _____

_____

NONFICTION TEXT FEATURES

Turn to page 2. Why do you think the author put a heading at the top of this page?

_____

_____

Turn to the web on page 15. What does this web show you?

_____

_____

AFTER READING

Summary

Write 2 important facts in your own words for each heading. You may use the book to help you.

Animal Helpers _____

_____

_____

Service Animals _____

_____

_____

_____

Dogs _____

_____

_____

Monkeys _____

_____

_____

Horses _____

_____

_____

Animals Can Help

Animals Can Help

Literal Comprehension

List 2 ways animals help in hospitals and nursing homes.

Animals in Hospitals and Nursing Homes
1. _____
2. _____

Interpretation

Why do you think a dog must be trained before it can help someone who cannot see?

_____

_____

_____

Reflection

What do you think is the most important thing you learned from reading this book?

_____

_____

_____

Tell why you think it is important._____

_____

_____

Reread what you have written to make sure your answers are the way you want them before you hand in your booklet.

Name/Date _____   Teacher/Grade _____

Scores: Reading Engagement ___/8   Oral Reading Fluency ___/16   Comprehension ___/28
Independent Range: 6–7   11–14   19–25

Book Selection   Text selected by: ☐ teacher   ☐ student

1. READING ENGAGEMENT

Ask the student to bring his or her reading record to the conference. If the Student Reading Survey was not completed prior to the assessment conference, read aloud the questions on the survey and record the student's responses.

2. ORAL READING FLUENCY

INTRODUCTION

T: This book is called From Peanuts to Peanut Butter. *It tells how peanuts are grown and then made into peanut butter. Please read aloud pages 2 through 6.* Show the student where to stop reading at the ✱.

RECORD OF ORAL READING

Record the student's oral reading behaviors. Note the student's fluency (expression and phrasing). Be sure to time the student's reading.

Page 2

Peanut Butter

You can find a jar of peanut butter in most homes.
Lots of kids like to eat peanut butter. Did you know
that millions of pounds of peanut butter are eaten in
the United States and Canada each year? That's a
lot of peanut butter!

Page 4

Growing Peanuts

Peanut butter is made from
peanuts. Peanuts are grown on
farms. About half of the peanuts
grown on farms are used to
make peanut butter.

Page 5

Most peanuts are grown in the southern part of the United States. There, the weather is warm. The soil is very sandy. Peanuts need rich, sandy soil and warm days and nights to grow.

Page 6

Peanuts are planted in April. They are planted in rows. The peanut plant starts to come through the soil after two weeks. It looks like a small bush.

When the plant is 18 inches tall, small yellow flowers bloom. First, the flowers fall off. Then, **pegs** grow down into the ground. Soon, the peanuts begin to grow on the pegs.

Time: _____ minutes:seconds

ORAL READING WORDS PER MINUTE, PERCENT OF ACCURACY
Use the student's oral reading time to circle the WPM range.

Word Count: 168

	INTRVN	INSTR	IND	ADV
Minutes:Seconds	2:37 or more	2:36–2:16	2:15–1:36	1:35 or less
WPM	64 or less	65–74	75–105	106 or more

Count the number of miscues that are not self-corrected. Circle the percent of accuracy based on the number of miscues.

	INTRVN	INSTR	IND				ADV	
Number of Miscues	11 or more	10	8–9	6–7	5	3–4	1–2	0
Percent of Accuracy	93 or less	94	95	96	97	98	99	100

- If the student's score falls in a shaded area for either WPM or Accuracy, STOP! Reassess with a lower-level text.
- If the student is reading below the grade-level benchmark, administer *DRA Word Analysis*, beginning with Task 28, at another time.

From Peanuts to Peanut Butter 28

3. COMPREHENSION

TEXT FEATURES and STUDENT PREDICTION

Read aloud the questions/prompts on page 1 in the Student Booklet, and record the student's responses on the same page. Do not give additional prompts. Students may use the indicated book pages when responding to the Prediction and Nonfiction Text Features questions/prompts.

Note: Continue with the assessment if time permits. Otherwise, have the student read the book and complete the Student Booklet at another time.

STUDENT READS AND RESPONDS

All students may use the text to complete pages 2–3 of the Student Booklet.

T: Read the book. When you are finished, write a summary of what you have read and answer the remaining questions in the Student Booklet. If you have questions, please come to me (or raise your hand).

Note: For students who have an Individual Education Plan in place for reading and/or written communication, follow the directions in their plan. You may read aloud the prompts on pages 2 and 3 of the Student Booklet and/or scribe their responses if required. Give <u>no</u> additional prompts.

While the student reads the text independently, complete the Teacher Analysis of Oral Reading on the next page and circle the descriptors on the *DRA*2 Continuum that best describe the student's oral reading fluency.

From Peanuts to Peanut Butter 28

4. TEACHER ANALYSIS

ORAL READING

If the student had 5 or more different miscues, use the information recorded on the Record of Oral Reading to complete the chart.

Student problem-solves words using:		
☐ beginning letter(s)/sound(s) ☐ letter-sound clusters ☐ blending letters/sounds ☐ onset and rime ☐ knowledge of spelling patterns (analogies) ☐ syllables ☐ rereading ☐ no observable behaviors	Number of miscues self-corrected: ____ Number of miscues not self-corrected: ____ Number of words told to the student: ____	

	Miscues interfered with meaning:
	 ☐ never
	 ☐ at times
	 ☐ often
		Miscues included:
		 ☐ omissions
		 ☐ insertions
		 ☐ reversals
		 ☐ substitutions that were
		   ☐ visually similar
		   ☐ not visually similar

Copy each substitution to help analyze the student's attention to visual information.

e.g., <u>pages</u> (substitution)
      pegs (text)

Oral Reading Rate: (Optional) Use the formula below to determine the student's exact oral reading rate. Convert the student's reading time to all seconds.

$$168 \text{ (words)} \div \underline{\hspace{1.5cm}} \text{ total seconds} = \underline{\hspace{1.5cm}} \text{ WPS} \times 60 = \underline{\hspace{1.5cm}} \text{ WPM}$$

*DRA*2 Continuum

- Use the information from the Student Reading Survey and the Student Booklet to circle the descriptors that best describe the student's responses for Reading Engagement and Comprehension.
- Add the circled numbers to obtain a total score for each section.
- Record the total scores at the top of page 1. Record the Comprehension score at the top of page 5 after the colon.

Note: If the Comprehension score is less than 14, administer *DRA*2 with a lower-level text.

Name/Date _____ Teacher/Grade _____

DRA2 CONTINUUM	LEVEL 28		EXTENDING READER	
	INTERVENTION	**INSTRUCTIONAL**	**INDEPENDENT**	**ADVANCED**
Reading Engagement				
Wide Reading	**1** Title(s) below grade level; limited reading experiences and book knowledge	**2** Titles slightly below grade level; rather limited reading experiences	**3** Titles within 2 genres or multiple books within a genre; generally on-grade-level texts	**4** Titles across 3 or more genres; many on- and above-grade-level texts
Self-Assessment/ Goal Setting	**1** No strengths and/or goals	**2** General strength(s) and goal(s) related to the reading process	**3** 2 specific strengths and 2 specific goals related to the reading process	**4** 3 specific strengths and 3 specific goals that reflect a higher level of thinking
Score	2 3	4 5	6 7	8
Oral Reading Fluency				
Expression	**1** Little expression; monotone	**2** Some expression that conveys meaning	**3** Expression emphasizing key phrases and words at times	**4** Expression emphasizing key phrases and words most of the time
Phrasing	**1** Mostly word-by-word	**2** Short phrases most of the time; inappropriate pauses	**3** Longer phrases most of the time; heeds most punctuation	**4** Consistently longer, meaningful phrases; heeds all punctuation
Rate	**1** 64 WPM or less	**2** 65–74 WPM	**3** 75–105 WPM	**4** 106 WPM or more
Accuracy	**1** 93% or less	**2** 94%	**3** 95%–98%	**4** 99%–100%
Score	4 5 6	7 8 9 10	11 12 13 14	15 16
Comprehension				
Prediction	**1** Unrelated question(s) or no response	**2** At least 1 reasonable question related to the text	**3** At least 2 reasonable questions that go beyond page(s) read aloud	**4** 3 thoughtful questions that go beyond page(s) read aloud
Nonfiction Text Features	**1** Limited information accessed from text features or no response	**2** Partial information accessed from text features	**3** Accurate information accessed from text features	**4** Detailed information accessed from text features
Scaffolded Summary	**1** 1–2 ideas/facts in own language and/or copied text; may include incorrect information	**2** Partial summary; generally in own language; some important ideas/facts; may include misinterpretations	**3** Summary in own language; includes important ideas and a few supporting facts from each section	**4** Summary in own language; includes the most important ideas and some supporting facts from each section
Scaffolded Summary: Vocabulary	**1** General terms or labels; limited understanding of key words/concepts	**2** Some language/ vocabulary from the text; some understanding of key words/concepts	**3** Most language/ vocabulary from the text; basic understanding of most key words/concepts	**4** All important language/vocabulary from the text; good understanding of key words/concepts
Literal Comprehension	**1** Incorrect response or no response	**2** Partial response; may include misinterpretation	**3** Accurate response	**4** Accurate response with specific details
Interpretation	**1** Little or no understanding of important text implications	**2** Some understanding of important text implications; no supporting details	**3** Understands important text implications; may include supporting details	**4** Insightful understanding of important text implications with supporting details or rationale
Reflection	**1** Insignificant message; no reason for opinion or no response	**2** Less significant message and/or a general reason for opinion	**3** Significant message and a relevant reason for opinion	**4** Significant message and reason for opinion that reflects higher-level thinking
Score	7 8 9 10 11 12 13	14 15 16 17 18	19 20 21 22 23 24 25	26 27 28

Choose three to five teaching/learning activities on the *DRA2* Focus for Instruction on the next page.

From Peanuts to Peanut Butter **28**

DRA2 FOCUS FOR INSTRUCTION FOR EXTENDING READERS

READING ENGAGEMENT

Wide Reading
- ☐ Teach student strategies to select appropriately leveled texts for independent reading
- ☐ Introduce student to reading materials from a variety of genres
- ☐ Teach strategies to build reading stamina
- ☐ Create structures and/or routines to support reading at home
- ☐ Develop clear expectations for amount of independent reading
- ☐ Teach student how to use a reading log to monitor book selection and set reading goals
- ☐ Model/teach how to read for different purposes

Self-Assessment/Goal Setting
- ☐ Model and discuss strategies good readers use
- ☐ Help student identify 1–2 reading goals and a plan of action to improve reading
- ☐ Support revision of ongoing reading goals

ORAL READING FLUENCY

Expression and Phrasing
- ☐ Model and support reading in longer, meaningful phrases with appropriate expression
- ☐ Have student practice appropriate expression with familiar texts
- ☐ Teach student to recognize and emphasize key phrases and words in nonfiction texts
- ☐ Teach student to heed punctuation

Rate
- ☐ Provide materials and time for repeated reading to increase reading rate
- ☐ Teach student to read lower-level and/or familiar texts at an appropriate rate

Accuracy: Word Analysis
- ☐ Support and reinforce self-corrections of miscues
- ☐ Model and support how to take words apart (e.g., onset and rime, syllables) to problem-solve unknown words
- ☐ Teach how to use word chunks and analogies to problem-solve unknown words
- ☐ Provide spelling activities and word sorts to help student recognize patterns in words

COMPREHENSION

Prediction
- ☐ Provide opportunities for student to make predictions based on title, table of contents, and headings
- ☐ Model and support using background information to make meaningful predictions
- ☐ Model and teach student how to pose questions as a basis for predictions

Nonfiction Text Features
- ☐ Model and support how to read and interpret charts, graphs, maps, tables, etc.
- ☐ Model and teach how to use table of contents, headings, glossary, etc.

Summary
- ☐ Share and identify characteristics of good summaries
- ☐ Model and co-construct written summaries of texts read aloud
- ☐ Model and support how to distinguish between more important and less important ideas and facts
- ☐ Model and support how to write a summary in one's own words
- ☐ Model and support how to use examples from the text
- ☐ Teach student how to use headings to organize a summary of an informational/nonfiction text

Literal Comprehension
- ☐ Show student how to use key words to identify specific information from the text
- ☐ Provide opportunities for student to answer and construct literal questions
- ☐ Teach student how to use graphic organizers to keep track of key ideas and facts

Interpretation
- ☐ Teach and share examples of inferences
- ☐ Provide opportunities for student to support inferences with information or examples from the text
- ☐ Give student opportunities to respond to inference questions orally and in writing
- ☐ Model and support how to interpret nonfiction text features (e.g., how to read a chart or diagram)

Reflection
- ☐ Help student identify important information and key vocabulary
- ☐ Demonstrate how to support opinion with details from the text

Name _____   Date _____

Teacher _____   Grade _____

The teacher reads aloud the prompts/questions and records the student's responses on this Before Reading page only.

BEFORE READING

PREDICTION

Open the book to the title and table of contents page. What are 3 questions you think may be answered as you read this book?

1. _____

_____

2. _____

_____

3. _____

_____

NONFICTION TEXT FEATURES

Turn to page 4. Why do you think the author put a heading at the top of this page?

_____

_____

Now read the map, and tell me what it shows you.

_____

_____

From Peanuts to Peanut Butter

AFTER READING

Summary

Write 2 important facts in your own words for each heading. You may use the book to help you.

Growing Peanuts _____

_____

_____

_____

Gathering Peanuts_____

_____

_____

_____

Making Peanut Butter _____

_____

_____

_____

Peanut Butter Treats_____

_____

_____

_____

Literal Comprehension

List 2 reasons that most peanuts are grown in the southern part of the United States.

Peanuts grow well in the South because ...

1. _____

2. _____

Interpretation

Why do you think people use machines to gather peanuts and make peanut butter?

_____

_____

_____

Reflection

What do you think is the most important thing you learned from reading this book?

_____

_____

Tell why you think it is important. _____

_____

_____

Reread what you have written to make sure your answers are the way you want them before you hand in your booklet.

Name/Date _____   Teacher/Grade _____

Scores: Reading Engagement ___/8   Oral Reading Fluency ___/16   Comprehension ___/28
Independent Range: 6–7   11–14   19–25

Book Selection   Text selected by: ☐ teacher   ☐ student

1. READING ENGAGEMENT

Ask the student to bring his or her reading record to the conference. If the Student Reading Survey was not completed prior to the assessment conference, read aloud the questions on the survey and record the student's responses.

2. ORAL READING FLUENCY

INTRODUCTION

T: In this story, Missing Sneakers, *Sara and her family are getting ready to move and Sara can't find her pet cat, Sneakers. Please read aloud pages 2 through 4.* Show the student where to stop reading at the ✱.

RECORD OF ORAL READING

Record the student's oral reading behaviors. Note the student's fluency (expression and phrasing). Be sure to time the student's reading.

Page 2

Sara put all of her stuffed animals in a packing box. Sneakers, her black cat with white paws, jumped off her bed. He reached up and put his front paws on the box.

"No, Sneakers, you're not going inside the box," Sara laughed. "We'll take you in your crate when we move."

Sara's mother peeked inside her room. "The moving truck is coming early tomorrow. Are you almost done packing?"

"Yes," said Sara. "I just need to pack up Sneakers' toys."

"Remember to put Sneakers in his crate first thing in the morning," her mother said. "We don't want to lose him during the move!"

Sara knew that watching her cat was an important job. Sneakers loved to sneak out of the house. He could be very hard to find!

Page 4

The next day, Sara woke up early. Sneakers rubbed against her and purred. "Sneakers, are you ready to move?" Sara asked.

A small plastic jingle ball fell off the bed. Sneakers jumped off the bed and chased it. The ball made a jingle sound as he hit it with his paw. Sara picked up the ball and put it in the box with his other toys.

Time: _____ minutes:seconds

ORAL READING WORDS PER MINUTE, PERCENT OF ACCURACY

Use the student's oral reading time to circle the WPM range.

Word Count: 196

	INTRVN	INSTR	IND	ADV
Minutes:Seconds	3:03 or more	3:02–2:38	2:37–1:52	1:51 or less
WPM	64 or less	65–74	75–105	106 or more

Count the number of miscues that are not self-corrected. Circle the percent of accuracy based on the number of miscues.

	INTRVN	INSTR	IND				ADV	
Number of Miscues	13 or more	11–12	9–10	7–8	5–6	3–4	1–2	0
Percent of Accuracy	93 or less	94	95	96	97	98	99	100

- If the student's score falls in a shaded area for either WPM or Accuracy, STOP! Reassess with a lower-level text.
- If the student is reading below the grade-level benchmark, administer *DRA Word Analysis*, beginning with Task 28, at another time.

Missing Sneakers 28

3. COMPREHENSION

TEXT FEATURES and STUDENT PREDICTION

Read aloud the questions/prompts on page 1 of the Student Booklet, and record the student's responses on the same page. Do not give additional prompts. Students do not use the book as you record their responses on the first page of the Student Booklet.

Note: Continue with the assessment if time permits. Otherwise, have the student read the book and complete the Student Booklet at another time.

STUDENT READS AND RESPONDS

All students may use the text to complete pages 2–3 of the Student Booklet.

T: Read the story. When you are finished, write a summary of what you have read and answer the remaining questions in the Student Booklet. If you have questions, please come to me (or raise your hand).

Note: For students who have an Individual Education Plan in place for reading and/or written communication, follow the directions in their plan. You may read aloud the prompts on pages 2 and 3 of the Student Booklet and/or scribe their responses if required. Give <u>no</u> additional prompts.

While the student reads the text independently, complete the Teacher Analysis of Oral Reading on the next page and circle the descriptors on the *DRA2* Continuum that best describe the student's oral reading fluency.

4. TEACHER ANALYSIS

ORAL READING

If the student had 5 or more different miscues, use the information recorded on the Record of Oral Reading to complete the chart.

<table>
<tr><td>Student problem-solves words using:
☐ beginning letter(s)/sound(s)
☐ letter-sound clusters
☐ blending letters/sounds
☐ onset and rime
☐ knowledge of spelling patterns (analogies)
☐ syllables
☐ rereading
☐ no observable behaviors</td><td colspan="2">Number of miscues self-corrected: _____
Number of miscues not self-corrected: _____
Number of words told to the student: _____</td></tr>
<tr><td></td><td>Miscues interfered with meaning:
☐ never
☐ at times
☐ often</td><td>Miscues included:
☐ omissions
☐ insertions
☐ reversals
☐ substitutions that were
   ☐ visually similar
   ☐ not visually similar</td></tr>
<tr><td colspan="3">Copy each substitution to help analyze the student's attention to visual information.
e.g., <u>package</u> (substitution)
    packing (text)</td></tr>
</table>

Oral Reading Rate: (Optional) Use the formula below to determine the student's exact oral reading rate. Convert the student's reading time to all seconds.

196 (words) ÷ _____ total seconds = _____ WPS × 60 = _____ WPM

DRA2 Continuum

• Use the information from the Student Reading Survey and the Student Booklet to circle the descriptors that best describe the student's responses for Reading Engagement and Comprehension.
• Add the circled numbers to obtain a total score for each section.
• Record the total scores at the top of page 1. Record the Comprehension score at the top of page 5 after the colon.

Note: If the Comprehension score is less than 14, administer *DRA2* with a lower-level text.

Name/Date _____ Teacher/Grade _____

*DRA*2 CONTINUUM	LEVEL 28		EXTENDING READER	
	INTERVENTION	**INSTRUCTIONAL**	**INDEPENDENT**	**ADVANCED**
Reading Engagement				
Wide Reading	**1** Title(s) below grade level; limited reading experiences and book knowledge	**2** Titles slightly below grade level; rather limited reading experiences	**3** Titles within 2 genres or multiple books within a genre; generally on-grade-level texts	**4** Titles across 3 or more genres; many on- and above-grade-level texts
Self-Assessment/ Goal Setting	**1** No strengths and/or goals	**2** General strength(s) and goal(s) related to the reading process	**3** 2 specific strengths and 2 specific goals related to the reading process	**4** 3 specific strengths and 3 specific goals that reflect a higher level of thinking
Score	2 3	4 5	6 7	8
Oral Reading Fluency				
Expression	**1** Little expression; monotone	**2** Some expression that conveys meaning	**3** Expression reflects mood, pace, and tension at times	**4** Expression reflects mood, pace, and tension most of the time
Phrasing	**1** Mostly word-by-word	**2** Short phrases most of the time; inappropriate pauses	**3** Longer phrases most of the time; heeds most punctuation	**4** Consistently longer, meaningful phrases; heeds all punctuation
Rate	**1** 64 WPM or less	**2** 65–74 WPM	**3** 75–105 WPM	**4** 106 WPM or more
Accuracy	**1** 93% or less	**2** 94%	**3** 95%–98%	**4** 99%–100%
Score	4 5 6	7 8 9 10	11 12 13 14	15 16
Comprehension				
Use of Text Features	**1** Limited or no description of the characters	**2** Partial description of the characters; general statements	**3** Description of each character; includes at least 2 specific details	**4** Description of each character; includes at least 3 specific details
Prediction	**1** Unrelated predictions or no response	**2** At least 1 reasonable prediction related to the text	**3** At least 2 reasonable predictions that go beyond the text read aloud	**4** 3 thoughtful predictions that go beyond the text read aloud
Scaffolded Summary	**1** 1–2 events in own language and/or copied text; may include incorrect information	**2** Partial summary; generally in own language; some important characters/events; may include misinterpretations	**3** Summary in own language; includes important characters, many of the important events, and some details from the beginning, middle, and end	**4** Summary in own language; includes all important characters, events, and details from the beginning, middle, and end
Scaffolded Summary: Vocabulary	**1** General terms or labels; limited understanding of key words/concepts	**2** Some language/ vocabulary from the text; some understanding of key words/concepts	**3** Most language/ vocabulary from the text; basic understanding of most key words/concepts	**4** All important language/ vocabulary from the text; good understanding of key words/concepts
Literal Comprehension	**1** Incorrect response or no response	**2** Partial response; may include misinterpretation	**3** Accurate response	**4** Accurate response with specific details
Interpretation	**1** Little or no understanding of important text implications	**2** Some understanding of important text implications; no supporting details	**3** Understands important text implications; may include supporting details	**4** Insightful understanding of important text implications; with supporting details or rationale
Reflection	**1** Insignificant event; no reason for opinion or no response	**2** Less significant event and/or a general reason for opinion	**3** Significant event <u>and</u> a relevant reason for opinion	**4** Significant event <u>and</u> reason for opinion that reflects higher-level thinking
Score	7 8 9 10 11 12 13	14 15 16 17 18	19 20 21 22 23 24 25	26 27 28

Choose three to five teaching/learning activities on the *DRA*2 Focus for Instruction on the next page.

Missing Sneakers **28**

DRA2 FOCUS FOR INSTRUCTION FOR EXTENDING READERS

READING ENGAGEMENT

Wide Reading
- ☐ Teach student strategies to select appropriately leveled texts for independent reading
- ☐ Introduce student to reading materials from a variety of genres
- ☐ Teach strategies to build reading stamina
- ☐ Create structures and/or routines to support reading at home
- ☐ Develop clear expectations for amount of independent reading
- ☐ Teach student how to use a reading log to monitor book selection and set reading goals
- ☐ Model/teach how to read for different purposes

Self-Assessment/Goal Setting
- ☐ Model and discuss strategies good readers use
- ☐ Help student identify 1–2 reading goals and a plan of action to improve reading
- ☐ Support revision of ongoing reading goals

ORAL READING FLUENCY

Expression and Phrasing
- ☐ Model and support reading in longer, meaningful phrases with appropriate expression
- ☐ Have student practice appropriate expression with familiar texts
- ☐ Have student participate in choral reading and/or reader's theater
- ☐ Teach student to heed punctuation

Rate
- ☐ Provide materials and time for repeated reading to increase reading rate
- ☐ Teach student to read lower level and/or familiar texts at an appropriate rate

Accuracy: Word Analysis
- ☐ Support and reinforce self-corrections of miscues
- ☐ Model and support how to take words apart (e.g., onset and rime, syllables) to problem-solve unknown words
- ☐ Teach how to use word chunks and analogies to problem-solve unknown words
- ☐ Provide spelling activities and word sorts to help student recognize patterns in words

COMPREHENSION

Use of Text Features
- ☐ Provide opportunities for student to discuss what he or she knows about the characters based on title and book cover, as well as opening paragraphs and texts read aloud
- ☐ Teach student how to describe characters, using information from fiction text features (e.g., title, illustrations, and text)

Prediction
- ☐ Teach student how to make predictions based on title and book cover, as well as opening paragraphs of texts read aloud
- ☐ Model and support using background information to make meaningful predictions

Summary
- ☐ Share and identify characteristics of good summaries
- ☐ Model and co-construct written summaries of texts read aloud
- ☐ Model and support how to distinguish between more important and less important ideas and details
- ☐ Model and support how to write a summary in one's own words
- ☐ Teach student how to use a graphic organizer as an aid to creating a summary
- ☐ Teach student how to identify story elements (e.g., characters, setting, plot)

Literal Comprehension
- ☐ Show student how to use key words to identify specific information from the text
- ☐ Provide opportunities for student to answer and construct literal questions
- ☐ Help student locate and record specific details
- ☐ Teach student how to use graphic organizers to keep track of story information

Interpretation
- ☐ Teach and share examples of inferences
- ☐ Model and teach student how to think about *Why?* questions while and after reading a text
- ☐ Model and teach how to support inferences with examples from the text
- ☐ Give student opportunities to respond to inference questions orally and in writing

Reflection
- ☐ Help student identify important message in a story
- ☐ Provide opportunities to identify and discuss the most important event in a story
- ☐ Demonstrate and teach student how to support opinion with details from the text

Name _____ Date _____

Teacher _____ Grade _____

The teacher reads aloud the prompts/questions and records the student's responses on this Before Reading page only.

BEFORE READING

TEXT FEATURES

Think about the title, the pictures you have seen, and what you have read so far. Tell me what you know about Sara and Sneakers.

Sara: _____

_____

Sneakers: _____

_____

_____

PREDICTION

What are 3 things you think might happen in the rest of this story?

1. _____

_____

_____

2. _____

_____

_____

3. _____

_____

Missing Sneakers

AFTER READING

Summary

Write a summary of this story in your own words. Include the important characters, events, and details. You may use the book and the words below to help you write your summary.

In the beginning, _____

_____

_____

Next, _____

_____

_____

Then, _____

_____

_____

After that, _____

_____

_____

In the end, _____

_____

_____

Missing Sneakers

Literal Comprehension

List 2 places where Sara looked for Sneakers.

Sara looked for Sneakers ...

1. _____

2. _____

Interpretation

What do you think Sara learned? _____

_____

_____

_____

Reflection

What do you think is the most important event in this story?

_____

_____

_____

Tell why you think it is important. _____

_____

_____

_____

Reread what you have written to make sure your answers are the way you want them before you hand in your booklet.

Teacher Observation Guide   *You Don't Look Beautiful to Me*   Level 28, Page 1

Name/Date _____   Teacher/Grade _____

Scores: Reading Engagement ___/8   Oral Reading Fluency ___/16   Comprehension ___/28
Independent Range: 6–7   11–14   19–25

Book Selection   Text selected by: ☐ teacher   ☐ student

1. READING ENGAGEMENT

Ask the student to bring his or her reading record to the conference. If the Student Reading Survey was not completed prior to the assessment conference, read aloud the questions on the survey and record the student's responses.

2. ORAL READING FLUENCY

INTRODUCTION

T: *In this story,* You Don't Look Beautiful to Me, *Mother Skunk thinks Little Skunk is beautiful. The other animals don't think so. Please read aloud page 2.* Show the student where to stop reading at the ✱.

RECORD OF ORAL READING

Record the student's oral reading behaviors. Note the student's fluency (expression and phrasing). Be sure to time the student's reading.

Page 2

"You are so beautiful," Mother Skunk said as she looked down at Little Skunk beside her on the warm rock. She ruffled up his fur with her nose and tickled his feet.

Little Skunk rolled over and off the rock.

The spring day was beautiful. The robins were making nests. Trees had little green buds on them. Yellow and blue flowers poked their heads out of the ground. The warm sun shone brightly.

"This is the best day in my whole life," Little Skunk said, shaking the dirt out of his shiny fur.

Little Skunk was so happy that he ran off to talk to the other animals in the woods. He hadn't gone very far when he met Little Rabbit.

"Hello, Little Rabbit," he said. "My mother says I'm beautiful." He drew circles in the air with his long tail.

Little Rabbit looked at him and wrinkled up his nose. "Your tail looks too long to me. And how can you hear anything with such short ears? You're not beautiful at all." He hopped away.

Time: _____ minutes:seconds

ORAL READING WORDS PER MINUTE, PERCENT OF ACCURACY
Use the student's oral reading time to circle the WPM range.

Word Count: 176

	INTRVN	INSTR	IND	ADV
Minutes: Seconds	2:44 or more	2:43–2:22	2:21–1:41	1:40 or less
WPM	64 or less	65–74	75–105	106 or more

Count the number of miscues that are not self-corrected. Circle the percent of accuracy based on the number of miscues.

	INTRVN	INSTR	IND				ADV	
Number of Miscues	12 or more	10–11	8–9	7	5–6	3–4	1–2	0
Percent of Accuracy	93 or less	94	95	96	97	98	99	100

- If the student's score falls in a shaded area for either WPM or Accuracy, STOP! Reassess with a lower-level text.
- If the student is reading below the grade-level benchmark, administer *DRA Word Analysis*, beginning with Task 28, at another time.

3. COMPREHENSION

TEXT FEATURES and STUDENT PREDICTION

Read aloud the questions/prompts on page 1 of the Student Booklet, and record the student's responses on the same page. Do not give additional prompts. Students do not use the book as you record their responses on the first page of the Student Booklet.

Note: Continue with the assessment if time permits. Otherwise, have the student read the book and complete the Student Booklet at another time.

STUDENT READS AND RESPONDS

All students may use the text to complete pages 2–3 of the Student Booklet.

T: Read the story. When you are finished, write a summary of what you have read and answer the remaining questions in the Student Booklet. If you have questions, please come to me (or raise your hand).

Note: For students who have an Individual Education Plan in place for reading and/or written communication, follow the directions in their plan. You may read aloud the prompts on pages 2 and 3 of the Student Booklet and/or scribe their responses if required. Give <u>no</u> additional prompts.

While the student reads the text independently, complete the Teacher Analysis of Oral Reading on the next page and circle the descriptors on the *DRA2* Continuum that best describe the student's oral reading fluency.

4. TEACHER ANALYSIS

ORAL READING

If the student had 5 or more different miscues, use the information recorded on the Record of Oral Reading to complete the chart.

Student problem-solves words using:	
☐ beginning letter(s)/sound(s) ☐ letter-sound clusters ☐ blending letters/sounds ☐ onset and rime ☐ knowledge of spelling patterns (analogies) ☐ syllables ☐ rereading ☐ no observable behaviors	Number of miscues self-corrected: _____ Number of miscues not self-corrected: _____ Number of words told to the student: _____

Miscues interfered with meaning:	Miscues included:

☐ never
☐ at times
☐ often
	☐ omissions
	☐ insertions
	☐ reversals
	☐ substitutions that were
	   ☐ visually similar
	   ☐ not visually similar

Copy each substitution to help analyze the student's attention to visual information.

e.g., <u>shined</u> (substitution)

   shone (text)

Oral Reading Rate: (Optional) Use the formula below to determine the student's exact oral reading rate. Convert the student's reading time to all seconds.

$$176 \text{ (words)} \div \underline{\hspace{2cm}} \text{ total seconds} = \underline{\hspace{2cm}} \text{ WPS} \times 60 = \underline{\hspace{2cm}} \text{ WPM}$$

DRA2 Continuum

- Use the information from the Student Reading Survey and the Student Booklet to circle the descriptors that best describe the student's responses for Reading Engagement and Comprehension.
- Add the circled numbers to obtain a total score for each section.
- Record the total scores at the top of page 1. Record the Comprehension score at the top of page 5 after the colon.

Note: If the Comprehension score is less than 14, administer *DRA2* with a lower-level text.

Name/Date _____ Teacher/Grade _____

DRA2 CONTINUUM	LEVEL 28		EXTENDING READER	
	INTERVENTION	**INSTRUCTIONAL**	**INDEPENDENT**	**ADVANCED**
Reading Engagement				
Wide Reading	**1** Title(s) below grade level; limited reading experiences and book knowledge	**2** Titles slightly below grade level; rather limited reading experiences	**3** Titles within 2 genres or multiple books within a genre; generally on-grade-level texts	**4** Titles across 3 or more genres; many on- and above-grade-level texts
Self-Assessment/ Goal Setting	**1** No strengths and/or goals	**2** General strength(s) and goal(s) related to the reading process	**3** 2 specific strengths and 2 specific goals related to the reading process	**4** 3 specific strengths and 3 specific goals that reflect a higher level of thinking
Score	2 3	4 5	6 7	8
Oral Reading Fluency				
Expression	**1** Little expression; monotone	**2** Some expression that conveys meaning	**3** Expression reflects mood, pace, and tension at times	**4** Expression reflects mood, pace, and tension most of the time
Phrasing	**1** Mostly word-by-word	**2** Short phrases most of the time; inappropriate pauses	**3** Longer phrases most of the time; heeds most punctuation	**4** Consistently longer, meaningful phrases; heeds all punctuation
Rate	**1** 64 WPM or less	**2** 65–74 WPM	**3** 75–105 WPM	**4** 106 WPM or more
Accuracy	**1** 93% or less	**2** 94%	**3** 95%–98%	**4** 99%–100%
Score	4 5 6	7 8 9 10	11 12 13 14	15 16
Comprehension				
Use of Text Features	**1** Limited or no description of the characters	**2** Partial description of the characters; general statements	**3** Description of each character; includes at least 2 specific details	**4** Description of each character; includes at least 3 specific details
Prediction	**1** Unrelated predictions or no response	**2** At least 1 reasonable prediction related to the text	**3** At least 2 reasonable predictions that go beyond the text read aloud	**4** 3 thoughtful predictions that go beyond the text read aloud
Scaffolded Summary	**1** 1–2 events in own language and/or copied text; may include incorrect information	**2** Partial summary; generally in own language; some important characters/events; may include misinterpretations	**3** Summary in own language; includes important characters, many of the important events, and some details from the beginning, middle, and end	**4** Summary in own language; includes all important characters, events, and details from the beginning, middle, and end
Scaffolded Summary: Vocabulary	**1** General terms or labels; limited understanding of key words/concepts	**2** Some language/ vocabulary from the text; some understanding of key words/concepts	**3** Most language/ vocabulary from the text; basic understanding of most key words/concepts	**4** All important language/vocabulary from the text; good understanding of key words/concepts
Literal Comprehension	**1** Incorrect response or no response	**2** Partial response; may include misinterpretation	**3** Accurate response	**4** Accurate response with specific details
Interpretation	**1** Little or no understanding of important text implications	**2** Some understanding of important text implications; no supporting details	**3** Understands important text implications; may include supporting details	**4** Insightful understanding of important text implications with supporting details or rationale
Reflection	**1** Insignificant event; no reason for opinion or no response	**2** Less significant event and/or a general reason for opinion	**3** Significant event <u>and</u> a relevant reason for opinion	**4** Significant event <u>and</u> reason for opinion that reflects higher-level thinking
Score	7 8 9 10 11 12 13	14 15 16 17 18	19 20 21 22 23 24 25	26 27 28

Choose three to five teaching/learning activities on the *DRA2* Focus for Instruction on the next page.

DRA2 FOCUS FOR INSTRUCTION FOR EXTENDING READERS

READING ENGAGEMENT

Wide Reading

- ☐ Teach student strategies to select appropriately leveled texts for independent reading
- ☐ Introduce student to reading materials from a variety of genres
- ☐ Teach strategies to build reading stamina
- ☐ Create structures and/or routines to support reading at home
- ☐ Develop clear expectations for amount of independent reading
- ☐ Teach student how to use a reading log to monitor book selection and set reading goals
- ☐ Model/teach how to read for different purposes

Self-Assessment/Goal Setting

- ☐ Model and discuss strategies good readers use
- ☐ Help student identify 1–2 reading goals and a plan of action to improve reading
- ☐ Support revision of ongoing reading goals

ORAL READING FLUENCY

Expression and Phrasing

- ☐ Model and support reading in longer, meaningful phrases with appropriate expression
- ☐ Have student practice appropriate expression with familiar texts
- ☐ Have student participate in choral reading and/or reader's theater
- ☐ Teach student to heed punctuation

Rate

- ☐ Provide materials and time for repeated reading to increase reading rate
- ☐ Teach student to read lower-level and/or familiar texts at an appropriate rate

Accuracy: Word Analysis

- ☐ Support and reinforce self-corrections of miscues
- ☐ Model and support how to take words apart (e.g., onset and rime, syllables) to problem-solve unknown words
- ☐ Teach how to use word chunks and analogies to problem-solve unknown words
- ☐ Provide spelling activities and word sorts to help student recognize patterns in words

COMPREHENSION

Use of Text Features

- ☐ Provide opportunities for student to discuss what he or she knows about the characters based on title and book cover, as well as opening paragraphs and texts read aloud
- ☐ Teach student how to describe characters, using information from fiction text features (e.g., title, illustrations, and text)

Prediction

- ☐ Teach student how to make predictions based on title and book cover, as well as opening paragraphs of texts read aloud
- ☐ Model and support using background information to make meaningful predictions

Summary

- ☐ Share and identify characteristics of good summaries
- ☐ Model and co-construct written summaries of texts read aloud
- ☐ Model and support how to distinguish between more important and less important ideas and details
- ☐ Model and support how to write a summary in one's own words
- ☐ Teach student how to use a graphic organizer as an aid to creating a summary
- ☐ Teach student how to identify story elements (e.g., characters, setting, plot)

Literal Comprehension

- ☐ Show student how to use key words to identify specific information from the text
- ☐ Provide opportunities for student to answer and construct literal questions
- ☐ Help student locate and record specific details
- ☐ Teach student how to use graphic organizers to keep track of story information

Interpretation

- ☐ Teach and share examples of inferences
- ☐ Model and teach student how to think about *Why?* questions while and after reading a text
- ☐ Model and teach how to support inferences with examples from the text
- ☐ Give student opportunities to respond to inference questions orally and in writing

Reflection

- ☐ Help student identify important message in a story
- ☐ Provide opportunities to identify and discuss the most important event in a story
- ☐ Demonstrate and teach student how to support opinion with details from the text

Name _____   Date _____

Teacher _____   Grade _____

The teacher reads aloud the prompts/questions and records the student's responses on this Before Reading page only.

BEFORE READING

TEXT FEATURES

Think about the title, the pictures, and what you have read so far. Tell me what you know about Little Skunk and Little Rabbit.

Little Skunk: _____

_____

Little Rabbit: _____

_____

PREDICTION

What are 3 things you think might happen in the rest of this story?

1. _____

_____

_____

2. _____

_____

_____

3. _____

_____

AFTER READING

Summary

Write a summary of this story in your own words. Include the important characters, events, and details. You may use the book and the words below to help you write your summary.

In the beginning, _____

_____

_____

Next, _____

_____

_____

Then, _____

_____

_____

After that, _____

_____

_____

In the end, _____

_____

_____

Literal Comprehension

List 2 reasons why Little Deer did not think Little Skunk was beautiful.

Little Deer's Reasons
1. _____
2. _____

Interpretation

What do you think Little Skunk learned?_____

_____

_____

_____

Reflection

What do you think is the most important event in this story?

_____

_____

_____

Tell why you think it is important._____

_____

_____

_____

_____

Reread what you have written to make sure your answers are the way you want them before you hand in your booklet.

Name/Date _____   Teacher/Grade _____

Scores: Reading Engagement ___/8   Oral Reading Fluency ___/16   Comprehension ___/28
Independent Range: 6–7   11–14   19–25

Book Selection   Text selected by: ☐ teacher   ☐ student

1. READING ENGAGEMENT

Ask the student to bring his or her reading record to the conference. If the Student Reading Survey was not completed prior to the assessment conference, read aloud the questions on the survey and record the student's responses.

2. ORAL READING FLUENCY

INTRODUCTION

T: This book is called Busy Helpers. *It is about two friends, Pedro and Ann, and how they help Pedro's neighbor. Please read aloud pages 2 through 3.* Show the student where to stop reading at the ✱.

RECORD OF ORAL READING

Record the student's oral reading behaviors. Note the student's fluency (expression and phrasing). Be sure to time the student's reading.

Page 2

Most afternoons Pedro and Ann played in the backyard at Pedro's house. Sometimes they tossed a ball. Other times they jumped rope or took turns shooting the basketball.

They also liked to race each other.

Miss Clark and her dog, Zane, lived next door. When Pedro and Ann raced, Zane barked and ran with them on his side of the fence.

One day as Ann petted Zane through the fence, she told Pedro, "I really want a dog. But," she paused, "my brother is allergic, so we can't have one."

"You can come here to see Zane anytime. Miss Clark won't mind," Pedro said while Zane wagged his tail in approval.

The next day Ann and Pedro were surprised to see Miss Clark had broken her leg. Her left leg was in a cast, and she was walking with crutches.

"What happened?" they asked.

Page 3
Miss Clark explained to them, "I slipped and fell down my stairs."

"I'm really good at helping!" said Pedro. "Can we do anything to help?"

"That would be nice," Miss Clark answered.

Pedro and Ann went to Miss Clark's house every afternoon to do odd jobs. They pulled weeds from the yard, and Pedro made sure they got them all. Ann threw Zane's ball to keep the dog busy while Pedro worked.

Time: _____ minutes:seconds

ORAL READING WORDS PER MINUTE, PERCENT OF ACCURACY
Use the student's oral reading time to circle the WPM range.

Word Count: 216

	INTRVN	INSTR	IND	ADV
Minutes:Seconds	3:21 or more	3:20–2:44	2:43–1:58	1:57 or less
WPM	64 or less	65–79	80–110	111 or more

Busy Helpers **30**

Count the number of miscues that are not self-corrected. Circle the percent of accuracy based on the number of miscues.

	INTRVN	INSTR	IND			ADV	
Number of Miscues	12 or more	10–11	8–9	6–7	4–5	1–3	0
Percent of Accuracy	94 or less	95	96	97	98	99	100

- If the student's score falls in a shaded area for either WPM or Accuracy, STOP! Reassess with a lower-level text at another time.

3. COMPREHENSION

TEXT FEATURES and STUDENT PREDICTION

Read aloud the questions/prompts on page 1 of the Student Booklet, and record the student's responses on the same page. Do not give additional prompts. Students do not use the book as you record their responses on the first page of the Student Booklet.

Note: Continue with the assessment if time permits. Otherwise, have the student read the book and complete the Student Booklet at another time.

STUDENT READS AND RESPONDS

All students may use the text to complete pages 2–3 of the Student Booklet.

T: Read the story. When you are finished, write a summary of what you have read and answer the remaining questions in the Student Booklet. If you have questions, please come to me (or raise your hand).

Note: For students who have an Individual Education Plan in place for reading and/or written communication, follow the directions in their plan. You may read aloud the prompts on pages 2 and 3 of the Student Booklet and/or scribe their responses if required. Give <u>no</u> additional prompts.

While the student reads the text independently, complete the Teacher Analysis of Oral Reading on the next page and circle the descriptors on the *DRA2* Continuum that best describe the student's oral reading fluency.

4. TEACHER ANALYSIS

ORAL READING

If the student had 5 or more different miscues, use the information recorded on the Record of Oral Reading to complete the chart.

Student problem-solves words using:	Number of miscues self-corrected: _____
☐ beginning letter(s)/sound(s)	Number of miscues not self-corrected: _____
☐ letter-sound clusters	Number of words told to the student: _____

Student problem-solves words using:	Miscues interfered with meaning:	Miscues included:
☐ blending letters/sounds	☐ never	☐ omissions
☐ onset and rime	☐ at times	☐ insertions
☐ knowledge of spelling patterns (analogies)	☐ often	☐ reversals
☐ syllables		☐ substitutions that were
☐ rereading		☐ visually similar
☐ no observable behaviors		☐ not visually similar

Copy each substitution to help analyze the student's attention to visual information.

e.g., <u>old</u> (substitution)

    odd (text)

Oral Reading Rate: (Optional) Use the formula below to determine the student's exact oral reading rate. Convert the student's reading time to all seconds.

$$216 \text{ (words)} \div \underline{\hspace{1cm}} \text{ total seconds} = \underline{\hspace{1cm}} \text{ WPS} \times 60 = \underline{\hspace{1cm}} \text{ WPM}$$

DRA2 Continuum

- Use the information from the Student Reading Survey and the Student Booklet to circle the descriptors that best describe the student's responses for Reading Engagement and Comprehension.
- Add the circled numbers to obtain a total score for each section.
- Record the total scores at the top of page 1. Record the Comprehension score at the top of page 5 after the colon.

Note: If the Comprehension score is less than 14, administer *DRA2* with a lower-level text.

Busy Helpers **30**

Name/Date _____   Teacher/Grade _____

*DRA*2 CONTINUUM	LEVEL 30		EXTENDING READER	
	INTERVENTION	**INSTRUCTIONAL**	**INDEPENDENT**	**ADVANCED**
Reading Engagement				
Wide Reading	**1** Title(s) below grade level; limited reading experiences and book knowledge	**2** Titles slightly below grade level; rather limited reading experiences	**3** Titles within 2 genres or multiple books within a genre; generally on-grade-level texts	**4** Titles across 3 or more genres; many on- and above-grade-level texts
Self-Assessment/ Goal Setting	**1** No strengths and/or goals	**2** General strength(s) and goal(s) related to the reading process	**3** 2 specific strengths and 2 specific goals related to the reading process	**4** 3 specific strengths and 3 specific goals that reflect a higher level of thinking
Score	2 3	4 5	6 7	8
Oral Reading Fluency				
Expression	**1** Little expression; monotone	**2** Some expression that conveys meaning	**3** Expression reflects mood, pace, and tension at times	**4** Expression reflects mood, pace, and tension most of the time
Phrasing	**1** Mostly word-by-word	**2** Short phrases most of the time; inappropriate pauses	**3** Longer phrases most of the time; heeds most punctuation	**4** Consistently longer, meaningful phrases; heeds all punctuation
Rate	**1** 64 WPM or less	**2** 65–79 WPM	**3** 80–110 WPM	**4** 111 WPM or more
Accuracy	**1** 94% or less	**2** 95%	**3** 96%–98%	**4** 99%–100%
Score	4 5 6	7 8 9 10	11 12 13 14	15 16
Comprehension				
Use of Text Features	**1** Limited or no description of the characters	**2** Partial description of the characters; general statements	**3** Description of each character; includes at least 2 specific details	**4** Description of each character; includes at least 3 specific details
Prediction	**1** Unrelated predictions or no response	**2** At least 1 reasonable prediction related to the text	**3** At least 2 reasonable predictions that go beyond the text read aloud	**4** 3 thoughtful predictions that go beyond the text read aloud
Scaffolded Summary	**1** 1–2 events in own language and/or copied text; may include incorrect information	**2** Partial summary; generally in own language; some important characters/events; may include misinterpretations	**3** Summary in own language; includes important characters, many of the important events, and some details from the beginning, middle, and end	**4** Summary in own language; includes all important characters, events, and details from the beginning, middle, and end
Scaffolded Summary: Vocabulary	**1** General terms or labels; limited understanding of key words/concepts	**2** Some language/ vocabulary from the text; some understanding of key words/concepts	**3** Most language/vocabulary from the text; basic understanding of most key words/concepts	**4** All important language/vocabulary from the text; good understanding of key words/concepts
Literal Comprehension	**1** Incorrect response or no response	**2** Partial response; may include misinterpretation	**3** Accurate response	**4** Accurate response with specific details
Interpretation	**1** Little or no understanding of important text implications	**2** Some understanding of important text implications; no supporting details	**3** Understands important text implications; may include supporting details	**4** Insightful understanding of important text implications with supporting details or rationale
Reflection	**1** Insignificant event; no reason for opinion or no response	**2** Less significant event and/or a general reason for opinion	**3** Significant event <u>and</u> a relevant reason for opinion	**4** Significant event <u>and</u> reason for opinion that reflects higher-level thinking
Score	7 8 9 10 11 12 13	14 15 16 17 18	19 20 21 22 23 24 25	26 27 28

Choose three to five teaching/learning activities on the *DRA*2 Focus for Instruction on the next page.

DRA2 FOCUS FOR INSTRUCTION FOR EXTENDING READERS

READING ENGAGEMENT

Wide Reading
- ☐ Teach student strategies to select appropriately leveled texts for independent reading
- ☐ Introduce student to reading materials from a variety of genres
- ☐ Teach strategies to build reading stamina
- ☐ Create structures and/or routines to support reading at home
- ☐ Develop clear expectations for amount of independent reading
- ☐ Teach student how to use a reading log to monitor book selection and set reading goals
- ☐ Model/teach how to read for different purposes

Self-Assessment/Goal Setting
- ☐ Model and discuss strategies good readers use
- ☐ Help student identify 1–2 reading goals and a plan of action to improve reading
- ☐ Support revision of ongoing reading goals

ORAL READING FLEUNCY

Expression and Phrasing
- ☐ Model and support reading in longer, meaningful phrases with appropriate expression
- ☐ Have student practice appropriate expression with familiar texts
- ☐ Have student participate in choral reading and/or reader's theater
- ☐ Teach student to heed punctuation

Rate
- ☐ Provide materials and time for repeated reading to increase reading rate
- ☐ Teach student to read lower-level and/or familiar texts at an appropriate rate

Accuracy: Word Analysis
- ☐ Support and reinforce self-corrections of miscues
- ☐ Model and support how to take words apart (e.g., onset and rime, syllables) to problem-solve unknown words
- ☐ Teach how to use word chunks and analogies to problem-solve unknown words
- ☐ Provide spelling activities and word sorts to help student recognize patterns in words

COMPREHENSION

Use of Text Features
- ☐ Provide opportunities for student to discuss what he or she knows about the characters based on title and book cover, as well as opening paragraphs and texts read aloud
- ☐ Teach student how to describe characters using information from fiction text features (e.g., title, illustrations, and text)

Prediction
- ☐ Teach student how to make predictions based on title and book cover, as well as opening paragraphs of texts read aloud
- ☐ Model and support using background information to make meaningful predictions

Summary
- ☐ Share and identify characteristics of good summaries
- ☐ Model and co-construct written summaries of texts read aloud
- ☐ Model and support how to distinguish between more important and less important ideas and details
- ☐ Model and support how to write a summary in one's own words
- ☐ Teach student how to use a graphic organizer as an aid to creating a summary
- ☐ Teach student how to identify story elements (e.g., characters, setting, plot)

Literal Comprehension
- ☐ Show student how to use key words to identify specific information from the text
- ☐ Provide opportunities for student to answer and construct literal questions
- ☐ Help student locate and record specific details
- ☐ Teach student how to use graphic organizers to keep track of story information

Interpretation
- ☐ Teach and share examples of inferences
- ☐ Model and teach student how to think about *Why?* questions while and after reading a text
- ☐ Model and teach how to support inferences with examples from the text
- ☐ Give student opportunities to respond to inference questions orally and in writing

Reflection
- ☐ Help student identify important message in a story
- ☐ Provide opportunities to identify and discuss the most important event in a story
- ☐ Demonstrate and teach student how to support opinion with details from the text

Name _____ Date _____

Teacher _____ Grade _____

The teacher reads aloud the prompts/questions and records the student's responses on this Before Reading page only.

BEFORE READING

TEXT FEATURES

Think about the title, the pictures, and what you have read so far. Tell me what you know about Pedro and Ann.

Pedro: _____

_____

Ann: _____

_____

PREDICTION

What are 3 things you think might happen in the rest of this story?

1. _____

_____

_____

2. _____

_____

_____

3. _____

_____

_____

Busy Helpers

AFTER READING

Summary

Write a summary of this story in your own words. Include the important characters, events, and details. You may use the book and the words below to help you write your summary.

In the beginning, _____

_____

_____

Next, _____

_____

_____

Then, _____

_____

_____

After that, _____

_____

_____

In the end, _____

_____

_____

Busy Helpers

Literal Comprehension

List 3 ways that Pedro and Ann helped Miss Clark.

Busy Helpers

Ways Pedro and Ann Helped Miss Clark
1. _____
2. _____
3. _____

Interpretation

Why do you think Miss Clark said to Pedro and Ann that they would do better next time?

_____

_____

_____

Reflection

What do you think is the most important event in this story?

_____

_____

_____

Tell why you think it is important. _____

_____

_____

_____

Reread what you have written to make sure your answers are the way you want them before you hand in your booklet.

Name/Date _____   Teacher/Grade _____

Scores: Reading Engagement ___/8   Oral Reading Fluency ___/16   Comprehension ___/28
Independent Range: 6–7   11–14   19–25

Book Selection   Text selected by: ☐ teacher   ☐ student

1. READING ENGAGEMENT

Ask the student to bring his or her reading record to the conference. If the Student Reading Survey was not completed prior to the assessment conference, read aloud the questions on the survey and record the student's responses.

2. ORAL READING FLUENCY

INTRODUCTION

T: This book is called Tiger's Whirlwind Day. *It is about a girl named Karla who loses her cat Tiger. Please read aloud pages 2 through 3.* Show the student where to stop reading at the ✱.

RECORD OF ORAL READING

Record the student's oral reading behaviors. Note the student's fluency (expression and phrasing). Be sure to time the student's reading.

Page 2

"Quick, Karla, hand me that rope!" Dad yelled, as clouds swept across the sun. "We have to get these trash cans tied down because there's a storm heading this way."

"Where's Tiger, Mom?" asked Karla, handing Dad some rope. "We have to keep him in the house. You know my cat is a scaredy-cat. He doesn't like wind or water."

"I don't know where Tiger is, but I do know the storm's winds will be strong," said Mom. "I'll get the candles and flashlights ready in case the lights go out."

Karla searched for Tiger. She felt the wind pick up and watched the leaves swirl around in the backyard. Then she heard a soft meow under the porch.

"Come on out, Tiger," said Karla. "A dangerous storm is coming this way!" Tiger inched his way out and followed Karla.

Page 3

Dad was gathering up the lawn chairs and table. More clouds blew in as Karla helped Dad carry the chairs into the garage. The sky darkened, and it seemed like the whole world was in a shadow.

Gusts of wind made the rope ladder to Karla's treehouse dance like a puppet. The wind ruffled her hair and rippled Tiger's fur. Karla lifted him in her arms as darker clouds began to roll in. She made it into the house just as the first drops of rain fell.

Time: _____ minutes:seconds

ORAL READING WORDS PER MINUTE, PERCENT OF ACCURACY

Use the student's oral reading time to circle the WPM range.

Word Count: 228

	INTRVN	INSTR	IND	ADV
Minutes:Seconds	3:33 or more	3:32–2:53	2:52–2:04	2:03 or less
WPM	64 or less	65–79	80–110	111 or more

Count the number of miscues that are not self-corrected. Circle the percent of accuracy based on the number of miscues.

	INTRVN	INSTR	IND			ADV	
Number of Miscues	13 or more	11–12	8–10	6–7	4–5	1–3	0
Percent of Accuracy	94 or less	95	96	97	98	99	100

• If the student's score falls in a shaded area for either WPM or Accuracy, STOP! Reassess with a lower-level text at another time.

Tiger's Whirlwind Day **30**

3. COMPREHENSION

TEXT FEATURES and STUDENT PREDICTION

Read aloud the questions/prompts on page 1 of the Student Booklet, and record the student's responses on the same page. Do not give additional prompts. Students do not use the book as you record their responses on the first page of the Student Booklet.

Note: Continue with the assessment if time permits. Otherwise, have the student read the book and complete the Student Booklet at another time.

STUDENT READS AND RESPONDS

All students may use the text to complete pages 2–3 of in the Student Booklet.

T: Read the story. When you are finished, write a summary of what you have read and answer the remaining questions in the Student Booklet. If you have questions, please come to me (or raise your hand).

Note: For the students who have an Individual Education Plan in place for reading and/or written communication, follow the directions in their plan. You may read aloud the prompts on pages 2 and 3 of the Student Booklet and/or scribe their responses if required. Give <u>no</u> additional prompts.

While the student reads the text independently, complete the Teacher Analysis of Oral Reading on the next page and circle the descriptors on the *DRA2* Continuum that best describe the student's oral reading fluency.

Tiger's Whirlwind Day **30**

4. TEACHER ANALYSIS

ORAL READING

If the student had 5 or more miscues, use the information recorded on the Record of Oral Reading to complete the chart.

Student problem-solves words using:

- ☐ beginning letter(s)/sound(s)
- ☐ letter-sound clusters
- ☐ blending letters/sounds
- ☐ onset and rime
- ☐ knowledge of spelling patterns (analogies)
- ☐ syllables
- ☐ rereading
- ☐ no observable behaviors

Number of miscues self-corrected: _____
Number of miscues not self-corrected: _____
Number of words told to the student: _____

Miscues interfered with meaning:

- ☐ never
- ☐ at times
- ☐ often

Miscues included:

- ☐ omissions
- ☐ insertions
- ☐ reversals
- ☐ substitutions that were
    - ☐ visually similar
    - ☐ not visually similar

Copy each substitution to help analyze the student's attention to visual information.
e.g., <u>getting</u> (substitution)
        gathering (text)

Oral Reading Rate: (Optional) Use the formula below to determine the student's exact oral reading rate. Convert the student's reading time to all seconds.

$$228 \text{ (words)} \div \underline{\hspace{1cm}} \text{ total seconds} = \underline{\hspace{1cm}} \text{ WPS} \times 60 = \underline{\hspace{1cm}} \text{ WPM}$$

*DRA*2 Continuum

- Use the information from the Student Reading Survey and the Student Booklet to circle the descriptors that best describe the student's responses for Reading Engagement and Comprehension.
- Add the circled numbers to obtain a total score for each section.
- Record the total scores at the top of page 1. Record the Comprehension score at the top of page 5 after the colon.

Note: If the Comprehension score is less than 14, administer *DRA*2 with a lower-level text.

Name/Date _____   Teacher/Grade _____

*DRA*2 CONTINUUM	LEVEL 30		EXTENDING READER	
	INTERVENTION	**INSTRUCTIONAL**	**INDEPENDENT**	**ADVANCED**
Reading Engagement				
Wide Reading	**1** Title(s) below grade level; limited reading experiences and book knowledge	**2** Titles slightly below grade level; rather limited reading experiences	**3** Titles within 2 genres or multiple books within a genre; generally on-grade-level texts	**4** Titles across 3 or more genres; many on- and above-grade-level texts
Self-Assessment/ Goal Setting	**1** No strengths and/or goals	**2** General strength(s) and goal(s) related to the reading process	**3** 2 specific strengths and 2 specific goals related to the reading process	**4** 3 specific strengths and 3 specific goals that reflect a higher level of thinking
Score	2 3	4 5	6 7	8
Oral Reading Fluency				
Expression	**1** Little expression; monotone	**2** Some expression that conveys meaning	**3** Expression reflects mood, pace, and tension at times	**4** Expression reflects mood, pace, and tension most of the time
Phrasing	**1** Mostly word-by-word	**2** Short phrases most of the time; inappropriate pauses	**3** Longer phrases most of the time; heeds most punctuation	**4** Consistently longer, meaningful phrases; heeds all punctuation
Rate	**1** 64 WPM or less	**2** 65–79 WPM	**3** 80–110 WPM	**4** 111 WPM or more
Accuracy	**1** 94% or less	**2** 95%	**3** 96%–98%	**4** 99%–100%
Score	4 5 6	7 8 9 10	11 12 13 14	15 16
Comprehension				
Use of Text Features	**1** Limited or no description of the characters	**2** Partial description of the characters; general statements	**3** Description of each character; includes at least 2 specific details	**4** Description of each character; includes at least 3 specific details
Prediction	**1** Unrelated predictions or no response	**2** At least 1 reasonable prediction related to the text	**3** At least 2 reasonable predictions that go beyond the text read aloud	**4** 3 thoughtful predictions that go beyond the text read aloud
Scaffolded Summary	**1** 1–2 events in own language and/or copied text; may include incorrect information	**2** Partial summary; generally in own language; some important characters/events; may include misinterpretations	**3** Summary in own language; includes important characters, many of the important events, and some details from the beginning, middle, and end	**4** Summary in own language; includes all important characters, events, and details from the beginning, middle, and end
Scaffolded Summary: Vocabulary	**1** General terms or labels; limited understanding of key words/concepts	**2** Some language/ vocabulary from the text; some understanding of key words/concepts	**3** Most language/vocabulary from the text; basic understanding of most key words/concepts	**4** All important language/ vocabulary from the text; good understanding of key words/concepts
Literal Comprehension	**1** Incorrect response or no response	**2** Partial response; may include misinterpretation	**3** Accurate response	**4** Accurate response with specific details
Interpretation	**1** Little or no understanding of important text implications	**2** Some understanding of important text implications; no supporting details	**3** Understands important text implications; may include supporting details	**4** Insightful understanding of important text implications with supporting details or rationale
Reflection	**1** Insignificant event; no reason for opinion or no response	**2** Less significant event and/or a general reason for opinion	**3** Significant event <u>and</u> a relevant reason for opinion	**4** Significant event <u>and</u> reason for opinion that reflects higher-level thinking
Score	7 8 9 10 11 12 13	14 15 16 17 18	19 20 21 22 23 24 25	26 27 28

Choose three to five teaching/learning activities on the *DRA*2 Focus for Instruction on the next page.

Tiger's Whirlwind Day **30**

DRA2 FOCUS FOR INSTRUCTION FOR EXTENDING READERS

READING ENGAGEMENT
Wide Reading
- ☐ Teach student strategies to select appropriately leveled texts for independent reading
- ☐ Introduce student to reading materials from a variety of genres
- ☐ Teach strategies to build reading stamina
- ☐ Create structures and/or routines to support reading at home
- ☐ Develop clear expectations for amount of independent reading
- ☐ Teach student how to use a reading log to monitor book selection and set reading goals
- ☐ Model/teach how to read for different purposes

Self-Assessment/Goal Setting
- ☐ Model and discuss strategies good readers use
- ☐ Help student identify 1–2 reading goals and a plan of action to improve reading
- ☐ Support revision of ongoing reading goals

ORAL READING FLUENCY
Expression and Phrasing
- ☐ Model and support reading in longer, meaningful phrases with appropriate expression
- ☐ Have student practice appropriate expression with familiar texts
- ☐ Have student participate in choral reading and/or reader's theater
- ☐ Teach student to heed punctuation

Rate
- ☐ Provide materials and time for repeated reading to increase reading rate
- ☐ Teach student to read lower-level and/or familiar texts at an appropriate rate

Accuracy: Word Analysis
- ☐ Support and reinforce self-corrections of miscues
- ☐ Model and support how to take words apart (e.g., onset and rime, syllables) to problem-solve unknown words
- ☐ Teach how to use word chunks and analogies to problem-solve unknown words
- ☐ Provide spelling activities and word sorts to help student recognize patterns in words

COMPREHENSION
Use of Text Features
- ☐ Provide opportunities for student to discuss what he or she knows about the characters based on title and book cover, as well as opening paragraphs and texts read aloud
- ☐ Teach student how to describe characters, using information from fiction text features (e.g., title, illustrations, and text)

Prediction
- ☐ Teach student how to make predictions based on title and book cover, as well as opening paragraphs of texts read aloud
- ☐ Model and support using background information to make meaningful predictions

Summary
- ☐ Share and identify characteristics of good summaries
- ☐ Model and co-construct written summaries of texts read aloud
- ☐ Model and support how to distinguish between more important and less important ideas and details
- ☐ Model and support how to write a summary in one's own words
- ☐ Teach student how to use a graphic organizer as an aid to creating a summary
- ☐ Teach student how to identify story elements (e.g., characters, setting, plot)

Literal Comprehension
- ☐ Show student how to use key words to identify specific information from the text
- ☐ Provide opportunities for student to answer and construct literal questions
- ☐ Help student locate and record specific details
- ☐ Teach student how to use graphic organizers to keep track of story information

Interpretation
- ☐ Teach and share examples of inferences
- ☐ Model and teach student how to think about *Why?* questions while and after reading a text
- ☐ Model and teach how to support inferences with examples from the text
- ☐ Give student opportunities to respond to inference questions orally and in writing

Reflection
- ☐ Help student identify important message in a story
- ☐ Provide opportunities to identify and discuss the most important event in a story
- ☐ Demonstrate and teach student how to support opinion with details from the text

Name _____   Date _____

Teacher _____   Grade _____

The teacher reads aloud the prompts/questions and records the student's responses on this Before Reading page only.

BEFORE READING

TEXT FEATURES

Think about the title, the pictures you have seen, and what you have read so far. Tell me what you know about Karla and Tiger.

Karla: _____

_____

Tiger: _____

_____

PREDICTION

What are 3 things you think might happen in the rest of this story?

1. _____

_____

_____

2. _____

_____

_____

3. _____

_____

_____

Tiger's Whirlwind Day

AFTER READING

Summary

Write a summary of this story in your own words. Include the important characters, events, and details. You may use the book and the words below to help you write your summary.

In the beginning, _____

_____

_____

Next, _____

_____

_____

Then, _____

_____

_____

After that, _____

_____

_____

In the end, _____

_____

_____

Literal Comprehension

List 3 things that happened when something crashed against Karla's house during the storm.

The crash caused . . .

1. _____

2. _____

3. _____

Interpretation

Why do you think Karla said Tiger had a whirlwind of a day?

_____

_____

_____

Reflection

What do you think is the most important event in this story?

_____

_____

_____

Tell why you think it is important. _____

_____

_____

_____

Reread what you have written to make sure your answers are the way you want them before you hand in your booklet.

Tiger's Whirlwind Day

Name/Date _____   Teacher/Grade _____

Scores: Reading Engagement ___/8   Oral Reading Fluency ___/16   Comprehension ___/28
Independent Range: 6–7   11–14   19–25

Book Selection   Text selected by: ☐ teacher   ☐ student

1. READING ENGAGEMENT

Ask the student to bring his or her reading record to the conference. If the Student Reading Survey was not completed prior to the assessment conference, read aloud the questions on the survey and record the student's responses.

2. ORAL READING FLUENCY

INTRODUCTION

T: *In this story,* The Mystery at the Mays' House, *Zoe and Sam Mays are puzzled because things keep mysteriously disappearing in their house. Please read aloud pages 3 and 4.* Show the student where to stop reading at the ✱.

RECORD OF ORAL READING

Record the student's oral reading behaviors. Note the student's fluency (expression and phrasing). Be sure to time the student's reading.

Page 3

"Wait a minute!" said Zoe. "Where is my necklace?"

She looked on and under her dresser, but she couldn't find her necklace with a silver heart. Today she had a spelling test, and Zoe liked wearing her heart necklace on test days. She liked holding the heart with her right hand while she took the test with her left hand.

Zoe's twin brother, Sam, stopped by her room. "What are you looking for?" he asked.

"My heart necklace is missing," Zoe said.

"Ha-ha, you have no heart!" Sam teased. He and Zoe were very close, but they liked teasing each other.

"Very funny," said Zoe.

"I'll help you look," said Sam, but the twins didn't find the heart before the school bus came.

Page 4

The next day Zoe wanted to wear her bracelet with a silver horse, but she couldn't find it anywhere.

"What did you lose now?" asked Sam when he saw Zoe looking under her desk.

Zoe bumped her head as she got up. "Ow!" she said. "I didn't lose anything. My bracelet with the silver horse is missing."

"Maybe it galloped off to find your heart!" Sam teased.

Zoe wasn't in a good mood. "If you took the bracelet as a joke," she said, "it's not funny! It was a gift from Aunt Clara."

Time: _____ minutes:seconds

ORAL READING WORDS PER MINUTE, PERCENT OF ACCURACY

Use the student's oral reading time to circle the WPM range.

Word Count: 216

	INTRVN	INSTR	IND	ADV
Minutes:Seconds	3:21 or more	3:20–2:44	2:43–1:53	1:52 or less
WPM	64 or less	65–79	80–115	116 or more

Count the number of miscues that are not self-corrected. Circle the percent of accuracy based on the number of miscues.

	INTRVN	INSTR	IND			ADV	
Number of Miscues	12 or more	10–11	8–9	6–7	4–5	1–3	0
Percent of Accuracy	94 or less	95	96	97	98	99	100

- If the student's score falls in a shaded area for either WPM or Accuracy, STOP! Reassess with a lower-level text at another time.

3. COMPREHENSION

TEXT FEATURES and STUDENT PREDICTION

Read aloud the questions/prompts on page 1 of the Student Booklet, and record the student's responses on the same page. Do not give additional prompts. Students do not use the book as you record their responses on the first page of the Student Booklet.

Note: Continue with the assessment if time permits. Otherwise, have the student read the book and complete the Student Booklet at another time.

STUDENT READS AND RESPONDS

All students may use the text to complete pages 2–3 of the Student Booklet.

T: Read the story. When you are finished, write a summary of what you have read and answer the remaining questions in the Student Booklet. If you have questions, please come to me (or raise your hand).

Note: For students who have an Individual Education Plan in place for reading and/or written communication, follow the directions in their plan. You may read aloud the prompts on pages 2 and 3 of the Student Booklet and/or scribe their responses if required. Give <u>no</u> additional prompts.

While the student reads the text independently, complete the Teacher Analysis of Oral Reading on the next page and circle the descriptors on the *DRA2* Continuum that best describe the student's oral reading fluency.

4. TEACHER ANALYSIS

ORAL READING

If the student had 5 or more different miscues, use the information recorded on the Record of Oral Reading to complete the chart below.

Student problem-solves words using:

☐ beginning letter(s)/sound(s)

☐ letter-sound clusters

☐ blending letters/sounds

☐ onset and rime

☐ knowledge of spelling patterns
   (analogies)

☐ syllables

☐ rereading

☐ no observable behaviors

Number of miscues self-corrected: _____

Number of miscues not self-corrected: _____

Number of words told to the student: _____

Miscues interfered with meaning:

☐ never

☐ at times

☐ often

Miscues included:

☐ omissions

☐ insertions

☐ reversals

☐ substitutions that were

    ☐ visually similar

    ☐ not visually similar

Copy each substitution to help analyze the student's attention to visual information.

e.g., <u>gulped</u> (substitution)
    galloped (text)

Oral Reading Rate: (Optional) Use the formula below to determine the student's exact oral reading rate. Convert the student's reading time to all seconds.

$$216 \text{ (words)} \div \underline{\hspace{1cm}} \text{ total seconds} = \underline{\hspace{1cm}} \text{ WPS} \times 60 = \underline{\hspace{1cm}} \text{ WPM}$$

DRA2 Continuum

- Use the information from the Student Reading Survey and the Student Booklet to circle the descriptors that best describe the student's responses for Reading Engagement and Comprehension.
- Add the circled numbers to obtain a total score for each section.
- Record the total scores at the top of page 1. Record the Comprehension score at the top of page 5 after the colon.

Note: If the Comprehension score is less than 14, administer *DRA2* with a lower-level text.

Name/Date _____ Teacher/Grade _____

DRA2 CONTINUUM	LEVEL 34		EXTENDING READER	
	INTERVENTION	**INSTRUCTIONAL**	**INDEPENDENT**	**ADVANCED**
Reading Engagement				
Wide Reading	**1** Title(s) below grade level; limited reading experiences and book knowledge	**2** Titles slightly below grade level; rather limited reading experiences	**3** Titles within 2 genres or multiple books within a genre; generally on-grade-level texts	**4** Titles across 3 or more genres; many on- and above-grade-level texts
Self-Assessment/ Goal Setting	**1** No strengths and/or goals	**2** General strength(s) and goal(s) related to the reading process	**3** 2 specific strengths and 2 specific goals related to the reading process	**4** 3 specific strengths and 3 specific goals that reflect a higher level of thinking
Score	2 3	4 5	6 7	8
Oral Reading Fluency				
Expression	**1** Little expression; monotone	**2** Some expression that conveys meaning	**3** Expression reflects mood, pace, and tension at times	**4** Expression reflects mood, pace, and tension most of the time
Phrasing	**1** Mostly word-by-word	**2** Short phrases most of the time; inappropriate pauses	**3** Longer phrases most of the time; heeds most punctuation	**4** Consistently longer, meaningful phrases; heeds all punctuation
Rate	**1** 64 WPM or less	**2** 65–79 WPM	**3** 80–115 WPM	**4** 116 WPM or more
Accuracy	**1** 94% or less	**2** 95%	**3** 96%–98%	**4** 99%–100%
Score	4 5 6	7 8 9 10	11 12 13 14	15 16
Comprehension				
Use of Text Features	**1** Limited or no description of the characters	**2** Partial description of the characters; general statements	**3** Description of each character; includes at least 2 specific details	**4** Description of each character; includes at least 3 specific details
Prediction	**1** Unrelated predictions or no response	**2** At least 1 reasonable prediction related to the text	**3** At least 2 reasonable predictions that go beyond the text read aloud	**4** 3 thoughtful predictions that go beyond the text read aloud
Scaffolded Summary	**1** 1–2 events in own language and/or copied text; may include incorrect information	**2** Partial summary; generally in own language; some important characters/events; may include misinterpretations	**3** Summary in own language; includes important characters, many of the important events, and some details from the beginning, middle, and end	**4** Summary in own language; includes all important characters, events, and details from the beginning, middle, and end
Scaffolded Summary: Vocabulary	**1** General terms or labels; limited understanding of key words/concepts	**2** Some language/ vocabulary from the text; some understanding of key words/concepts	**3** Most language/ vocabulary from the text; basic understanding of most key words/concepts	**4** All important language/vocabulary from the text; good understanding of key words/concepts
Literal Comprehension	**1** Incorrect response or no response	**2** Partial response; may include misinterpretation	**3** Accurate response	**4** Accurate response with specific details
Interpretation	**1** Little or no understanding of important text implications	**2** Some understanding of important text implications; no supporting details	**3** Understands important text implications; may include supporting details	**4** Insightful understanding of important text implications with supporting details or rationale
Reflection	**1** Insignificant event; no reason for opinion or no response	**2** Less significant event and/or a general reason for opinion	**3** Significant event and a relevant reason for opinion	**4** Significant event and reason for opinion that reflects higher-level thinking
Score	7 8 9 10 11 12 13	14 15 16 17 18	19 20 21 22 23 24 25	26 27 28

Choose three to five teaching/learning activities on the *DRA2* Focus for Instruction on the next page.

The Mystery at the Mays' House **34**

DRA2 FOCUS FOR INSTRUCTION FOR EXTENDING READERS

READING ENGAGEMENT
Wide Reading
- ☐ Teach student strategies to select appropriately leveled texts for independent reading
- ☐ Introduce student to reading materials from a variety of genres
- ☐ Teach strategies to build reading stamina
- ☐ Create structures and/or routines to support reading at home
- ☐ Develop clear expectations for amount of independent reading
- ☐ Teach student how to use a reading log to monitor book selection and set reading goals
- ☐ Model/teach how to read for different purposes

Self-Assessment/Goal Setting
- ☐ Model and discuss strategies good readers use
- ☐ Help student identify 1–2 reading goals and a plan of action to improve reading
- ☐ Support revision of ongoing reading goals

ORAL READING FLUENCY
Expression and Phrasing
- ☐ Model and support reading in longer, meaningful phrases with appropriate expression
- ☐ Have student practice appropriate expression with familiar texts
- ☐ Have student participate in choral reading and/or reader's theater
- ☐ Teach student to heed punctuation

Rate
- ☐ Provide materials and time for repeated reading to increase reading rate
- ☐ Teach student to read lower-level and/or familiar texts at an appropriate rate

Accuracy: Word Analysis
- ☐ Support and reinforce self-corrections of miscues
- ☐ Model and support how to take words apart (e.g., onset and rime, syllables) to problem-solve unknown words
- ☐ Teach how to use word chunks and analogies to problem-solve unknown words
- ☐ Provide spelling activities and word sorts to help student recognize patterns in words

COMPREHENSION
Use of Text Features
- ☐ Provide opportunities for student to discuss what he or she knows about the characters based on title and book cover, as well as opening paragraphs and texts read aloud
- ☐ Teach student how to describe characters, using information from fiction text features (e.g., title, illustrations, and text)

Prediction
- ☐ Teach student how to make predictions based on title and book cover, as well as opening paragraphs of texts read aloud
- ☐ Model and support using background information to make meaningful predictions

Summary
- ☐ Share and identify characteristics of good summaries
- ☐ Model and co-construct written summaries of texts read aloud
- ☐ Model and support how to distinguish between more important and less important ideas and details
- ☐ Model and support how to write a summary in one's own words
- ☐ Teach student how to use a graphic organizer as an aid to creating a summary
- ☐ Teach student how to identify story elements (e.g., characters, setting, plot)

Literal Comprehension
- ☐ Show student how to use key words to identify specific information from the text
- ☐ Provide opportunities for student to answer and construct literal questions
- ☐ Help student locate and record specific details
- ☐ Teach student how to use graphic organizers to keep track of story information

Interpretation
- ☐ Teach and share examples of inferences
- ☐ Model and teach student how to think about *Why?* questions while and after reading a text
- ☐ Model and teach how to support inferences with examples from the text
- ☐ Give student opportunities to respond to inference questions orally and in writing

Reflection
- ☐ Help student identify important message in a story
- ☐ Provide opportunities to identify and discuss the most important event in a story
- ☐ Demonstrate and teach student how to support opinion with details from the text

The Mystery at the Mays' House 34

Name _____   Date _____

Teacher _____   Grade _____

The teacher reads aloud the prompts/questions and records the student's responses on this Before Reading page only.

BEFORE READING

TEXT FEATURES

Think about the title, the pictures you have seen, and what you have read so far. Tell me what you know about Zoe and Sam.

Zoe: _____

_____

Sam: _____

_____

PREDICTION

What are 3 things you think might happen in the rest of this story?

1. _____

_____

_____

2. _____

_____

_____

3. _____

_____

AFTER READING

Summary

Write a summary of this story in your own words. Include the important characters, events, and details. You may use the book and the words below to help you write your summary.

In the beginning, _____

_____

_____

Next, _____

_____

_____

Then, _____

_____

_____

After that, _____

_____

_____

In the end, _____

_____

_____

Literal Comprehension

List 2 things that Zoe and Sam were each missing.

Zoe	Sam
1. _____	1. _____
2. _____	2. _____

Interpretation

Why do you think Sam and Zoe did not suspect the cat?

_____

_____

_____

Reflection

What do you think is the most important event in this story?

_____

_____

_____

Tell why you think it is important._____

_____

_____

_____

Reread what you have written to make sure your answers are the way you want them before you hand in your booklet.

Name/Date _____   Teacher/Grade _____

Scores: Reading Engagement ___/8   Oral Reading Fluency ___/16   Comprehension ___/28
Independent Range: 6–7   11–14   19–25

Book Selection   Text selected by: ☐ teacher   ☐ student

1. READING ENGAGEMENT

Ask the student to bring his or her reading record to the conference. If the Student Reading Survey was not completed prior to the assessment conference, read aloud the questions on the survey and record the student's responses.

2. ORAL READING FLUENCY

INTRODUCTION

T: Have you ever felt angry or let down because you had to go somewhere you didn't want to go? This happens to Noah in Summer Discovery. *Please read aloud page 3.* Show the student where to stop reading at the ✱.

RECORD OF ORAL READING

Record the student's oral reading behaviors. Note the student's fluency (expression and phrasing). Be sure to time the student's reading.

Page 3

Noah opened his lunch box. He found the note from his mom. Even though he enjoyed finding his mom's notes, he made sure the other kids didn't see it. He didn't know how they felt about getting notes.

"Happy Last Day of School!" the note read. "I love you, Mom."

The last couple of months had been hard at Noah's house, but summer vacation was always great. It was something he could count on. He had time to play with friends and to go to the pool.

Noah was looking forward to working on the rock collection he'd started. He had some great samples already. He hoped to find a piece of peacock ore— all red, green, and purple. That was his goal.

When Noah got home later that day, his mom was still at work. After Noah's dad had died, she had started working at the hospital. It was an okay job, but sometimes she had to work late.

There was another note next to his snack. It read, "I have something exciting to tell you! Go next door and play with Jake until I come home. Love, Mom."

During dinner that night, Mom said that she had talked with his grandparents, and they had invited him to spend the summer with them.

Time: _____ minutes:seconds

ORAL READING WORDS PER MINUTE, PERCENT OF ACCURACY

Use the student's oral reading time to circle the WPM range.

Word Count: 214

	INTRVN	INSTR	IND	ADV
Minutes:Seconds	3:20 or more	3:19–2:42	2:41–1:52	1:51 or less
WPM	64 or less	65–79	80–115	116 or more

Count the number of miscues that are not self-corrected. Circle the percent of accuracy based on the number of miscues.

	INTRVN	INSTR	IND			ADV	
Number of Miscues	12 or more	10–11	8–9	6–7	4–5	1–3	0
Percent of Accuracy	94 or less	95	96	97	98	99	100

• If the student's score falls in a shaded area for either WPM or Accuracy, STOP! Reassess with a lower-level text at another time.

3. COMPREHENSION

TEXT FEATURES and STUDENT PREDICTION

Read aloud the questions/prompts on page 1 of the Student Booklet, and record the student's responses on the same page. Do not give additional prompts. Students do not use the book as you record their responses on the first page of the Student Booklet.

Note: Continue with the assessment if time permits. Otherwise, have the student read the book and complete the Student Booklet at another time.

STUDENT READS AND RESPONDS

All students may use the text to complete pages 2–3 of the Student Booklet.

T: Read the story. When you are finished, write a summary of what you have read and answer the remaining questions in the Student Booklet. If you have questions, please come to me (or raise your hand).

Note: For students who have an Individual Education Plan in place for reading and/or written communication, follow the directions in their plan. You may read aloud the prompts on pages 2 and 3 of the Student Booklet and/or scribe their responses if required. Give <u>no</u> additional prompts.

While the student reads the text independently, complete the Teacher Analysis of Oral Reading on the next page and circle the descriptors on the *DRA2* Continuum that best describe the student's oral reading fluency.

4. TEACHER ANALYSIS

ORAL READING

If the student had 5 or more different miscues, use the information recorded on the Record of Oral Reading to complete the chart below.

Student problem-solves words using:	Number of miscues self-corrected: _____	
☐ beginning letter(s)/sound(s)	Number of miscues not self-corrected: _____	
☐ letter-sound clusters	Number of words told to the student: _____	
☐ blending letters/sounds	**Miscues interfered with meaning:**	**Miscues included:**
☐ onset and rime	☐ never	☐ omissions
☐ knowledge of spelling patterns (analogies)	☐ at times	☐ insertions
☐ syllables	☐ often	☐ reversals
☐ rereading		☐ substitutions that were
☐ no observable behaviors		☐ visually similar
		☐ not visually similar

Copy each substitution to help analyze the student's attention to visual information.

e.g., <u>not</u> (substitution)

   note (text)

Oral Reading Rate: (Optional) Use the formula below to determine the student's exact oral reading rate. Convert the student's reading time to all seconds.

214 (words) ÷ _____ total seconds = _____ WPS × 60 = _____ WPM

*DRA*2 Continuum

- Use the information from the Student Reading Survey and the Student Booklet to circle the descriptors that best describe the student's responses for Reading Engagement and Comprehension.
- Add the circled numbers to obtain a total score for each section.
- Record the total scores at the top of page 1. Record the Comprehension score at the top of page 5 after the colon.

Note: If the Comprehension score is less than 14, administer *DRA*2 with a lower-level text.

Name/Date _____ Teacher/Grade _____

*DRA*2 CONTINUUM	LEVEL 34		EXTENDING READER	
	INTERVENTION	**INSTRUCTIONAL**	**INDEPENDENT**	**ADVANCED**
Reading Engagement				
Wide Reading	1 Title(s) below grade level; limited reading experiences and book knowledge	2 Titles slightly below grade level; rather limited reading experiences	3 Titles within 2 genres or multiple books within a genre; generally on-grade-level texts	4 Titles across 3 or more genres; many on- and above-grade-level texts
Self-Assessment/ Goal Setting	1 No strengths and/or goals	2 General strength(s) and goal(s) related to the reading process	3 2 specific strengths and 2 specific goals related to the reading process	4 3 specific strengths <u>and</u> 3 specific goals that reflect a higher level of thinking
Score	2 3	4 5	6 7	8
2. Oral Reading Fluency				
Expression	1 Little expression; monotone	2 Some expression that conveys meaning	3 Expression reflects mood, pace, and tension at times	4 Expression reflects mood, pace, and tension most of the time
Phrasing	1 Mostly word-by-word	2 Short phrases most of the time; inappropriate pauses	3 Longer phrases most of the time; heeds most punctuation	4 Consistently longer, meaningful phrases; heeds all punctuation
Rate	1 64 WPM or less	2 65–79 WPM	3 80–115 WPM	4 116 WPM or more
Accuracy	1 94% or less	2 95%	3 96%–98%	4 99%–100%
Score	4 5 6	7 8 9 10	11 12 13 14	15 16
Comprehension				
Use of Text Features	1 Limited or no description of the characters	2 Partial description of the characters; general statements	3 Description of each character; includes at least 2 specific details	4 Description of each character; includes at least 3 specific details
Prediction	1 Unrelated predictions or no response	2 At least 1 reasonable prediction related to the text	3 At least 2 reasonable predictions that go beyond the text read aloud	4 3 thoughtful predictions that go beyond the text read aloud
Scaffolded Summary	1 1–2 events in own language and/or copied text; may include incorrect information	2 Partial summary; generally in own language; some important characters/events; may include misinterpretations	3 Summary in own language; includes important characters, many of the important events, and some details from the beginning, middle, and end	4 Summary in own language; includes all important characters, events, and details from the beginning, middle, and end
Scaffolded Summary: Vocabulary	1 General terms or labels; limited understanding of key words/concepts	2 Some language/ vocabulary from the text; some understanding of key words/concepts	3 Most language/ vocabulary from the text; basic understanding of most key words/concepts	4 All important language/vocabulary from the text; good understanding of key words/concepts
Literal Comprehension	1 Incorrect response or no response	2 Partial response; may include misinterpretation	3 Accurate response	4 Accurate response with specific details
Interpretation	1 Little or no understanding of important text implications	2 Some understanding of important text implications; no supporting details	3 Understands important text implications; may include supporting details	4 Insightful understanding of important text implications with supporting details or rationale
Reflection	1 Insignificant event; no reason for opinion or no response	2 Less significant event and/or a general reason for opinion	3 Significant event <u>and</u> a relevant reason for opinion	4 Significant event <u>and</u> reason for opinion that reflects higher-level thinking
Score	7 8 9 10 11 12 13	14 15 16 17 18	19 20 21 22 23 24 25	26 27 28

Choose three to five teaching/learning activities on the *DRA*2 Focus for Instruction on the next page.

DRA2 FOCUS FOR INSTRUCTION FOR EXTENDING READERS

READING ENGAGEMENT

Wide Reading
- ☐ Teach student strategies to select appropriately leveled texts for independent reading
- ☐ Introduce student to reading materials from a variety of genres
- ☐ Teach strategies to build reading stamina
- ☐ Create structures and/or routines to support reading at home
- ☐ Develop clear expectations for amount of independent reading
- ☐ Teach student how to use a reading log to monitor book selection and set reading goals
- ☐ Model/teach how to read for different purposes

Self-Assessment/Goal Setting
- ☐ Model and discuss strategies good readers use
- ☐ Help student identify 1–2 reading goals and a plan of action to improve reading
- ☐ Support revision of ongoing reading goals

ORAL READING FLUENCY

Expression and Phrasing
- ☐ Model and support reading in longer, meaningful phrases with appropriate expression
- ☐ Have student practice appropriate expression with familiar texts
- ☐ Have student participate in choral reading and/or reader's theater
- ☐ Teach student to heed punctuation

Rate
- ☐ Provide materials and time for repeated reading to increase reading rate
- ☐ Teach student to read lower-level and/or familiar texts at an appropriate rate

Accuracy: Word Analysis
- ☐ Support and reinforce self-corrections of miscues
- ☐ Model and support how to take words apart (e.g., onset and rime, syllables) to problem-solve unknown words
- ☐ Teach how to use word chunks and analogies to problem-solve unknown words
- ☐ Provide spelling activities and word sorts to help student recognize patterns in words

COMPREHENSION

Use of Text Features
- ☐ Provide opportunities for student to discuss what he or she knows about the characters based on title and book cover, as well as opening paragraphs and texts read aloud
- ☐ Teach student how to describe characters, using information from fiction text features (e.g., title, illustrations, and text)

Prediction
- ☐ Teach student how to make predictions based on title and book cover, as well as opening paragraphs of texts read aloud
- ☐ Model and support using background information to make meaningful predictions

Summary
- ☐ Share and identify characteristics of good summaries
- ☐ Model and co-construct written summaries of texts read aloud
- ☐ Model and support how to distinguish between more important and less important ideas and details
- ☐ Model and support how to write a summary in one's own words
- ☐ Teach student how to use a graphic organizer as an aid to creating a summary
- ☐ Teach student how to identify story elements (e.g., characters, setting, plot)

Literal Comprehension
- ☐ Show student how to use key words to identify specific information from the text
- ☐ Provide opportunities for student to answer and construct literal questions
- ☐ Help student locate and record specific details
- ☐ Teach student how to use graphic organizers to keep track of story information

Interpretation
- ☐ Teach and share examples of inferences
- ☐ Model and teach student how to think about *Why?* questions while and after reading a text
- ☐ Model and teach how to support inferences with examples from the text
- ☐ Give student opportunities to respond to inference questions orally and in writing

Reflection
- ☐ Help student identify the important message in a story
- ☐ Provide opportunities to identify and discuss the most important event in a story
- ☐ Demonstrate and teach student how to support opinion with details from the text

Name _____ Date _____

Teacher _____ Grade _____

The teacher reads aloud the prompts/questions and records the student's responses on this Before Reading page only.

BEFORE READING

TEXT FEATURES

Think about the title, the pictures you have seen, and what you have read so far. Tell me what you know about Noah and his mom.

Noah: _____

_____

Noah's Mom: _____

_____

PREDICTION

What are 3 things you think might happen in the rest of this story?

1. _____

_____

_____

2. _____

_____

_____

3. _____

_____

_____

AFTER READING

Summary

Write a summary of this story in your own words. Include the important characters, events, and details. You may use the book and the words below to help you write your summary.

In the beginning, _____

_____

_____

Next, _____

_____

_____

Then, _____

_____

_____

After that, _____

_____

_____

In the end, _____

_____

_____

Literal Comprehension

List 3 things that Noah thought about the detective stories Gramps found in the attic.

The Detective Stories
I. _____
2. _____
3. _____

Interpretation

What do you think Noah learned? _____

_____

_____

Reflection

What do you think is the most important event in this story?

_____

_____

Tell why you think it is important. _____

_____

_____

_____

Reread what you have written to make sure your answers are the way you want them before you hand in your booklet.

Name/Date _____   Teacher/Grade _____

Scores: Reading Engagement ___/8   Oral Reading Fluency ___/16   Comprehension ___/28
Independent Range: 6–7   11–14   19–25

Book Selection   Text selected by: ☐ teacher   ☐ student

1. READING ENGAGEMENT

Ask the student to bring his or her reading record to the conference. If the Student Reading Survey was not completed prior to the assessment conference, read aloud the questions on the survey and record the student's responses.

2. ORAL READING FLUENCY

INTRODUCTION

*T: **This book is called** Mae Jemison: Shooting for the Stars. **It is a biography about a woman who wanted to be an astronaut. Please read aloud pages 2 through 4.** Show the student where to stop reading at the ✱.*

RECORD OF ORAL READING

Record the student's oral reading behaviors. Note the student's fluency (expression and phrasing). Be sure to time the student's reading.

Page 2

Mae's Childhood

Lots of little hands waved high in the air. The children in this kindergarten class in Chicago couldn't wait to share what they wanted to be when they grew up. One little girl with short brown hair said that she wanted to be a scientist. The teacher looked very surprised. She asked the girl if she meant a nurse. The young girl shook her head "no." She put her hands on her hips. The young Mae Jemison could read, and she knew all her numbers. She knew exactly what she wanted to be — a scientist.

Page 3

Mae Jemison was born in Alabama in 1956. She was the youngest of three children. Her family moved to Chicago, Illinois, when she was three years old. From the time she was a young girl, Mae worked hard. She was an excellent student.

Mae loved visiting the library. It was just a mile from her house. She read all sorts of books about space. By the time she was ten years old, Mae knew she would travel in space someday.

Page 4

Mae as a Young Woman

When she was sixteen years old, Mae finished high school. She went to college. She earned two **degrees**. Then she went to medical school to become a doctor.

Time: _____ minutes:seconds

ORAL READING WORDS PER MINUTE, PERCENT OF ACCURACY

Use the student's oral reading time to circle the WPM range.

Word Count: 210

	INTRVN	INSTR	IND	ADV
Minutes:Seconds	3:02 or more	3:01–2:21	2:20–1:41	1:40 or less
WPM	69 or less	70–89	90–125	126 or more

Count the number of miscues that are not self-corrected. Circle the percent of accuracy based on the number of miscues.

	INTRVN	INSTR	IND			ADV	
Number of Miscues	12 or more	10–11	8–9	6–7	4–5	1–3	0
Percent of Accuracy	94 or less	95	96	97	98	99	100

- If the student's score falls in a shaded area for either WPM or Accuracy, STOP! Reassess with a lower-level text at another time.

Mae Jemison **38**

3. COMPREHENSION

TEXT FEATURES AND STUDENT PREDICTION

Read aloud the questions/prompts on page 1 of the Student Booklet, and record the student's responses on the same page. Do not give additional prompts. Students may use the indicated book pages when responding to the Prediction and Nonfiction Text Features questions/prompts.

Note: Continue with the assessment if time permits. Otherwise, have the student read the book and complete the Student Booklet at another time.

STUDENT READS and RESPONDS

All students may use the text to complete pages 2–3 of the Student Booklet.

T: Read the book. When you are finished, write a summary of what you have read and answer the remaining questions in the Student Booklet. If you have questions, please come to me (or raise your hand).

Note: For students who have an Individual Education Plan in place for reading and/or written communication, follow the directions in their plan. You may read aloud the prompts on pages 2 and 3 of the Student Booklet and/or scribe their responses if required. Give <u>no</u> additional prompts.

While the student reads the text independently, complete the Teacher Analysis of Oral Reading on the next page and circle the descriptors on the *DRA2* Continuum that best describe the student's oral reading fluency.

4. TEACHER ANALYSIS

ORAL READING

If the student had 5 or more different miscues, use the information recorded on the Record of Oral Reading to complete the chart below.

Student problem-solves words using:	Number of miscues self-corrected: _____	
☐ beginning letter(s)/sound(s) ☐ letter-sound clusters ☐ blending letters/sounds ☐ onset and rime ☐ knowledge of spelling patterns (analogies) ☐ syllables ☐ rereading ☐ no observable behaviors	Number of miscues not self-corrected: _____ Number of words told to the student: _____	
	Miscues interfered with meaning: ☐ never ☐ at times ☐ often	**Miscues included:** ☐ omissions ☐ insertions ☐ reversals ☐ substitutions that were ☐ visually similar ☐ not visually similar

Copy each substitution to help analyze the student's attention to visual information.
e.g., <u>wouldn't</u> (substitution)
    couldn't (text)

Oral Reading Rate: (Optional) Use the formula below to determine the student's exact oral reading rate. Convert the student's reading time to all seconds.

210 (words) ÷ _____ **total seconds** = _____ **WPS × 60** = _____ **WPM**

*DRA*2 Continuum

- Use the information from the Student Reading Survey and the Student Booklet to circle the descriptors that best describe the student's responses for Reading Engagement and Comprehension.
- Add the circled numbers to obtain a total score for each section.
- Record the total scores at the top of page 1. Record the Comprehension score at the top of page 5 after the colon.

Note: If the Comprehension score is less than 14, administer *DRA*2 with a lower-level text.

Mae Jemison 38

Name/Date _____ Teacher/Grade _____

Mae Jemison 38

*DRA*2 CONTINUUM	LEVEL 38		EXTENDING READER	
	INTERVENTION	**INSTRUCTIONAL**	**INDEPENDENT**	**ADVANCED**
Reading Engagement				
Wide Reading	1 Title(s) below grade level; limited reading experiences and book knowledge	2 Titles slightly below grade level; rather limited reading experiences	3 Titles within 2 genres or multiple books within a genre; generally on-grade-level texts	4 Titles across 3 or more genres; many on- and above-grade-level texts
Self-Assessment/ Goal Setting	1 No strengths and/or goals	2 General strength(s) and goal(s) related to the reading process	3 2 specific strengths and 2 specific goals related to the reading process	4 3 specific strengths and 3 specific goals that reflect a higher level of thinking
Score	2 3	4 5	6 7	8
Oral Reading Fluency				
Expression	1 Little expression; monotone	2 Some expression that conveys meaning	3 Expression emphasizing key phrases and words at times	4 Expression emphasizing key phrases and words most of the time
Phrasing	1 Mostly word-by-word	2 Short phrases most of the time; inappropriate pauses	3 Longer phrases most of the time; heeds most punctuation	4 Consistently longer, meaningful phrases; heeds all punctuation
Rate	1 69 WPM or less	2 70–89 WPM	3 90–125 WPM	4 126 WPM or more
Accuracy	1 94% or less	2 95%	3 96%–98%	4 99%–100%
Score	4 5 6	7 8 9 10	11 12 13 14	15 16
Comprehension				
Prediction	1 Unrelated question(s) or no response	2 At least 1 reasonable question related to the text	3 At least 2 reasonable questions that go beyond page(s) read aloud	4 3 thoughtful questions that go beyond page(s) read aloud
Nonfiction Text Features	1 Limited information accessed from text features or no response	2 Partial information accessed from text features	3 Accurate information accessed from text features	4 Detailed information accessed from text features
Scaffolded Summary	1 1–2 ideas/facts in own language and/or copied text; may include incorrect information	2 Partial summary; generally in own language; some important ideas/facts; may include misinterpretations	3 Summary in own language; includes important ideas and few supporting facts from each section	4 Summary in own language; includes the most important ideas and some supporting facts from each section
Scaffolded Summary: Vocabulary	1 General terms or labels; limited understanding of key words/concepts	2 Some language/ vocabulary from the text; some understanding of key words/concepts	3 Most language/vocabulary from the text; basic understanding of most key words/concepts	4 All important language/vocabulary from the text; good understanding of key words/concepts
Literal Comprehension	1 Incorrect response or no response	2 Partial response; may include misinterpretation	3 Accurate response	4 Accurate response with specific details
Interpretation	1 Little or no understanding of important text implications	2 Some understanding of important text implications; no supporting details	3 Understands important text implications; may include supporting details	4 Insightful understanding of important text implications with supporting details or rationale
Reflection	1 Insignificant message; no reason for opinion or no response	2 Less significant message and/or a general reason for opinion	3 Significant message and a relevant reason for opinion	4 Significant message and reason for opinion that reflects higher-level thinking
Score	7 8 9 10 11 12 13	14 15 16 17 18	19 20 21 22 23 24 25	26 27 28

Choose three to five teaching/learning activities on the *DRA*2 Focus for Instruction on the next page.

DRA2 FOCUS FOR INSTRUCTION FOR EXTENDING READERS

READING ENGAGEMENT

Wide Reading
- ☐ Teach student strategies to select appropriately leveled texts for independent reading
- ☐ Introduce student to reading materials from a variety of genres
- ☐ Teach strategies to build reading stamina
- ☐ Create structures and/or routines to support reading at home
- ☐ Develop clear expectations for amount of independent reading
- ☐ Teach student how to use a reading log to monitor book selection and set reading goals
- ☐ Model/teach how to read for different purposes

Self-Assessment/Goal Setting
- ☐ Model and discuss strategies good readers use
- ☐ Help student identify 1–2 reading goals and a plan of action to improve reading
- ☐ Support revision of ongoing reading goals

ORAL READING FLUENCY

Expression and Phrasing
- ☐ Model and support reading in longer, meaningful phrases with appropriate expression
- ☐ Have student practice appropriate expression with familiar texts
- ☐ Teach student to recognize and emphasize key phrases and words in nonfiction texts
- ☐ Teach student to heed punctuation

Rate
- ☐ Provide materials and time for repeated reading to increase reading rate
- ☐ Teach student to read lower-level and/or familiar texts at an appropriate rate

Accuracy: Word Analysis
- ☐ Support and reinforce self-corrections of miscues
- ☐ Model and support how to take words apart (e.g., onset and rime, syllables) to problem-solve unknown words in nonfiction texts
- ☐ Teach how to use word chunks and analogies to problem-solve unknown words

COMPREHENSION

Prediction
- ☐ Provide opportunities for student to make predictions based on title, table of contents, and headings
- ☐ Model and support using background information to make meaningful predictions
- ☐ Model and teach student how to pose questions as a basis for predictions

Nonfiction Text Features
- ☐ Model and support how to read and interpret charts, graphs, maps, tables, etc.
- ☐ Model and teach how to use table of contents, headings, glossary, etc.

Summary
- ☐ Share and identify characteristics of good summaries
- ☐ Model and co-construct written summaries of texts read aloud
- ☐ Model and support how to distinguish between more important and less important ideas and facts
- ☐ Model and support how to write a summary in one's own words
- ☐ Model and support how to use examples from the text
- ☐ Teach student how to use headings to organize a summary of an informational/nonfiction text

Literal Comprehension
- ☐ Show student how to use key words to identify specific information from the text
- ☐ Provide opportunities for student to answer and construct literal questions
- ☐ Teach student how to use graphic organizers to keep track of key ideas and facts

Interpretation
- ☐ Teach and share examples of inferences
- ☐ Provide opportunities for student to support inferences with information or examples from the text
- ☐ Give student opportunities to respond to inference questions orally and in writing
- ☐ Model and support how to interpret nonfiction text features (e.g., how to read a chart or diagram)

Reflection
- ☐ Help student identify important information and key vocabulary
- ☐ Demonstrate how to support opinion with details from the text

Mae Jemison **38**

Name _____   Date _____

Teacher _____   Grade _____

The teacher reads aloud the prompts/questions and records the student's responses on this Before Reading page only.

BEFORE READING

TEXT FEATURES

PREDICTION

Open the book to the title and table of contents page. What are 3 questions you think may be answered as you read this book?

1. _____

   _____

2. _____

   _____

3. _____

   _____

NONFICTION TEXT FEATURES

Turn to page 4. Read the map and tell me what this map shows you.

_____

_____

_____

Turn to the glossary. What does the word *degrees* mean in this book?

_____

_____

_____

AFTER READING

Summary

Write a summary of this book in your own words. Include the important ideas and facts. You may use the book and the headings below to help you write your summary.

Mae's Childhood _____

_____

_____

Mae as a Young Woman _____

_____

_____

Mae's Space Training _____

_____

_____

Mae's First Flight in Space _____

_____

_____

In the Spacelab _____

_____

_____

A Dream Come True _____

_____

Literal Comprehension

List 3 things that Mae learned to do in the astronaut training program.

Mae learned ...
1. _____
2. _____
3. _____

Interpretation

Why do you think Mae wanted to be an astronaut? _____

_____

_____

Reflection

What do you think is the most important thing that you learned from
this book?

_____

_____

_____

Tell why you think it is important. _____

_____

_____

_____

**Reread what you have written to make sure your answers are the way you
want them before you hand in your booklet.**

Name/Date _____   Teacher/Grade _____

Scores: Reading Engagement ___/8   Oral Reading Fluency ___/16   Comprehension ___/28
Independent Range: 6–7   11–14   19–25

Book Selection   Text selected by: ☐ teacher   ☐ student

1. READING ENGAGEMENT

Ask the student to bring his or her reading record to the conference. If the Student Reading Survey was not completed prior to the assessment conference, read aloud the questions on the survey and record the student's responses.

2. ORAL READING FLUENCY

INTRODUCTION

T: This book is called Slammin' Sammy: A Real Hero. *Sammy Sosa is a famous baseball player. Please read aloud pages 2 through 4.* Show the student where to stop reading at the ✱.

RECORD OF ORAL READING

Record the student's oral reading behaviors. Note the student's fluency (expression and phrasing). Be sure to time the student's reading.

Page 2

Meet Sammy Sosa

It's a sunny Saturday afternoon at the **ballpark**. The fans watch as Sammy Sosa steps up to the plate. He pulls back on his bat and swings with all his might.

Crack! The crowd watches as the ball flies out of the park. It's another **home run** for Slammin' Sammy. As he runs around the bases, Sammy kisses his fingers, touches his heart, and then blows a kiss. This is how Sammy sends a message to his mother.

Sammy's smile shines when he crosses home plate. The fans are on their feet chanting, "Sam-my! Sam-my!"

Page 4

Sammy as a Boy

Sammy Sosa is one of baseball's great stars. He grew up in a small town in the Dominican Republic. As a kid, Sammy helped his mother, four brothers, and two sisters. His father died when he was seven years old. Sammy did all sorts of things to help make money. Sometimes he would shine shoes or wash cars. Other times he would sell oranges.

Like many kids on the island, Sammy dreamed of playing baseball in the United States. He didn't have a baseball or a bat. When he played baseball, he used a milk carton as a glove. He used stuffed socks as a ball. A tree branch was used as a bat. That is all he had.

Time: _____ minutes:seconds

ORAL READING WORDS PER MINUTE, PERCENT OF ACCURACY

Use the student's oral reading time to circle the WPM range.

Word Count: 221

	INTRVN	INSTR	IND	ADV
Minutes:Seconds	3:11 or more	3:10–2:29	2:28–1:46	1:45 or less
WPM	69 or less	70–89	90–125	126 or more

Count the number of miscues that are not self-corrected. Circle the percent of accuracy based on the number of miscues.

	INTRVN	INSTR	IND			ADV	
Number of Miscues	13 or more	10–12	8–9	6–7	4–5	1–3	0
Percent of Accuracy	94 or less	95	96	97	98	99	100

- If the student's score falls in a shaded area for either WPM or Accuracy, STOP! Reassess with a lower-level text at another time.

3. COMPREHENSION

TEXT FEATURES and STUDENT PREDICTION

Read aloud the questions/prompts on page 1 of the Student Booklet, and record the student's responses on the same page. Do not give additional prompts. Students may use the indicated book pages when responding to the Prediction and Nonfiction Text Features questions/prompts.

Note: Continue with the assessment if time permits. Otherwise, have the student read the book and complete the Student Booklet at another time.

STUDENT READS AND RESPONDS

All students may use the text to complete pages 2–3 of the Student Booklet.

T: Read the book. When you are finished, write a summary of what you have read and answer the remaining questions in the Student Booklet. If you have questions, please come to me (or raise your hand).

Note: For students who have an Individual Education Plan in place for reading and/or written communication, follow the directions in their plan. You may read aloud the prompts on pages 2 and 3 of the Student Booklet and/or scribe their responses if required. Give <u>no</u> additional prompts.

While the student reads the text independently, complete the Teacher Analysis of Oral Reading on the next page and circle the descriptors on the *DRA2* Continuum that best describe the student's oral reading fluency.

Slammin' Sammy 38

4. TEACHER ANALYSIS

ORAL READING

If the student had 5 or more different miscues, use the information recorded on the Record of Oral Reading to complete the chart below.

Student problem-solves words using:	Number of miscues self-corrected: _____ Number of miscues not self-corrected: _____ Number of words told to the student: _____	

☐ beginning letter(s)/sound(s)
☐ letter-sound clusters
☐ blending letters/sounds
☐ onset and rime
☐ knowledge of spelling patterns
  (analogies)
☐ syllables
☐ rereading
☐ no observable behaviors
	Miscues interfered with meaning:
	☐ never
	☐ at times
	☐ often
		Miscues included:
		☐ omissions
		☐ insertions
		☐ reversals
		☐ substitutions that were
		    ☐ visually similar
		    ☐ not visually similar

Copy each substitution to help analyze the student's attention to visual information.
e.g., <u>chatting</u> (substitution)
    chanting (text)

Oral Reading Rate: (Optional) Use the formula below to determine the student's exact oral reading rate. Convert the student's reading time to all seconds.

$$221 \text{ (words)} \div \underline{\hspace{1cm}} \text{ total seconds} = \underline{\hspace{1cm}} \text{ WPS} \times 60 = \underline{\hspace{1cm}} \text{ WPM}$$

DRA2 Continuum

- Use the information from the Student Reading Survey and the Student Booklet to circle the descriptors that best describe the student's responses for Reading Engagement and Comprehension.
- Add the circled numbers to obtain a total score for each section.
- Record the total scores at the top of page 1. Record the Comprehension score at the top of page 5 after the colon.

Note: If the Comprehension score is less than 14, administer *DRA2* with a lower-level text.

Name/Date _____   Teacher/Grade _____

*DRA*2 CONTINUUM	LEVEL 38		EXTENDING READER	
	INTERVENTION	**INSTRUCTIONAL**	**INDEPENDENT**	**ADVANCED**
Reading Engagement				
Wide Reading	**1** Title(s) below grade level; limited reading experiences and book knowledge	**2** Titles slightly below grade level; rather limited reading experiences	**3** Titles within 2 genres or multiple books within a genre; generally on-grade-level texts	**4** Titles across 3 or more genres; many on- and above-grade-level texts
Self-Assessment/ Goal Setting	**1** No strengths and/or goals	**2** General strength(s) and goal(s) related to the reading process	**3** 2 specific strengths and 2 specific goals related to the reading process	**4** 3 specific strengths and 3 specific goals that reflect a higher level of thinking
Score	2 3	4 5	6 7	8
Oral Reading Fluency				
Expression	**1** Little expression; monotone	**2** Some expression that conveys meaning	**3** Expression emphasizing key phrases and words at times	**4** Expression emphasizing key phrases and words most of the time
Phrasing	**1** Mostly word-by-word	**2** Short phrases most of the time; inappropriate pauses	**3** Longer phrases most of the time; heeds most punctuation	**4** Consistently longer, meaningful phrases; heeds all punctuation
Rate	**1** 69 WPM or less	**2** 70–89 WPM	**3** 90–125 WPM	**4** 126 WPM or more
Accuracy	**1** 94% or less	**2** 95%	**3** 96%–98%	**4** 99%–100%
Score	4 5 6	7 8 9 10	11 12 13 14	15 16
Comprehension				
Prediction	**1** Unrelated question(s) or no response	**2** At least 1 reasonable question related to the text	**3** At least 2 reasonable questions that go beyond page(s) read aloud	**4** 3 thoughtful questions that go beyond page(s) read aloud
Nonfiction Text Features	**1** Limited information accessed from text features or no response	**2** Partial information accessed from text features	**3** Accurate information accessed from text features	**4** Detailed information accessed from text features
Scaffolded Summary	**1** 1–2 ideas/facts in own language and/or copied text; may include incorrect information	**2** Partial summary; generally in own language; some important ideas/facts; may include misinterpretations	**3** Summary in own language; includes important ideas <u>and</u> a few supporting facts from each section	**4** Summary in own language; includes the most important ideas <u>and</u> some supporting facts from each section
Scaffolded Summary: Vocabulary	**1** General terms or labels; limited understanding of key words/concepts	**2** Some language/ vocabulary from the text; some understanding of key words/concepts	**3** Most language/ vocabulary from the text; basic understanding of most key words/concepts	**4** All important language/vocabulary from the text; good understanding of key words/concepts
Literal Comprehension	**1** Incorrect response or no response	**2** Partial response; may include misinterpretation	**3** Accurate response	**4** Accurate response with specific details
Interpretation	**1** Little or no understanding of important text implications	**2** Some understanding of important text implications; no supporting details	**3** Understands important text implications; may include supporting details	**4** Insightful understanding of important text implications with supporting details or rationale
Reflection	**1** Insignificant message; no reason for opinion or no response	**2** Less significant message and/or a general reason for opinion	**3** Significant message <u>and</u> a relevant reason for opinion	**4** Significant message <u>and</u> reason for opinion that reflects higher-level thinking
Score	7 8 9 10 11 12 13	14 15 16 17 18	19 20 21 22 23 24 25	26 27 28

Choose three to five teaching/learning activities on the *DRA*2 Focus for Instruction on the next page.

Slammin' Sammy **38**

DRA2 FOCUS FOR INSTRUCTION FOR EXTENDING READERS

READING ENGAGEMENT

Wide Reading
- ☐ Teach student strategies to select appropriately leveled texts for independent reading
- ☐ Introduce student to reading materials from a variety of genres
- ☐ Teach strategies to build reading stamina
- ☐ Create structures and/or routines to support reading at home
- ☐ Develop clear expectations for amount of independent reading
- ☐ Teach student how to use a reading log to monitor book selection and set reading goals
- ☐ Model/teach how to read for different purposes

Self-Assessment/Goal Setting
- ☐ Model and discuss strategies good readers use
- ☐ Help student identify 1–2 reading goals and a plan of action to improve reading
- ☐ Support revision of ongoing reading goals

ORAL READING FLUENCY

Expression and Phrasing
- ☐ Model and support reading in longer, meaningful phrases with appropriate expression
- ☐ Have student practice appropriate expression with familiar texts
- ☐ Teach student to recognize and emphasize key phrases and words in nonfiction texts
- ☐ Teach student to heed punctuation

Rate
- ☐ Provide materials and time for repeated reading to increase reading rate
- ☐ Teach student to read lower-level and/or familiar texts at an appropriate rate

Accuracy: Word Analysis
- ☐ Support and reinforce self-corrections of miscues
- ☐ Model and support how to take words apart (e.g., onset and rime, syllables) to problem-solve unknown words
- ☐ Teach how to use word chunks and analogies to problem-solve unknown words

COMPREHENSION

Prediction
- ☐ Provide opportunities for student to make predictions based on title, table of contents, and headings
- ☐ Model and support using background information to make meaningful predictions
- ☐ Model and teach student how to pose questions as a basis for predictions

Nonfiction Text Features
- ☐ Model and support how to read and interpret charts, graphs, maps, tables, etc.
- ☐ Model and teach how to use table of contents, headings, glossary, etc.

Summary
- ☐ Share and identify characteristics of good summaries
- ☐ Model and co-construct written summaries of texts read aloud
- ☐ Model and support how to distinguish between more important and less important ideas and facts
- ☐ Model and support how to write a summary in one's own words
- ☐ Model and support how to use examples from the text
- ☐ Teach student how to use headings to organize a summary of an informational/nonfiction text

Literal Comprehension
- ☐ Show student how to use key words to identify specific information from the text
- ☐ Provide opportunities for student to answer and construct literal questions
- ☐ Teach student how to use graphic organizers to keep track of key ideas and facts

Interpretation
- ☐ Teach and share examples of inferences
- ☐ Provide opportunities for student to support inferences with information or examples from the text
- ☐ Give student opportunities to respond to inference questions orally and in writing
- ☐ Model and support how to interpret nonfiction text features (e.g., how to read a chart or diagram)

Reflection
- ☐ Help student identify important information and key vocabulary
- ☐ Demonstrate how to support opinion with details from the text

Name _____   Date _____

Teacher _____   Grade _____

The teacher reads aloud the prompts/questions and records the student's responses on this Before Reading page only.

BEFORE READING

PREDICTION

Open the book to the title and table of contents page. What are 3 questions you think may be answered as you read this book?

1. _____

_____

2. _____

_____

3. _____

_____

NONFICTION TEXT FEATURES

Turn to page 13. Read the graph, and tell me what this graph shows you.

_____

_____

_____

Turn to the glossary. What does the word *scouts* mean in this book?

_____

_____

Slammin' Sammy

AFTER READING

Summary

Write a summary of this book in your own words. Include the important ideas and facts. You may use the book and the headings below to help you write your summary.

Sammy as a Boy _____

_____

_____

Sammy Tries Out for a Baseball Team _____

_____

_____

Sammy Begins to Hit Home Runs _____

_____

_____

The Great Home Run Race _____

_____

_____

A Hero on and off the Field _____

_____

_____

Slammin' Sammy

Literal Comprehension

List 3 things that Sammy used to play baseball when he was a young boy.

Sammy used...

1. _____

2. _____

3. _____

Interpretation

Why do you think Sammy wants to help the people in his home country?

_____

_____

_____

Reflection

What do you think is the most important thing that you learned from this book?

_____

_____

_____

Tell why you think it is important. _____

_____

_____

_____

Reread what you have written to make sure your answers are the way you want them before you hand in your booklet.

Slammin' Sammy

Name/Date _____   Teacher/Grade _____

Scores: Reading Engagement ___/8   Oral Reading Fluency ___/16   Comprehension ___/28
Independent Range: 6–7   11–14   19–25

Book Selection   Text selected by: ☐ teacher   ☐ student

1. READING ENGAGEMENT

Ask the student to bring his or her reading record to the conference. If the Student Reading Survey was not completed prior to the assessment conference, read aloud the questions on the survey and record the student's responses.

2. ORAL READING FLUENCY

INTRODUCTION

T: Have you ever thought something you had to do was going to be boring? This happens to Rosa and Hector in this story, A Trip Through Time. *Please read aloud pages 2 through 4.* Show the student where to stop reading at the ✱.

RECORD OF ORAL READING

Record the student's oral reading behaviors. Note the student's fluency (expression and phrasing). Be sure to time the student's reading.

Page 2

"Bye! See you in two weeks!" Rosa and Hector waved to their father as he backed the car down the driveway. Their grandparents waved, too.

Rosa and Hector looked at the old country home where their grandparents lived. They would be staying here for the next two weeks.

"Grandpa, what video games do you have?" Hector asked.

Grandpa shook his head. "We don't have video games."

"That's okay," Hector said. "We'll play computer games instead."

"Grandpa and I have no need for a computer, so we don't have one," Grandma said.

"No problem," Rosa said. "I brought my favorite videos and DVDs."

Grandma shook her head. "We have no VCR or DVD player."

"That's okay," Rosa said. "We'll just watch the TV." Grandpa and Grandma looked worried. Rosa and Hector had an awful feeling. "You have a TV, don't you?" Rosa asked.

Page 4

"We don't watch TV, so we gave our TV to a family in town," Grandpa told them.

Rosa and Hector tried to smile. They didn't say anything until they were alone together on the porch.

"Who doesn't have a TV these days?" Rosa asked. "What do they do for fun?"

Hector shrugged. "This is going to be a very long, boring two weeks."

"You're right," Rosa agreed.

"Let's walk around and see if we can find something to do," suggested Hector.

Time: _____ minutes:seconds

ORAL READING WORDS PER MINUTE, PERCENT OF ACCURACY

Use the student's oral reading time to circle the WPM range.

Word Count: 223

	INTRVN	INSTR	IND	ADV
Minutes:Seconds	3:13 or more	3:12–2:30	2:29–1:47	1:46 or less
WPM	69 or less	70–89	90–125	126 or more

Count the number of miscues that are not self-corrected. Circle the percent of accuracy based on the number of miscues.

	INTRVN	INSTR	IND			ADV	
Number of Miscues	13 or more	11–12	8–10	6–7	4–5	1–3	0
Percent of Accuracy	94 or less	95	96	97	98	99	100

- If the student's score falls in a shaded area for either WPM or Accuracy, STOP! Reassess with a lower-level text at another time.

3. COMPREHENSION

TEXT FEATURES and STUDENT PREDICTION

Read aloud the questions/prompts on page 1 of the Student Booklet, and record the student's responses on the same page. Do not give additional prompts. Students do not use the book as you record their responses on the first page of the Student Booklet.

Note: Continue with the assessment if time permits. Otherwise, have the student read the book and complete the Student Booklet at another time.

STUDENT READS AND RESPONDS

All students may use the text to complete pages 2–3 of the Student Booklet.

T: Read the story. When you are finished, write a summary of what you have read and answer the remaining questions in the Student Booklet. If you have questions, please come to me (or raise your hand).

Note: For students who have an Individual Education Plan in place for reading and/or written communication, follow the directions in their plan. You may read aloud the prompts on pages 2 and 3 of the Student Booklet and/or scribe their responses if required. Give <u>no</u> additional prompts.

While the student reads the text independently, complete the Teacher Analysis of Oral Reading on the next page and circle the descriptors on the *DRA2* Continuum that best describe the student's oral reading fluency.

A Trip Through Time **38**

4. TEACHER ANALYSIS

ORAL READING

If the student had 5 or more different miscues, use the information recorded on the Record of Oral Reading to complete the chart below.

Student problem-solves words using:	Number of miscues self-corrected: _____
☐ beginning letter(s)/sound(s)	Number of miscues not self-corrected: _____
☐ letter-sound clusters	Number of words told to the student: _____

Student problem-solves words using:	Miscues interfered with meaning:	Miscues included:
☐ blending letters/sounds	☐ never	☐ omissions
☐ onset and rime	☐ at times	☐ insertions
☐ knowledge of spelling patterns	☐ often	☐ reversals
(analogies)		☐ substitutions that were
☐ syllables		☐ visually similar
☐ rereading		☐ not visually similar
☐ no observable behaviors		

Copy each substitution to help analyze the student's attention to visual information.
e.g., <u>suggested</u> (substitution)
　　　shrugged (text)

Oral Reading Rate: (Optional) Use the formula below to determine the student's exact oral reading rate. Convert the student's reading time to all seconds.

223 (words) ÷ _____ total seconds = _____ WPS × 60 = _____ WPM

DRA2 Continuum

- Use the information from the Student Reading Survey and the Student Booklet to circle the descriptors that best describe the student's responses for Reading Engagement and Comprehension.
- Add the circled numbers to obtain a total score for each section.
- Record the total scores at the top of page 1. Record the Comprehension score at the top of page 5 after the colon.

Note: If the Comprehension score is less than 14, administer *DRA2* with a lower-level text.

Name/Date _____ Teacher/Grade _____

DRA2 CONTINUUM	LEVEL 38		EXTENDING READER	
	INTERVENTION	INSTRUCTIONAL	INDEPENDENT	ADVANCED
Reading Engagement				
Wide Reading	1 Title(s) below grade level; limited reading experiences and book knowledge	2 Titles slightly below grade level; rather limited reading experiences	3 Titles within 2 genres or multiple books within a genre; generally on-grade-level texts	4 Titles across 3 or more genres; many on- and above-grade-level texts
Self-Assessment/ Goal Setting	1 No strengths and/or goals	2 General strength(s) and goal(s) related to the reading process	3 2 specific strengths and 2 specific goals related to the reading process	4 3 specific strengths and 3 specific goals that reflect a higher level of thinking
Score	2 3	4 5	6 7	8
Oral Reading Fluency				
Expression	1 Little expression; monotone	2 Some expression that conveys meaning	3 Expression reflects mood, pace, and tension at times	4 Expression reflects mood, pace, and tension most of the time
Phrasing	1 Mostly word-by-word	2 Short phrases most of the time; inappropriate pauses	3 Longer phrases most of the time; heeds most punctuation	4 Consistently longer, meaningful phrases; heeds all punctuation
Rate	1 69 WPM or less	2 70–89 WPM	3 90–125 WPM	4 126 WPM or more
Accuracy	1 94% or less	2 95%	3 96%–98%	4 99%–100%
Score	4 5 6	7 8 9 10	11 12 13 14	15 16
Comprehension				
Use of Text Features	1 Limited or no description of the characters	2 Partial description of the characters; general statements	3 Description of each character; includes at least 2 specific details	4 Description of each character; includes at least 3 specific details
Prediction	1 Unrelated predictions or no response	2 At least 1 reasonable prediction related to the text	3 At least 2 reasonable predictions that go beyond the text read aloud	4 3 thoughtful predictions that go beyond the text read aloud
Scaffolded Summary	1 1–2 events in own language and/or copied text; may include incorrect information	2 Partial summary; generally in own language; some important characters/events; may include misinterpretations	3 Summary in own language; includes important characters, many of the important events, and some details from the beginning, middle, and end	4 Summary in own language; includes all important characters, events, and details from the beginning, middle, and end
Scaffolded Summary: Vocabulary	1 General terms or labels; limited understanding of key words/concepts	2 Some language/ vocabulary from the text; some understanding of key words/concepts	3 Most language/ vocabulary from the text; basic understanding of most key words/concepts	4 All important language/vocabulary from the text; good understanding of key words/concepts
Literal Comprehension	1 Incorrect response or no response	2 Partial response; may include misinterpretation	3 Accurate response	4 Accurate response with specific details
Interpretation	1 Little or no understanding of important text implications	2 Some understanding of important text implications; no supporting details	3 Understands important text implications; may include supporting details	4 Insightful understanding of important text implications with supporting details or rationale
Reflection	1 Insignificant event; no reason for opinion or no response	2 Less significant event and/or a general reason for opinion	3 Significant event and a relevant reason for opinion	4 Significant event and reason for opinion that reflects higher-level thinking
Score	7 8 9 10 11 12 13	14 15 16 17 18	19 20 21 22 23 24 25	26 27 28

Choose three to five teaching/learning activities on the DRA2 Focus for Instruction on the next page.

A Trip Through Time 38

254

DRA2 FOCUS FOR INSTRUCTION FOR EXTENDING READERS

READING ENGAGEMENT

Wide Reading
- ☐ Teach student strategies to select appropriately leveled texts for independent reading
- ☐ Introduce student to reading materials from a variety of genres
- ☐ Teach strategies to build reading stamina
- ☐ Create structures and/or routines to support reading at home
- ☐ Develop clear expectations for amount of independent reading
- ☐ Teach student how to use a reading log to monitor book selection and set reading goals
- ☐ Model/teach how to read for different purposes

Self-Assessment/Goal Setting
- ☐ Model and discuss strategies good readers use
- ☐ Help student identify 1–2 reading goals and a plan of action to improve reading
- ☐ Support revision of ongoing reading goals

Oral Reading Fluency

Expression and Phrasing
- ☐ Model and support reading longer, meaningful phrases with appropriate expression
- ☐ Have student practice appropriate expression with familiar texts
- ☐ Have student participate in choral reading and/or reader's theater
- ☐ Teach student to heed punctuation

Rate
- ☐ Provide materials and time for repeated reading to increase reading rate
- ☐ Teach student to read lower-level and/or familiar texts at an appropriate rate

Accuracy: Word Analysis
- ☐ Support and reinforce self-corrections of miscues
- ☐ Model and support how to take words apart (e.g., onset and rime, syllables) to problem-solve unknown words
- ☐ Teach how to use word chunks and analogies to problem-solve unknown words
- ☐ Provide spelling activities and word sorts to help student recognize patterns in words

COMPREHENSION

Use of Text Features
- ☐ Provide opportunities for student to discuss what he or she knows about the characters based on the title and book cover, as well as opening paragraphs and texts read aloud
- ☐ Teach student how to describe characters, using information from fiction text features (e.g., title, illustrations, and text)

Prediction
- ☐ Teach student how to make predictions based on title and book cover, as well as opening paragraphs of texts read aloud
- ☐ Model and support using background information to make meaningful predictions

Summary
- ☐ Share and identify characteristics of good summaries
- ☐ Model and co-construct written summaries of texts read aloud
- ☐ Model and support how to distinguish between more important and less important ideas and details
- ☐ Model and support how to write a summary in one's own words
- ☐ Teach student how to use a graphic organizer as an aid to creating a summary
- ☐ Teach student how to identify story elements (e.g., characters, setting, plot)

Literal Comprehension
- ☐ Show student how to use key words to identify specific information from the text
- ☐ Provide opportunities for student to answer and construct literal questions
- ☐ Help student locate and record specific details
- ☐ Teach student how to use graphic organizers to keep track of story information

Interpretation
- ☐ Teach and share examples of inferences
- ☐ Model and teach student how to think about *Why?* questions while and after reading a text
- ☐ Model and teach how to support inferences with examples from the text
- ☐ Give student opportunities to respond to inference questions orally and in writing

Reflection
- ☐ Help student identify important message in a story
- ☐ Provide opportunities to identify and discuss the most important event in a story
- ☐ Demonstrate and teach student how to support opinion with details from the text

A Trip Through Time **38**

Name _____   Date _____

Teacher _____   Grade _____

The teacher reads aloud the prompts/questions and records the student's responses on this Before Reading page only.

BEFORE READING

TEXT FEATURES

Think about the title, the pictures you have seen, and what you have read so far. Tell me what you know about Rosa and Hector.

Rosa: _____

_____

Hector: _____

_____

PREDICTION

What are 3 things you think might happen in the rest of this story?

1. _____

_____

_____

2. _____

_____

_____

3. _____

_____

_____

AFTER READING

Summary

Write a summary of this story in your own words. Include the important characters, events, and details. You may use the book and the words below to help you write your summary.

In the beginning, _____

_____

_____

Next, _____

_____

_____

Then, _____

_____

_____

After that, _____

_____

_____

In the end, _____

_____

_____

Literal Comprehension

List 3 things Rosa and Hector saw in the shed when they returned to their own time.

Rosa and Hector saw ...

1. _____

2. _____

3. _____

Interpretation

At the end of the story, why do you think Rosa and Hector felt it was going to be the most fun two weeks they'd ever spent?

_____

_____

_____

Reflection

What do you think is the most important event in the story?

_____

_____

_____

Tell why you think it is important. _____

_____

_____

Reread what you have written to make sure your answers are the way you want them before you hand in your booklet.

Name/Date _____   Teacher/Grade _____

Scores: Reading Engagement ___/8   Oral Reading Fluency ___/16   Comprehension ___/28
Independent Range: 6–7   11–14   19–25

Book Selection   Text selected by: ☐ teacher   ☐ student

1. READING ENGAGEMENT

Ask the student to bring his or her reading record to the conference. If the Student Reading Survey was not completed prior to the assessment conference, read aloud the questions on the survey and record the student's responses.

2. ORAL READING FLUENCY

INTRODUCTION

T: This wilderness story, Trouble at the Beaver Pond, *tells about a beaver family and how the mother saves her kits. Please read aloud pages 2 through 4.* Show the student where to stop reading at the ✱.

RECORD OF ORAL READING

Record the student's oral reading behaviors. Note the student's fluency (expression and phrasing). Be sure to time the student's reading.

Page 2

The mother beaver rested by the log dam for a moment. She watched her young son and daughter playing on the shore of the beaver pond. She was worried about them being on land. They belonged in the water. There they could move quickly. They could dive deep and swim underwater like two big, brown fish.

The mother beaver climbed out of the water. She began packing mud into the dam. Her hairless tail lay flat on the dam behind her, supporting her while she worked. Her strong front paws looked like little hands as they packed the mud into place.

Page 3

Again and again, the mother beaver stopped working to watch her kits. Their father was far upstream, cutting down more trees for the dam.

She looked now and then toward the beavers' lodge, which was built of sticks and mud piled up in deep water. The round, mud-covered roof of the lodge rose above the water. Under the roof was a high, dry room that could be entered only from an underwater tunnel. This room was the safest place the beaver kits would ever know.

Page 4

If the beaver kits were in any danger now, they did not know it. They battled playfully with each other, making faces and noises. They stood on their hind feet, pushing and pulling at each other with their front legs.

Time: _____ minutes:seconds

ORAL READING WORDS PER MINUTE, PERCENT OF ACCURACY

Use the student's oral reading time to circle the WPM range.

Word Count: 227

	INTRVN	INSTR	IND	ADV
Minutes:Seconds	3:16 or more	3:15–2:33	2:32–1:49	1:48 or less
WPM	69 or less	70–89	90–125	126 or more

Count the number of miscues that are not self-corrected. Circle the percent of accuracy based on the number of miscues.

	INTRVN	INSTR	IND			ADV	
Number of Miscues	13 or more	11–12	8–10	6–7	4–5	1–3	0
Percent of Accuracy	94 or less	95	96	97	98	99	100

- If the student's score falls in a shaded area for either WPM or Accuracy, STOP! Reassess with a lower-level text at another time.

3. COMPREHENSION

TEXT FEATURES and STUDENT PREDICTION

Read aloud the questions/prompts on page 1 of the Student Booklet, and record the student's responses on the same page. Do not give additional prompts. Students do not use the book as you record their responses on the first page of the Student Booklet.

Note: Continue with the assessment if time permits. Otherwise, have the student read the book and complete the Student Booklet at another time.

STUDENT READS AND RESPONDS

All students may use the text to complete pages 2–3 of the Student Booklet.

T: Read the story. When you are finished, write a summary of what you have read and answer the remaining questions in the Student Booklet. If you have questions, please come to me (or raise your hand).

Note: For students who have an Individual Education Plan in place for reading and/or written communication, follow the directions in their plan. You may read aloud the prompts on pages 2 and 3 of the Student Booklet and/or scribe their responses if required. Give <u>no</u> additional prompts.

While the student reads the text independently, complete the Teacher Analysis of Oral Reading on the next page and circle the descriptors on the *DRA2* Continuum that best describe the student's oral reading fluency.

38

4. TEACHER ANALYSIS

ORAL READING

If the student had 5 or more different miscues, use the information recorded on the Record of Oral Reading to complete the chart below.

Student problem-solves words using:	Number of miscues self-corrected: _____
☐ beginning letter(s)/sound(s)	Number of miscues not self-corrected: _____
☐ letter-sound clusters	Number of words told to the student: _____

Student problem-solves words using:	Miscues interfered with meaning:	Miscues included:
☐ blending letters/sounds	☐ never	☐ omissions
☐ onset and rime	☐ at times	☐ insertions
☐ knowledge of spelling patterns	☐ often	☐ reversals
(analogies)		☐ substitutions that were
☐ syllables		☐ visually similar
☐ rereading		☐ not visually similar
☐ no observable behaviors		

Copy each substitution to help analyze the student's attention to visual information.

e.g., <u>playful</u> (substitution)

      playfully (text)

Oral Reading Rate: (Optional) Use the formula below to determine the student's exact oral reading rate. Convert the student's reading time to all seconds.

$$227 \text{ (words)} \div \underline{\hspace{1cm}} \text{ total seconds} = \underline{\hspace{1cm}} \text{ WPS} \times 60 = \underline{\hspace{1cm}} \text{ WPM}$$

*DRA*2 Continuum

- Use the information from the Student Reading Survey and the Student Booklet to circle the descriptors that best describe the student's responses for Reading Engagement and Comprehension.
- Add the circled numbers to obtain a total score for each section.
- Record the total scores at the top of page 1. Record the Comprehension score at the top of page 5 after the colon.

Note: If the Comprehension score is less than 14, administer *DRA*2 with a lower-level text.

Name/Date _____ Teacher/Grade _____

DRA2 CONTINUUM	LEVEL 38		EXTENDING READER	
	INTERVENTION	**INSTRUCTIONAL**	**INDEPENDENT**	**ADVANCED**
Reading Engagement				
Wide Reading	**1** Title(s) below grade level; limited reading experiences and book knowledge	**2** Titles slightly below grade level; rather limited reading experiences	**3** Titles within 2 genres or multiple books within a genre; generally on-grade-level texts	**4** Titles across 3 or more genres; many on- and above-grade-level texts
Self-Assessment/ Goal Setting	**1** No strengths and/or goals	**2** General strength(s) and goal(s) related to the reading process	**3** 2 specific strengths and 2 specific goals related to the reading process	**4** 3 specific strengths and 3 specific goals that reflect a higher level of thinking
Score	2 3	4 5	6 7	8
Oral Reading Fluency				
Expression	**1** Little expression; monotone	**2** Some expression that conveys meaning	**3** Expression reflects mood, pace, and tension at times	**4** Expression reflects mood, pace, and tension most of the time
Phrasing	**1** Mostly word-by-word	**2** Short phrases most of the time; inappropriate pauses	**3** Longer phrases most of the time; heeds most punctuation	**4** Consistently longer, meaningful phrases; heeds all punctuation
Rate	**1** 69 WPM or less	**2** 70–89 WPM	**3** 90–125 WPM	**4** 126 WPM or more
Accuracy	**1** 94% or less	**2** 95%	**3** 96%–98%	**4** 99%–100%
Score	4 5 6	7 8 9 10	11 12 13 14	15 16
Comprehension				
Use of Text Features	**1** Limited or no description of the characters	**2** Partial description of the characters; general statements	**3** Description of each character; includes at least 2 specific details	**4** Description of each character; includes at least 3 specific details
Prediction	**1** Unrelated predictions or no response	**2** At least 1 reasonable prediction related to the text	**3** At least 2 reasonable predictions that go beyond the text read aloud	**4** 3 thoughtful predictions that go beyond the text read aloud
Scaffolded Summary	**1** 1–2 events in own language and/or copied text; may include incorrect information	**2** Partial summary; generally in own language; some important characters/events; may include misinterpretations	**3** Summary in own language; includes important characters, many of the important events, and some details from the beginning, middle, and end	**4** Summary in own language; includes all important characters, events, and details from the beginning, middle, and end
Scaffolded Summary: Vocabulary	**1** General terms or labels; limited understanding of key words/concepts	**2** Some language/ vocabulary from the text; some understanding of key words/concepts	**3** Most language/ vocabulary from the text; basic understanding of most key words/concepts	**4** All important language/vocabulary from the text; good understanding of key words/concepts
Literal Comprehension	**1** Incorrect response or no response	**2** Partial response; may include misinterpretation	**3** Accurate response	**4** Accurate response with specific details
Interpretation	**1** Little or no understanding of important text implications	**2** Some understanding of important text implications; no supporting details	**3** Understands important text implications; may include supporting details	**4** Insightful understanding of important text implications with supporting details or rationale
Reflection	**1** Insignificant event; no reason for opinion or no response	**2** Less significant event and/or a general reason for opinion	**3** Significant event and a relevant reason for opinion	**4** Significant event and reason for opinion that reflects higher-level thinking
Score	7 8 9 10 11 12 13	14 15 16 17 18	19 20 21 22 23 24 25	26 27 28

Choose three to five teaching/learning activities on the *DRA2* Focus for Instruction on the next page.

DRA2 FOCUS FOR INSTRUCTION FOR EXTENDING READERS

READING ENGAGEMENT
Wide Reading
- ☐ Teach student strategies to select appropriately leveled texts for independent reading
- ☐ Introduce student to reading materials from a variety of genres
- ☐ Teach strategies to build reading stamina
- ☐ Create structures and/or routines to support reading at home
- ☐ Develop clear expectations for amount of independent reading
- ☐ Teach student how to use a reading log to monitor book selection and set reading goals
- ☐ Model/teach how to read for different purposes

Self-Assessment/Goal Setting
- ☐ Model and discuss strategies good readers use
- ☐ Help student identify 1–2 reading goals and a plan of action to improve reading
- ☐ Support revision of ongoing reading goals

Oral Reading Fluency
Expression and Phrasing
- ☐ Model and support reading longer, meaningful phrases with appropriate expression
- ☐ Have student practice appropriate expression with familiar texts
- ☐ Have student participate in choral reading and/or reader's theater
- ☐ Teach student to heed punctuation

Rate
- ☐ Provide materials and time for repeated reading to increase reading rate
- ☐ Teach student to read lower-level and/or familiar texts at an appropriate rate

Accuracy: Word Analysis
- ☐ Support and reinforce self-corrections of miscues
- ☐ Model and support how to take words apart (e.g., onset and rime, syllables) to problem-solve unknown words
- ☐ Teach how to use word chunks and analogies to problem-solve unknown words
- ☐ Provide spelling activities and word sorts to help student recognize patterns in words

COMPREHENSION
Use of Text Features
- ☐ Provide opportunities for student to discuss what he or she knows about the characters based on the title and book cover, as well as opening paragraphs and texts read aloud.
- ☐ Teach student how to describe characters, using information from fiction text features (e.g., title, illustrations, and text)

Prediction
- ☐ Teach student how to make predictions based on title and book cover, as well as opening paragraphs of texts read aloud
- ☐ Model and support using background information to make meaningful predictions

Summary
- ☐ Share and identify characteristics of good summaries
- ☐ Model and co-construct written summaries of texts read aloud
- ☐ Model and support how to distinguish between more important and less important ideas and details
- ☐ Model and support how to write a summary in one's own words
- ☐ Teach student how to use a graphic organizer as an aid to creating a summary
- ☐ Teach student how to identify story elements (e.g., characters, setting, plot)

Literal Comprehension
- ☐ Show student how to use key words to identify specific information from the text
- ☐ Provide opportunities for student to answer and construct literal questions
- ☐ Help student locate and record specific details
- ☐ Teach student how to use graphic organizers to keep track of story information

Interpretation
- ☐ Teach and share examples of inferences
- ☐ Model and teach student how to think about *Why?* questions while and after reading a text
- ☐ Model and teach how to support inferences with examples from the text
- ☐ Give student opportunities to respond to inference questions orally and in writing

Reflection
- ☐ Help student identify important message in a story
- ☐ Provide opportunities to identify and discuss the most important event in a story
- ☐ Demonstrate and teach student how to support opinion with details from the text

Name _____ Date _____

Teacher _____ Grade _____

The teacher reads aloud the prompts/questions and records the student's responses on this Before Reading page only.

BEFORE READING

TEXT FEATURES

Think about the title, the pictures you have seen, and what you have read so far. Tell me what you know about the mother beaver and her kits.

Mother Beaver: _____

_____

Kits: _____

_____

PREDICTION

What are 3 things you think might happen in the rest of this story?

1. _____

_____

_____

2. _____

_____

_____

3. _____

_____

_____

AFTER READING

Summary

Write a summary of this story in your own words. Include the important characters, events, and details. You may use the book and the words below to help you write your summary.

In the beginning, ______________________________

____

____

Next, ______________________________

____

____

Then, ______________________________

____

____

After that, ______________________________

____

____

In the end, ______________________________

____

____

Literal Comprehension

List 3 ways the bear was described.

The bear was...

1. _____

2. _____

3. _____

Interpretation

At the end of the story, why wouldn't the mother beaver let the kits go more than a few feet from the water?

_____

_____

_____

Reflection

What do you think is the most important event in this story?

_____

_____

_____

Tell why you think it is important. _____

_____

_____

_____

Reread what you have written to make sure your answers are the way you want them before you hand in your booklet.

Name/Date _____   Teacher/Grade _____

Scores: Reading Engagement ___/8   Oral Reading Fluency ___/16   Comprehension ___/24
Independent Range: 6–7   11–14   17–22

Book Selection   Text selected by: ☐ teacher   ☐ student

1. READING ENGAGEMENT

Ask the student to bring his or her completed Student Reading Survey to the conference.

2. ORAL READING FLUENCY

INTRODUCTION

T: In this story, All the Way Under, *Sonya and her cousin, Katie, spend a day at the beach. Please read aloud to the star on page 2.* Show the student where to stop reading at the ✱.

RECORD OF ORAL READING

Record the student's oral reading behaviors. Note the student's fluency (expression and phrasing). Be sure to time the student's reading.

Page 2

I didn't plan to tell a lie or to get into trouble. It just sort of happened. Katie, my cousin, had asked me to stay with her family for a week during the summer. Katie and I were both nine. We were going into fourth grade in the fall. We both enjoyed riding bikes, playing games, and dancing to our favorite music. For the first few days, we had a wonderful time. But that all changed when Uncle Jack decided that he would take us to the beach on his day off.

I tried to act happy about going to the beach. It was my first time. I should have been excited. But I didn't want Katie to know I hadn't learned to swim yet.

"You can swim, can't you?" Uncle Jack asked as he turned into the beach parking lot the next day.

"Uh-huh," I nodded. It wasn't really a lie. I had started taking swimming lessons three times, but I never finished. The real problem was that I was afraid to go all the way under. Just thinking about putting my head in the water made me very nervous.

As soon as Uncle Jack parked the car, Katie jumped out of the back seat. She was ready to go swimming. Uncle Jack and Aunt Lisa grabbed the beach towels and umbrella and started looking for a good spot to enjoy the sun. I, on the other hand, stepped out of the car slowly. I had to come up with a plan of action.

Time: _____ minutes:seconds

ORAL READING WORDS PER MINUTE, PERCENT OF ACCURACY

Use the student's oral reading time to circle the WPM range.

Word Count: 255

	INTRVN	INSTR	IND	ADV
Minutes:Seconds	3:26 or more	3:25–2:27	2:26–1:49	1:48 or less
WPM	74 or less	75–104	105–140	141 or more

Count the number of miscues that are not self-corrected. Circle the percent of accuracy based on the number of miscues.

	INTRVN	INSTR	IND		ADV	
Number of Miscues	12 or more	9–11	7–8	4–6	1–3	0
Percent of Accuracy	95 or less	96	97	98	99	100

- If the student's score falls in a shaded area for either WPM or Accuracy, STOP! Reassess with a lower-level text at another time.

3. COMPREHENSION

PREDICTION

Students do not use the text when making their predictions.

T: Follow the directions on the first page of your Student Booklet. After you have finished your predictions, come to me (or raise your hand).

Note: For students who have an Individual Education Plan in place for reading and/or written communication, follow the directions in their plan. You may read aloud the prompts in the Student Booklet and/or scribe their responses if required. Give <u>no</u> additional prompts.

While the student completes the Prediction page, complete the Teacher Analysis of Oral Reading below and circle the descriptors on the *DRA2* Continuum that best describe the student's oral reading fluency.

Note: After the student has completed the Prediction page, continue with the assessment if time permits. Otherwise, have the student read the book and complete the Student Booklet at another time.

STUDENT READS AND RESPONDS

All students may use the text to complete pages 2–4 of the Student Booklet.

T: Read the story. When you are finished, write a summary of what you have read and answer the remaining questions in the Student Booklet. If you have questions, please come to me (or raise your hand).

4. TEACHER ANALYSIS

ORAL READING

If the student had 5 or more different miscues, use the information recorded on the Record of Oral Reading to complete the chart below.

Student problem-solves words using:		
☐ blending letters/sounds ☐ letter-sound clusters	Number of miscues not self-corrected: ____ Number of words told to the student: ____	

☐ onset and rime
☐ knowledge of spelling patterns (analogies)
☐ syllables
☐ rereading
☐ no observable behaviors
	Miscues interfered with meaning:
	☐ never
	☐ at times
	☐ often
		Miscues included:
		☐ omissions
		☐ insertions
		☐ reversals
		☐ substitutions that were
		    ☐ visually similar
		    ☐ not visually similar

Copy each substitution to help analyze the student's attention to visual information. e.g., <u>already</u> (substitution) ready (text)		

Oral Reading Rate: (Optional) Use the formula below to determine the student's exact oral reading rate. Convert the student's reading time to all seconds.

$$255 \text{ (words)} \div \underline{\hspace{2cm}} \text{ total seconds} = \underline{\hspace{2cm}} \text{ WPS} \times 60 = \underline{\hspace{2cm}} \text{ WPM}$$

DRA2 Continuum

- Use the information from the Student Reading Survey and the Student Booklet to circle the descriptors that best describe the student's responses.
- Add the circled numbers to obtain a total score for each section.
- Record the scores at the top of page 1. Record the Comprehension score at the top of page 4 after the colon.

Note: If the Comprehension score is less than 12, administer *DRA2* with a lower-level text.

Name/Date _____   Teacher/Grade _____

DRA2 CONTINUUM

	INTERVENTION	INSTRUCTIONAL	INDEPENDENT	ADVANCED
Reading Engagement				
Wide Reading	**1** Title(s) below grade level; limited reading experiences and book knowledge	**2** 2–3 titles slightly below grade level; some reading experiences	**3** At least 4 titles from 2–3 genres or multiple books from 1 genre; generally on-grade-level texts	**4** Wide variety of titles across 3 or more genres; many on- and above-grade-level texts
Self-Assessment/ Goal Setting	**1** No strengths and/or goals related to the reading process; no real plan	**2** General strengths and goals (e.g., read more); general plan	**3** At least 1–2 specific strengths and goals related to the reading process; relevant plan	**4** 3 specific strengths and goals related to the reading process; 2–3-step plan
Score	2 3	4 5	6 7	8
Oral Reading Fluency				
Expression	**1** Monotone; little expression	**2** Some expression that conveys meaning	**3** Expression reflects mood, pace, and tension at times	**4** Expression reflects mood, pace, and tension most of the time
Phrasing	**1** Mostly word-by-word	**2** Inappropriate pauses; shorter phrases most of the time	**3** Generally appropriate pauses; heeds most punctuation; longer, meaningful phrases most of the time	**4** Appropriate pauses; heeds all punctuation; consistently longer, meaningful phrases
Rate	**1** 74 WPM or less	**2** 75–104 WPM	**3** 105–140 WPM	**4** 141 WPM or more
Accuracy	**1** 95% or less	**2** 96%	**3** 97%–98%	**4** 99%–100%
Score	4 5 6	7 8 9 10	11 12 13 14	15 16
Comprehension				
Questioning/Prediction	**1** Illogical or unrelated questions(s) and/or prediction(s)	**2** 1–2 reasonable questions and/or predictions related to the text	**3** At least 2 reasonable questions and predictions that go beyond the text read aloud	**4** At least 3 thoughtful questions and predictions that go beyond the text read aloud
Summary	**1** 1–2 events in own language and/or copied text; may include incorrect information	**2** Partial summary; generally in own language; some important characters/events; may include misinterpretations	**3** Summary in own language; includes most of the important characters' names, some details, and many of the important events in sequence from the beginning, middle, and end	**4** Well-organized summary in own language; includes all important characters' names, specific details, and all important events from the beginning, middle, and end
Literal Comprehension	**1** Little information from the text and/or incorrect information	**2** Partial information from the text; may include misinterpretation	**3** Information from the text that accurately responds to question(s) or prompt(s)	**4** All important information from the text that effectively responds to question(s) or prompt(s)
Interpretation	**1** Little or no understanding of important text implication(s)	**2** Partial understanding of important text implication(s); little or no detail	**3** Understands important text implication(s); relevant supporting details	**4** Insightful understanding of important text implication(s); important supporting details
Reflection	**1** Insignificant or unrelated message or event; no reason for opinion or no response	**2** Less significant message or event and general reason(s) for opinion	**3** Significant message or event and a relevant reason for opinion	**4** Significant message or event and reason(s) for opinion that reflect higher-level thinking
Metacognitive Awareness	**1** Unrelated or no example(s); may copy a strategy	**2** General or limited example(s)	**3** At least 1 specific example from the text related to the identified strategy; may include details	**4** At least 2 specific examples from the text related to the identified strategy; includes details
Score	6 7 8 9 10 11	12 13 14 15 16	17 18 19 20 21 22	23 24

Choose three to five teaching/learning activities on the *DRA2* Focus for Instruction on the next page.

All the Way Under **40**

DRA2 FOCUS FOR INSTRUCTION

READING ENGAGEMENT

Wide Reading

- ☐ Teach student strategies to select appropriately leveled texts for independent reading
- ☐ Introduce student to reading materials from a variety of genres and purposes
- ☐ Teach strategies to build reading stamina
- ☐ Create structures and/or routines to support reading at home
- ☐ Develop and monitor clear expectations for amount of independent reading
- ☐ Teach student how to use a reading log to monitor book selection and set reading goals

Self-Assessment/Goal Setting

- ☐ Model and discuss strategies good readers use
- ☐ Help student identify 1–2 reading goals and a plan of action to improve reading
- ☐ Support revision of ongoing reading goals

ORAL READING FLUENCY

Expression and Phrasing

- ☐ Model and teach reading in longer, meaningful phrases with appropriate expression
- ☐ Have student practice appropriate expression with familiar texts
- ☐ Have student participate in choral reading and/or reader's theater
- ☐ Teach student to heed punctuation

Rate

- ☐ Provide materials and time for repeated readings and timed readings to increase reading rate
- ☐ Give opportunities for student to read lower-level and/or familiar texts at an appropriate rate

Accuracy: Word Analysis

- ☐ Support and reinforce self-corrections of miscues
- ☐ Model and support how to take words apart (e.g., onset and rime, syllables) to problem-solve unknown words
- ☐ Teach how to use word chunks and analogies to problem-solve unknown words
- ☐ Provide spelling activities and word sorts to help student recognize patterns in words

COMPREHENSION

Questioning/Prediction

- ☐ Provide opportunities for student to discuss what he or she knows about the characters and setting based on title and book cover, as well as opening paragraphs and illustrations of texts read aloud
- ☐ Teach student how to make and confirm predictions prior to and during reading
- ☐ Model and support using background information to make meaningful predictions
- ☐ Model and support using knowledge of text structures/genre characteristics to make predictions

Summary

- ☐ Share and identify characteristics of good summaries
- ☐ Model and co-construct written summaries of texts read aloud
- ☐ Model and support how to distinguish between more important and less important ideas and details
- ☐ Model and support how to write a summary in one's own words
- ☐ Teach student how to use a graphic organizer as an aid to creating a summary
- ☐ Teach student how to identify story elements (e.g., characters, setting, plot)
- ☐ Provide time for student how to practice oral and written summaries

Literal Comprehension

- ☐ Show student how to use key words to identify specific information from the text
- ☐ Provide opportunities for student to answer and construct literal questions
- ☐ Help student locate and record specific details
- ☐ Teach student how to use and construct graphic organizers to keep track of story information

Interpretation

- ☐ Teach and share examples of inferences
- ☐ Model and support how to identify important text implications
- ☐ Provide opportunities for student to support inferences with examples from the text
- ☐ Give student opportunities to respond to and construct inference questions orally and in writing

Reflection

- ☐ Help student identify important information and/or key vocabulary in a variety of texts
- ☐ Provide opportunities to identify and discuss a significant message or event in a story
- ☐ Provide opportunities to discuss theme/most important idea of stories read aloud
- ☐ Demonstrate and teach student how to support opinion with details from the text

Metacognitive Awareness

- ☐ Model and teach comprehension strategies for fiction texts
- ☐ Provide opportunities for student to practice using a specific comprehension strategy (e.g., making connections, visualizing, responding emotionally)
- ☐ Help student identify examples in a text where he or she used a specific strategy

OTHER

_____

_____

Name _____   Date _____

Teacher _____   Grade _____

BEFORE READING

PREDICTION

List 3 questions that you had while reading the first part of this story.

1. _____

   _____

2. _____

   _____

3. _____

   _____

What are 3 things that you think might happen in the rest of this story?

1. _____

   _____

2. _____

   _____

3. _____

   _____

Let your teacher know when you have completed this page.

All the Way Under

AFTER READING

SUMMARY

Write a summary of this story in your own words. Include the important characters, events, and details from the beginning, middle, and end of the story. You may use the book to help you write your summary.

_____

_____

_____

_____

_____

_____

_____

_____

_____

_____

_____

_____

_____

_____

_____

_____

LITERAL COMPREHENSION

List 3 things that you know about Sonya.

Sonya

1. _____

2. _____

3. _____

INTERPRETATION

How did Sonya's feeling about being at the beach change in this story? _____

_____

_____

_____

_____

REFLECTION

What do you think is the most important event in this story? _____

_____

_____

_____

_____

Tell why you think that event is important. _____

_____

_____

_____

_____

All the Way Under

METACOGNITIVE AWARENESS

Check 1 strategy that you used to help you understand this story.

☐   I thought about similar experiences and stories.

☐   I asked myself questions as I read.

☐   I pictured what was happening.

☐   I thought about the reason why things happened.

☐   I understood the character's feelings.

Give at least 2 specific examples from this story that show how you used this comprehension strategy.

_____

_____

_____

_____

_____

Reread what you have written to make sure your answers are the way you want them before you hand in your booklet.

Name/Date _____   Teacher/Grade _____

Scores: Reading Engagement ___/8   Oral Reading Fluency ___/16   Comprehension ___/24
Independent Range: 6–7   11–14   17–22

Book Selection   Text selected by: ☐ teacher   ☐ student

1. READING ENGAGEMENT

Ask the student to bring his or her completed Student Reading Survey to the conference.

2. ORAL READING FLUENCY

INTRODUCTION

T: *This informational text,* The Amazing Octopus, *tells some interesting facts about the octopus. Please read aloud to the star on page 2.* Show the student where to stop reading at the ✱.

RECORD OF ORAL READING

Record the student's oral reading behaviors. Note the student's fluency (expression and phrasing). Be sure to time the student's reading.

Page 2

The   Octopus

Deep in the ocean lives a creature known for its tricks. It can get out of the tightest places. It can change its shape and its color in less than a second. This creature is **coldblooded** and is called an octopus. More than 150 kinds of octopuses can be found around the world. The smallest is the size of a thumb. The biggest is more than 20 feet from arm tip to arm tip.

An octopus has no **backbone**. It has a body shaped like a balloon that is covered by a **mantle**. It has eight arms. Each arm has rows of **suckers**. Most kinds of octopuses have about 2,000 suckers. These suckers help an octopus to pick up and eat food. They also help it to cling to a hiding place. Octopus arms are always busy. They use their arms to walk, crawl, dig, and eat.

An octopus has two eyes. It can turn its eyes in half circles without moving its head. Its eyesight is very sharp. An octopus uses **gills** and a **funnel** for breathing. Its funnel also helps the octopus move through water.

Time: _____ minutes:seconds

ORAL READING WORDS PER MINUTE, PERCENT OF ACCURACY
Use the student's oral reading time to circle the WPM range.

Word Count: 189

	INTRVN	INSTR	IND	ADV
Minutes:Seconds	2:44 or more	2:43–1:54	1:53–1:24	1:23 or less
WPM	69 or less	70–99	100–135	136 or more

Count the number of miscues that are not self-corrected. Circle the percent of accuracy based on the number of miscues.

	INTRVN	INSTR	IND		ADV	
Number of Miscues	9 or more	7–8	5–6	3–4	1–2	0
Percent of Accuracy	95 or less	96	97	98	99	100

- If the student's score falls in a shaded area for either WPM or Accuracy, STOP! Reassess with a lower-level text at another time.

3. COMPREHENSION

PREDICTION
Students do not use the text when making their predictions.

T: Follow the directions on the first page of your Student Booklet. After you have finished your predictions, come to me (or raise your hand).

Note: For students who have an Individual Education Plan in place for reading and/or written communication, follow the directions in their plan. You may read aloud the prompts in the Student Booklet and/or scribe their responses if required. Give <u>no</u> additional prompts.

While the student completes the Prediction page, complete the Teacher Analysis of Oral Reading on the next page and circle the descriptors on the *DRA2* Continuum that best describe the student's oral reading fluency.

Note: After the student has completed the Prediction page, continue with the assessment if time permits. Otherwise, have the student read the book and complete the Student Booklet at another time.

STUDENT READS AND RESPONDS

All students may use the text to complete pages 2–4 of the Student Booklet.

T: Read the book. When you are finished, write a summary of what you have read and answer the remaining questions in the Student Booklet. If you have questions, please come to me (or raise your hand).

4. TEACHER ANALYSIS

ORAL READING

If the student had 5 or more different miscues, use the information recorded on the Record of Oral Reading to complete the chart below.

Student problem-solves words using:	Number of miscues not self-corrected: ____ Number of words told to the student: ____	

☐ blending letters/sounds
 ☐ letter-sound clusters
 ☐ onset and rime
 ☐ knowledge of spelling patterns (analogies)
 ☐ syllables
 ☐ rereading
 ☐ no observable behaviors
	Miscues interfered with meaning:
	 ☐ never
	 ☐ at times
	 ☐ often
		Miscues included:
		 ☐ omissions
		 ☐ insertions
		 ☐ reversals
		 ☐ substitutions that were
		     ☐ visually similar
		     ☐ not visually similar

Copy each substitution to help analyze the student's attention to visual information. e.g., <u>stickers</u> (substitution) suckers (text)		

Oral Reading Rate: (Optional) Use the formula below to determine the student's exact oral reading rate. Convert the student's reading time to all seconds.

189 (words) ÷ _____ total seconds = _____ WPS × 60 = _____ WPM

DRA2 Continuum

- Use the information from the Student Reading Survey and the Student Booklet to circle the descriptors that best describe the student's responses.
- Add the circled numbers to obtain a total score for each section.
- Record the scores at the top of page 1. Record the Comprehension score at the top of page 4 after the colon.

Note: If the Comprehension score is less than 12, administer *DRA2* with a lower-level text.

The Amazing Octopus **40**

Name/Date _____ Teacher/Grade _____

DRA2 CONTINUUM

	INTERVENTION	INSTRUCTIONAL	INDEPENDENT	ADVANCED
Reading Engagement				
Wide Reading	1 Title(s) below grade level; limited reading experiences and book knowledge	2 2–3 titles slightly below grade level; some reading experiences	3 At least 4 titles from 2–3 genres or multiple books from 1 genre; generally on-grade-level texts	4 Wide variety of titles across 3 or more genres; many on- and above-grade-level texts
Self-Assessment/ Goal Setting	1 No strengths and/or goals related to the reading process; no real plan	2 General strengths and goals (e.g., read more); general plan	3 At least 1–2 specific strengths and goals related to the reading process; relevant plan	4 3 specific strengths and goals related to the reading process; 2–3-step plan
Score	2 3	4 5	6 7	8
Oral Reading Fluency				
Expression	1 Monotone; very little expression	2 Some expression that conveys meaning	3 Expression emphasizing key phrases and words at times	4 Expression emphasizing key phrases and words effectively
Phrasing	1 Mostly word-by-word	2 Inappropriate pauses; shorter phrases most of the time	3 Generally appropriate pauses; heeds most punctuation; longer, meaningful phrases most of the time	4 Appropriate pauses; heeds all punctuation; consistently longer, meaningful phrases
Rate	1 69 WPM or less	2 70–99 WPM	3 100–135 WPM	4 136 WPM or more
Accuracy	1 95% or less	2 96%	3 97%–98%	4 99%–100%
Score	4 5 6	7 8 9 10	11 12 13 14	15 16
Comprehension				
Questioning/Prediction	1 Illogical or unrelated question(s) and/or prediction(s)	2 1–2 reasonable questions and/or predictions related to the text	3 At least 2 reasonable questions and predictions that go beyond the text read aloud	4 At least 3 thoughtful questions and predictions that go beyond the text read aloud
Summary	1 1–2 ideas/facts in own language and/or copied text; may include incorrect information	2 Partial summary; generally in own language; some important ideas/facts; may include misinterpretations	3 Summary in own language; includes many important ideas, some vocabulary, and supporting facts from each section	4 Summary in own language; includes all important ideas, key vocabulary, and supporting facts from each section
Literal Comprehension	1 Little information from the text and/or incorrect information	2 Partial information from the text; may include misinterpretation	3 Information from the text that accurately responds to question(s) or prompt(s)	4 All important information from the text that effectively responds to question(s) or prompt(s)
Interpretation	1 Little or no understanding of important text implication(s)	2 Partial understanding of important text implication(s); little or no detail	3 Understands important text implication(s); relevant supporting details	4 Insightful understanding of important text implication(s); important supporting details
Reflection	1 Insignificant or unrelated message or information; no reason for opinion or no response	2 Less significant message or information and general reason(s) for opinion	3 Significant message or information and a relevant reason for opinion	4 Significant message or information and reason(s) for opinion that reflect higher-level thinking
Metacognitive Awareness	1 Unrelated or no example(s); may copy a strategy	2 General or limited example(s)	3 At least 1 specific example from the text related to the identified strategy; may include details	4 At least 2 specific examples from the text related to the identified strategy; includes details
Score	6 7 8 9 10 11	12 13 14 15 16	17 18 19 20 21 22	23 24

Choose three to five teaching/learning activities on the *DRA2* Focus for Instruction on the next page.

The Amazing Octopus 40

DRA2 FOCUS FOR INSTRUCTION

READING ENGAGEMENT

Wide Reading
- ☐ Teach student strategies to select appropriately leveled texts for independent reading
- ☐ Introduce student to reading materials from a variety of genres and purposes
- ☐ Teach strategies to build reading stamina
- ☐ Create structures and/or routines to support reading at home
- ☐ Develop and monitor clear expectations for amount of independent reading
- ☐ Teach student how to use a reading log to monitor book selection and set reading goals

Self-Assessment/Goal Setting
- ☐ Model and discuss strategies good readers use
- ☐ Help student identify 1–2 reading goals and a plan of action to improve reading
- ☐ Support revision of ongoing reading goals

ORAL READING FLUENCY

Expression and Phrasing
- ☐ Model and teach reading in longer, meaningful phrases with appropriate expression
- ☐ Have student practice appropriate expression with familiar texts
- ☐ Teach student to recognize and emphasize key phrases and words
- ☐ Teach student to heed punctuation

Rate
- ☐ Provide materials and time for repeated readings and timed readings to increase reading rate
- ☐ Give opportunities for student to read lower-level and/or familiar texts at an appropriate rate

Accuracy: Word Analysis
- ☐ Support and reinforce self-corrections of miscues
- ☐ Model and support how to take words apart (e.g., onset and rime, syllables) to problem-solve unknown words
- ☐ Teach how to use word chunks and analogies to problem-solve unknown words
- ☐ Provide spelling activities and word sorts to help student recognize patterns in words

COMPREHENSION

Questioning/Prediction
- ☐ Provide opportunities for student to make and confirm predictions based on title, table of contents, and headings
- ☐ Model and support using background information to make meaningful predictions
- ☐ Model and teach student how to pose questions as a basis for predictions

Summary
- ☐ Share and identify characteristics of good summaries
- ☐ Model and co-construct written summaries of texts read aloud
- ☐ Model and support how to distinguish between more important and less important ideas and facts
- ☐ Model and support how to write a summary in one's own words
- ☐ Model and support how to use examples from the text
- ☐ Teach student how to use headings to organize a summary of an informational/nonfiction text
- ☐ Provide time for student to practice oral and written summaries

Literal Comprehension
- ☐ Show student how to use key words to identify specific information from the text
- ☐ Provide opportunities for student to answer and construct literal questions
- ☐ Model and support how to locate and use nonfiction text features (e.g., charts, graphs, maps, tables, headings, glossary, bold words, etc.)
- ☐ Teach student how to use and construct graphic organizers to keep track of key ideas and facts

Interpretation
- ☐ Teach and share examples of inferences
- ☐ Provide opportunities for student to support inferences with information or examples from the text
- ☐ Give student opportunities to respond to and construct inference questions orally and in writing
- ☐ Model and support how to interpret nonfiction text features (e.g., how to read a chart or diagram)

Reflection
- ☐ Help student identify important information and/or key vocabulary in a variety of texts
- ☐ Demonstrate how to support opinion with details from the text

Metacognitive Awareness
- ☐ Model and teach comprehension strategies for nonfiction texts
- ☐ Provide opportunities for student to practice using a specific comprehension strategy (e.g., making connections, visualizing, etc.)
- ☐ Help student identify examples in a text where he or she used a specific strategy

OTHER

_____

_____

_____

Name _____   Date _____

Teacher _____   Grade _____

BEFORE READING

PREDICTION

What questions did you have as you were reading the first part of this text?

1. _____

_____

2. _____

_____

3. _____

_____

What do you think you will learn from reading the rest of this text?

1. _____

_____

2. _____

_____

3. _____

_____

Let your teacher know when you have completed this page.

AFTER READING

SUMMARY

Write a summary of this book in your own words. Include the important ideas and facts from each section. You may use the book to help you write your summary.

_____

_____

_____

_____

_____

_____

_____

_____

_____

_____

_____

_____

_____

_____

_____

_____

The Amazing Octopus

Literal Comprehension

List 3 facts about an octopus.

Octopus Facts
1. _____
2. _____
3. _____

INTERPRETATION

What do you think would happen if there were no octopus predators in the ocean?

_____

_____

_____

_____

REFLECTION

What do you think is the most important thing about octopuses? _____

_____

_____

_____

Tell why you think this is important. _____

_____

_____

_____

METACOGNITIVE AWARENESS

Check 1 strategy that you used to help you understand this text.

☐   I recalled what I know about the topic.

☐   I asked myself questions as I read.

☐   I made connections.

☐   I thought about the reason why things happened.

☐   I pictured what was happening.

Give at least 2 specific examples from this book that show how you used this comprehension strategy.

_____

_____

_____

_____

_____

Reread what you have written to make sure your answers are the way you want them before you hand in your booklet.

The Amazing Octopus

Name/Date _____   Teacher/Grade _____

Scores: Reading Engagement ___/8   Oral Reading Fluency ___/16   Comprehension ___/24
Independent Range: 6–7   11–14   17–22

Book Selection   Text selected by: ☐ teacher   ☐ student

1. READING ENGAGEMENT

Ask the student to bring his or her completed Student Reading Survey to the conference.

2. ORAL READING FLUENCY

INTRODUCTION

T: In this story, A Journey to Freedom, *Bess and her son, Jed, run away from their home in the South to escape slavery. Please read aloud to the star on page 3.* Show the student where to stop reading at the ✱.

RECORD OF ORAL READING

Record the student's oral reading behaviors. Note the student's fluency (expression and phrasing). Be sure to time the student's reading.

Page 2

After a hard day of picking cotton, Jed went into the slave cabin. He lay down on the narrow board that was his bed. A few minutes later he heard his mother, Bess, come in. Jed expected to feel his mother's soft kiss and to hear her whisper, "Good night."

Instead, Jed heard her whisper, "We have to leave this place tonight. Master Boyd is dying. When I was sewing in the plantation house, I overheard Master Boyd's son. He said that he plans to sell some of the young slaves as soon as his father dies."

Jed shuddered. He knew that Master Boyd had promised never to separate him from his mother, but Mr. Boyd's son had made no such promise. Slave mothers and children were often separated, forever. His mother had always told him that she would never let that happen. But what could his mother do to prevent it?

"Get up, Jed," said his mother. "Get your coat and hat, and be as quiet as you can. Not a word until I tell you it's safe!"

Jed quickly grabbed his things and followed his mother. Jed was sure his beating heart would wake the others before they left the rundown slave cabin.

Page 3

Bess held her son's hand tightly as they darted for the woods. Jed stumbled along after his mother. His mind was full of questions. Where were they running to? How did his mother know which way to run? Neither of them had ever been outside of the plantation.

Time: _____ minutes:seconds

ORAL READING WORDS PER MINUTE, PERCENT OF ACCURACY

Use the student's oral reading time to circle the WPM range.

Word Count: 253

	INTRVN	INSTR	IND	ADV
Minutes:Seconds	3:24 or more	3:23–2:26	2:25–1:49	1:48 or less
WPM	74 or less	75–104	105–140	141 or more

Count the number of miscues that are not self-corrected. Circle the percent of accuracy based on the number of miscues.

	INTRVN	INSTR	IND		ADV	
Number of Miscues	12 or more	9–11	7–8	4–6	1–3	0
Percent of Accuracy	95 or less	96	97	98	99	100

- If the student's score falls in a shaded area for either WPM or Accuracy, STOP! Reassess with a lower-level text at another time.

3. COMPREHENSION

PREDICTION

Students do not use the text when making their predictions.

T: Follow the directions on the first page of your Student Booklet. After you have finished your predictions, come to me (or raise your hand).

Note: For students who have an Individual Education Plan in place for reading and/or written communication, follow the directions in their plan. You may read aloud the prompts in the Student Booklet and/or scribe their responses if required. Give <u>no</u> additional prompts.

While the student completes the Prediction page, complete the Teacher Analysis of Oral Reading on the next page and circle the descriptors on the *DRA2* Continuum that best describe the student's oral reading fluency.

Note: After the student has completed the Prediction page, continue with the assessment if time permits. Otherwise, have the student read the book and complete the Student Booklet at another time.

STUDENT READS AND RESPONDS

All students may use the text to complete pages 2–4 of the Student Booklet.

T: Read the story. When you are finished, write a summary of what you have read and answer the remaining questions in the Student Booklet. If you have questions, please come to me (or raise your hand).

4. TEACHER ANALYSIS

ORAL READING

If the student had 5 or more different miscues, use the information recorded on the Record of Oral Reading to complete the chart below.

Student problem-solves words using:	Number of miscues not self-corrected: ____ Number of words told to the student: ____	

☐ blending letters/sounds
☐ letter-sound clusters
☐ onset and rime
☐ knowledge of spelling patterns (analogies)
☐ syllables
☐ rereading
☐ no observable behaviors
	Miscues interfered with meaning:
	☐ never
	☐ at times
	☐ often
		Miscues included:
		☐ omissions
		☐ insertions
		☐ reversals
		☐ substitutions that were
		     ☐ visually similar
		     ☐ not visually similar

Copy each substitution to help analyze the student's attention to visual information. e.g., <u>plantain</u> (substitution)
                                                                                                      plantation (text)

Oral Reading Rate: (Optional) Use the formula below to determine the student's exact oral reading rate. Convert the student's reading time to all seconds.

$$253 \text{ (words)} \div \underline{\hspace{1cm}} \text{ total seconds} = \underline{\hspace{1cm}} \text{ WPS} \times 60 = \underline{\hspace{1cm}} \text{ WPM}$$

DRA2 Continuum

- Use the information from the Student Reading Survey and the Student Booklet to circle the descriptors that best describe the student's responses.
- Add the circled numbers to obtain a total score for each section.
- Record the scores at the top of page 1. Record the Comprehension score at the top of page 5 after the colon.

Note: If the Comprehension score is less than 12, administer *DRA2* with a lower-level text.

Name/Date _____ Teacher/Grade _____

Comprehension Score
40:

DRA2 CONTINUUM

	INTERVENTION	INSTRUCTIONAL	INDEPENDENT	ADVANCED
Reading Engagement				
Wide Reading	1 Title(s) below grade level; limited reading experiences and book knowledge	2 2–3 titles slightly below grade level; some reading experiences	3 At least 4 titles from 2–3 genres or multiple books from 1 genre; generally on-grade-level texts	4 Wide variety of titles across 3 or more genres; many on- and above-grade-level texts
Self-Assessment/ Goal Setting	1 No strengths and/or goals related to the reading process; no real plan	2 General strengths and goals (e.g., read more); general plan	3 At least 1–2 specific strengths and goals related to the reading process; relevant plan	4 3 specific strengths and goals related to the reading process; 2–3-step plan
Score	2 3	4 5	6 7	8
Oral Reading Fluency				
Expression	1 Monotone; very little expression	2 Some expression that conveys meaning	3 Expression reflects mood, pace, and tension at times	4 Expression reflects mood, pace, and tension most of the time
Phrasing	1 Mostly word-by-word	2 Inappropriate pauses; shorter phrases most of the time	3 Generally appropriate pauses; heeds most punctuation; longer, meaningful phrases most of the time	4 Appropriate pauses; heeds all punctuation; consistently longer, meaningful phrases
Rate	1 74 WPM or less	2 75–104 WPM	3 105–140 WPM	4 141 WPM or more
Accuracy	1 95% or less	2 96%	3 97%–98%	4 99%–100%
Score	4 5 6	7 8 9 10	11 12 13 14	15 16
Comprehension				
Questioning/Prediction	1 Illogical or unrelated questions(s) and/or prediction(s)	2 1–2 reasonable questions and/or predictions related to the text	3 At least 2 reasonable questions and predictions that go beyond the text read aloud	4 At least 3 thoughtful questions and predictions that go beyond the text read aloud
Summary	1 1–2 events in own language and/or copied text; may include incorrect information	2 Partial summary; generally in own language; some important characters/events; may include misinterpretations	3 Summary in own language; includes most of the important characters' names, some details, and many of the important events in sequence from the beginning, middle, and end	4 Well-organized summary in own language; includes all important characters' names, specific details, and all important events from the beginning, middle, and end
Literal Comprehension	1 Little information from the text and/or incorrect information	2 Partial information from the text; may include misinterpretation	3 Information from the text that accurately responds to question(s) or prompt(s)	4 All important information from the text that effectively responds to question(s) or prompt(s)
Interpretation	1 Little or no understanding of important text implication(s)	2 Partial understanding of important text implication(s); little or no detail	3 Understands important text implication(s); relevant supporting details	4 Insightful understanding of important text implication(s); important supporting details
Reflection	1 Insignificant or unrelated message or event; no reason for opinion or no response	2 Less significant message or event and general reason(s) for opinion	3 Significant message or event and a relevant reason for opinion	4 Significant message or event and reason(s) for opinion that reflect higher-level thinking
Metacognitive Awareness	1 Unrelated or no example(s); may copy a strategy	2 General or limited example(s)	3 At least 1 specific example from the text related to the identified strategy; may include details	4 At least 2 specific examples from the text related to the identified strategy; includes details
Score	6 7 8 9 10 11	12 13 14 15 16	17 18 19 20 21 22	23 24

Choose three to five learning/teaching activities on the *DRA2* Focus for Instruction on the next page.

A Journey to Freedom 40

DRA2 FOCUS FOR INSTRUCTION

READING ENGAGEMENT

Wide Reading
☐ Teach student strategies to select appropriately leveled texts for independent reading
☐ Introduce student to reading materials from a variety of genres and purposes
☐ Teach strategies to build reading stamina
☐ Create structures and/or routines to support reading at home
☐ Develop and monitor clear expectations for amount of independent reading
☐ Teach student how to use a reading log to monitor book selection and set reading goals

Self-Assessment/Goal Setting
☐ Model and discuss strategies good readers use
☐ Help student identify 1–2 reading goals and a plan of action to improve reading
☐ Support revision of ongoing reading goals

ORAL READING FLUENCY

Expression and Phrasing
☐ Model and teach reading in longer, meaningful phrases with appropriate expression
☐ Have student practice appropriate expression with familiar texts
☐ Have student participate in choral reading and/or reader's theater
☐ Teach student to heed punctuation

Rate
☐ Provide materials and time for repeated readings and timed readings to increase reading rate
☐ Give opportunities for student to read lower-level and/or familiar texts at an appropriate rate

Accuracy: Word Analysis
☐ Support and reinforce self-corrections of miscues
☐ Model and support how to take words apart (e.g., onset and rime, syllables) to problem-solve unknown words
☐ Teach how to use word chunks and analogies to problem-solve unknown words
☐ Provide spelling activities and word sorts to help student recognize patterns in words

COMPREHENSION

Questioning/Prediction
☐ Provide opportunities for student to discuss what he or she knows about the characters and setting based on title and book cover, as well as opening paragraphs and illustrations of texts read aloud
☐ Teach student how to make and confirm predictions prior to and during reading
☐ Model and support using background information to make meaningful predictions
☐ Model and support using knowledge of text structures/genre characteristics to make predictions

Summary
☐ Share and identify characteristics of good summaries
☐ Model and co-construct written summaries of texts read aloud
☐ Model and support how to distinguish between more important and less important ideas and details
☐ Model and support how to write a summary in one's own words
☐ Teach student how to use a graphic organizer as an aid to creating a summary
☐ Teach student how to identify story elements (e.g., characters, setting, plot)
☐ Provide time for student to practice oral and written summaries

Literal Comprehension
☐ Show student how to use key words to identify specific information from the text
☐ Provide opportunities for student to answer and construct literal questions
☐ Help student locate and record specific details
☐ Teach student how to use and construct graphic organizers to keep track of story information

Interpretation
☐ Teach and share examples of inferences
☐ Model and support how to identify important text implications
☐ Provide opportunities for student to support inferences with examples from the text
☐ Give student opportunities to respond to inference questions orally and in writing

Reflection
☐ Help student identify important information and/or key vocabulary in a variety of texts
☐ Provide opportunities to identify and discuss a significant message or event in a story
☐ Provide opportunities to discuss theme/most important idea of stories read aloud
☐ Demonstrate and teach student how to support opinion with details from the text

Metacognitive Awareness
☐ Model and teach comprehension strategies for fiction texts
☐ Provide opportunities for student to practice using a specific comprehension strategy (e.g., making connections, visualizing, responding emotionally)
☐ Help student identify examples in a text where he or she used a specific strategy

OTHER

_____

_____

Name _____ Date _____

Teacher _____ Grade _____

BEFORE READING

PREDICTION

List 3 questions that you had while reading the first part of this story.

1. _____

_____

2. _____

_____

3. _____

_____

What are 3 things that you think might happen in the rest of this story?

1. _____

_____

2. _____

_____

3. _____

_____

Let your teacher know when you have completed this page.

AFTER READING

Summary

Write a summary of this story in your own words. Include the important characters, events, and details from the beginning, middle, and end of the story. You may use the book to help you write your summary.

_____

_____

_____

_____

_____

_____

_____

_____

_____

_____

_____

_____

_____

_____

_____

_____

LITERAL COMPREHENSION

List 3 things that you know about Jed.

Jed

1. _____

2. _____

3. _____

INTERPRETATION

Why do you think Jed wanted to be an Underground Railroad conductor? _____

_____

_____

_____

_____

_____

_____

REFLECTION

What do you think is the most important event in this story? _____

_____

_____

_____

Tell why you think that event is important. _____

_____

_____

_____

A Journey to Freedom

Metacognitive Awareness

Check 1 strategy that you used to help you understand this story.

☐   I thought about similar experiences and stories.

☐   I asked myself questions as I read.

☐   I pictured what was happening.

☐   I thought about the reason why things happened.

☐   I understood the character's feelings.

Give at least 2 specific examples from this story that show how you used this comprehension strategy.

_____

_____

_____

_____

_____

_____

Reread what you have written to make sure your answers are the way you want them before you hand in your booklet.

Name/Date _____　　　Teacher/Grade _____

Scores: 　　Reading Engagement ___/8　　Oral Reading Fluency ___/16　　Comprehension ___/24
Independent Range: 　　　　　　6–7　　　　　　　　　　11–14　　　　　　　　　17–22

Book Selection 　　Text selected by:　　☐ teacher　　　☐ student

1. READING ENGAGEMENT

Ask the student to bring his or her completed Student Reading Survey to the conference.

2. ORAL READING FLUENCY

INTRODUCTION

T: This informational text, A Pack of Wolves, *tells about wolves that live in North America. Please read aloud to the star on page 2.* Show the student where to stop reading at the ✱.

RECORD OF ORAL READING

Record the student's oral reading behaviors. Note the student's fluency (expression and phrasing). Be sure to time the student's reading.

Page 2

The Gray Wolf

Large numbers of gray wolves once lived in North America. For years, humans and wolves shared the land. Early hunters admired the wolf's skill. Then people started to farm, build cities, and raise cattle. They wanted to protect their cattle and pets. They killed about nine out of every ten wolves. That's why today, wolves have disappeared from most states.

Wolves are the largest members of the dog family. There are five types of gray wolves found in North America. They are the eastern timber, Great Plains, Rocky Mountain, Mexican, and Arctic wolves. Adult gray wolves can weigh between 50 and 145 pounds. Males tend to be larger than females. Gray wolves' fur ranges in color from white to gray to black. Their bushy tails are about 2 feet long. In cold climates, a wolf curls its tail around its nose for warmth when it rests.

Wolves have very good senses. With their yellow eyes, they can spot a rabbit trying to hide 400 yards away. Wolves can hear mice under the ground with their large, pointed ears. Their sense of smell is amazing, too. When the wind is just right, a wolf can sniff out its prey about a mile away.

Time: _____ **minutes:seconds**

ORAL READING WORDS PER MINUTE, PERCENT OF ACCURACY

Use the student's oral reading time to circle the WPM range.

Word Count: 205

	INTRVN	INSTR	IND	ADV
Minutes:Seconds	2:57 or more	2:56–2:04	2:03–1:31	1:30 or less
WPM	69 or less	70–99	100–135	136 or more

Count the number of miscues that are not self-corrected. Circle the percent of accuracy based on the number of miscues.

	INTRVN	INSTR	IND		ADV	
Number of Miscues	10 or more	8–9	6–7	4–5	1–3	0
Percent of Accuracy	95 or less	96	97	98	99	100

- If the student's score falls in a shaded area for either WPM or Accuracy, STOP! Reassess with a lower-level text at another time.

3. COMPREHENSION

PREDICTION

Students do not use the text when making their predictions.

T: Follow the directions on the first page of your Student Booklet. After you have finished your predictions, come to me (or raise your hand).

Note: For students who have an Individual Education Plan in place for reading and/or written communication, follow the directions in their plan. You may read aloud the prompts in the Student Booklet and/or scribe their responses if required. Give <u>no</u> additional prompts.

While the student completes the Prediction page, complete the Teacher Analysis of Oral Reading on the next page and circle the descriptors on the *DRA2* Continuum that best describe the student's oral reading fluency.

Note: After the student has completed the Prediction page, continue with the assessment if time permits. Otherwise, have the student read the book and complete the Student Booklet at another time.

STUDENT READS AND RESPONDS

All students may use the text to complete pages 2–4 of the Student Booklet.

T: Read the story. When you are finished, write a summary of what you have read and answer the remaining questions in the Student Booklet. If you have questions, please come to me (or raise your hand).

4. TEACHER ANALYSIS

ORAL READING

If the student had 5 or more different miscues, use the information recorded on the Record of Oral Reading to complete the chart below.

Student problem-solves words using:		
☐ blending letters/sounds ☐ letter-sound clusters ☐ onset and rime ☐ knowledge of spelling patterns (analogies) ☐ syllables ☐ rereading ☐ no observable behaviors	Number of miscues not self-corrected: ____ Number of words told to the student: ____	

	Miscues interfered with meaning:
	 ☐ never
	 ☐ at times
	 ☐ often
		Miscues included:
		 ☐ omissions
		 ☐ insertions
		 ☐ reversals
		 ☐ substitutions that were
		    ☐ visually similar
		    ☐ not visually similar

Copy each substitution to help analyze the student's attention to visual information. e.g., <u>skin</u> (substitution) skill (text)		

Oral Reading Rate: (Optional) Use the formula below to determine the student's exact oral reading rate. Convert the student's reading time to all seconds.

$$205 \text{ (words)} \div \underline{\hspace{1cm}} \text{ total seconds} = \underline{\hspace{1cm}} \text{ WPS} \times 60 = \underline{\hspace{1cm}} \text{ WPM}$$

*DRA*2 Continuum

- Use the information from the Student Reading Survey and the Student Booklet to circle the descriptors that best describe the student's responses.
- Add the circled numbers to obtain a total score for each section.
- Record the scores at the top of page 1. Record the Comprehension score at the top of page 4 after the colon.

Note: If the Comprehension score is less than 12, administer *DRA*2 with a lower-level text.

Comprehension Score
40:

Name/Date _____ Teacher/Grade _____

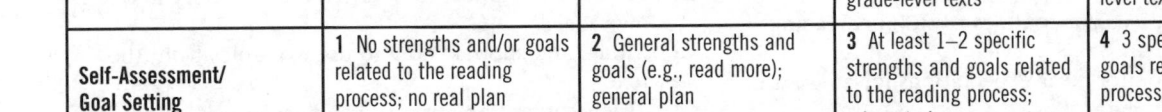

A Pack of Wolves **40**

DRA2 CONTINUUM

	INTERVENTION	INSTRUCTIONAL	INDEPENDENT	ADVANCED
Reading Engagement				
Wide Reading	**1** Title(s) below grade level; limited reading experiences and book knowledge	**2** 2–3 titles slightly below grade level; some reading experiences	**3** At least 4 titles from 2–3 genres or multiple books from 1 genre; generally on-grade-level texts	**4** Wide variety of titles across 3 or more genres; many on- and above-grade-level texts
Self-Assessment/ Goal Setting	**1** No strengths and/or goals related to the reading process; no real plan	**2** General strengths and goals (e.g., read more); general plan	**3** At least 1–2 specific strengths and goals related to the reading process; relevant plan	**4** 3 specific strengths and goals related to the reading process; 2–3-step plan
Score	2 3	4 5	6 7	8
Oral Reading Fluency				
Expression	**1** Monotone; very little expression	**2** Some expression that conveys meaning	**3** Expression emphasizing key phrases and words at times	**4** Expression emphasizing key phrases and words effectively
Phrasing	**1** Mostly word-by-word	**2** Inappropriate pauses; shorter phrases most of the time	**3** Generally appropriate pauses; heeds most punctuation; longer, meaningful phrases most of the time	**4** Appropriate pauses; heeds all punctuation; consistently longer, meaningful phrases
Rate	**1** 69 WPM or less	**2** 70–99 WPM	**3** 100–135 WPM	**4** 136 WPM or more
Accuracy	**1** 95% or less	**2** 96%	**3** 97%–98%	**4** 99%–100%
Score	4 5 6	7 8 9 10	11 12 13 14	15 16
Comprehension				
Questioning/Prediction	**1** Illogical or unrelated question(s) and/or prediction(s)	**2** 1–2 reasonable questions and/or predictions related to the text	**3** At least 2 reasonable questions and predictions that go beyond the text read aloud	**4** At least 3 thoughtful questions and predictions that go beyond the text read aloud
Summary	**1** 1–2 ideas/facts in own language and/or copied text; may include incorrect information	**2** Partial summary; generally in own language; some important ideas/facts; may include misinterpretations	**3** Summary in own language; includes many important ideas, some vocabulary, and supporting facts from each section	**4** Summary in own language; includes all important ideas, key vocabulary, and supporting facts from each section
Literal Comprehension	**1** Little information from the text and/or incorrect information	**2** Partial information from the text; may include misinterpretation	**3** Information from the text that accurately responds to question(s) or prompt(s)	**4** All important information from the text that effectively responds to question(s) or prompt(s)
Interpretation	**1** Little or no understanding of important text implication(s)	**2** Partial understanding of important text implication(s); little or no detail	**3** Understands important text implication(s); relevant supporting details	**4** Insightful understanding of important text implication(s); important supporting details
Reflection	**1** Insignificant or unrelated message or information; no reason for opinion or no response	**2** Less significant message or information and general reason(s) for opinion	**3** Significant message or information and a relevant reason for opinion	**4** Significant message or information and reason(s) for opinion that reflect higher-level thinking
Metacognitive Awareness	**1** Unrelated or no example(s); may copy a strategy	**2** General or limited example(s)	**3** At least 1 specific example from the text related to the identified strategy; may include details	**4** At least 2 specific examples from the text related to the identified strategy; includes details
Score	6 7 8 9 10 11	12 13 14 15 16	17 18 19 20 21 22	23 24

Choose three to five learning/teaching activities on the *DRA2* Focus for Instruction on the next page.

DRA2 FOCUS FOR INSTRUCTION

READING ENGAGEMENT
Wide Reading
- ☐ Teach student strategies to select appropriately leveled texts for independent reading
- ☐ Introduce student to reading materials from a variety of genres and purposes
- ☐ Teach strategies to build reading stamina
- ☐ Create structures and/or routines to support reading at home
- ☐ Develop and monitor clear expectations for amount of independent reading
- ☐ Teach student how to use a reading log to monitor book selection and set reading goals

Self-Assessment/Goal Setting
- ☐ Model and discuss strategies good readers use
- ☐ Help student identify 1–2 reading goals and a plan of action to improve reading
- ☐ Support revision of ongoing reading goals

ORAL READING FLUENCY
Expression and Phrasing
- ☐ Model and teach reading in longer, meaningful phrases with appropriate expression
- ☐ Have student practice appropriate expression with familiar texts
- ☐ Teach student to recognize and emphasize key phrases and words
- ☐ Teach student to heed punctuation

Rate
- ☐ Provide materials and time for repeated readings and timed readings to increase reading rate
- ☐ Give opportunities for student to read lower-level and/or familiar texts at an appropriate rate

Accuracy: Word Analysis
- ☐ Support and reinforce self-corrections of miscues
- ☐ Model and support how to take words apart (e.g., onset and rime, syllables) to problem-solve unknown words
- ☐ Teach how to use word chunks and analogies to problem-solve unknown words
- ☐ Provide spelling activities and word sorts to help student recognize patterns in words

COMPREHENSION
Questioning/Prediction
- ☐ Provide opportunities for student to make and confirm predictions based on title, table of contents, and headings
- ☐ Model and support using background information to make meaningful predictions
- ☐ Model and teach student how to pose questions as a basis for predictions

Summary
- ☐ Share and identify characteristics of good summaries
- ☐ Model and co-construct written summaries of texts read aloud
- ☐ Model and support how to distinguish between more important and less important ideas and facts
- ☐ Model and support how to write a summary in one's own words
- ☐ Model and support how to use examples from the text
- ☐ Teach student how to use headings to organize a summary of an informational/nonfiction text
- ☐ Provide time for student to practice oral and written summaries

Literal Comprehension
- ☐ Show student how to use key words to identify specific information from the text
- ☐ Provide opportunities for student to answer and construct literal questions
- ☐ Model and support how to locate and use nonfiction text features (e.g., charts, graphs, maps, tables, headings, glossary, bold words, etc.)
- ☐ Teach student how to use and construct graphic organizers to keep track of key ideas and facts

Interpretation
- ☐ Teach and share examples of inferences
- ☐ Provide opportunities for student to support inferences with information or examples from the text
- ☐ Give student opportunities to respond to inference questions orally and in writing
- ☐ Model and support how to interpret nonfiction text features (e.g., how to read a chart or diagram)

Reflection
- ☐ Help student identify important information and/or key vocabulary in a variety of texts
- ☐ Demonstrate how to support opinion with details from the text

Metacognitive Awareness
- ☐ Model and teach comprehension strategies for nonfiction texts
- ☐ Provide opportunities for student to practice using a specific comprehension strategy (e.g., making connections, visualizing, etc.)
- ☐ Help student identify examples in a text where he or she used a specific strategy

OTHER

_____

_____

_____

Name _____   Date _____

Teacher _____   Grade _____

BEFORE READING

PREDICTION

What questions did you have as you were reading the first part of this text?

1. _____

_____

2. _____

_____

3. _____

_____

What do you think you will learn from reading the rest of this text?

1. _____

_____

2. _____

_____

3. _____

_____

Let your teacher know when you have completed this page.

AFTER READING

Summary

Write a summary of this book in your own words. Include the important ideas and facts from each section. You may use the book to help you write your summary.

_____

_____

_____

_____

_____

_____

_____

_____

_____

_____

_____

_____

_____

_____

_____

_____

_____

_____

LITERAL COMPREHENSION

List 3 facts about gray wolves.

Gray Wolves

1. _____

2. _____

3. _____

INTERPRETATION

Why do you think wolves are able to survive in the wild? _____

_____

_____

_____

_____

REFLECTION

What do you think is the most important thing about gray wolves? _____

_____

_____

_____

Tell why you think this is important. _____

_____

_____

_____

A Pack of Wolves

METACOGNITIVE AWARENESS

Check 1 strategy that you used to help you understand this text.

☐   I recalled what I know about the topic.

☐   I asked myself questions as I read.

☐   I made connections.

☐   I decided what was important to remember.

☐   I thought about the reasons why things happened.

☐   I pictured what was happening.

Give at least 2 specific examples from this book that show how you used this comprehension strategy.

_____

_____

_____

_____

_____

Reread what you have written to make sure your answers are how you want them to be before you hand in your booklet.

Developmental Reading Assessment®

K–3

Additional Blackline Masters for Program Administration:

- Student Assessment Form
- Fiction and Nonfiction Records
- Student Book Graph
- Focus for Instruction: Class Profile for Emergent Readers
- Focus for Instruction: Class Profile for Early Readers
- Focus for Instruction: Class Profile for Transitional Readers
- Focus for Instruction: Class Profile for Extending Readers
- Class Reporting Form
- Student Reading Survey

Developmental Reading Assessment® K–3 Student Assessment Form

Name

Assessment Date	Grade	DRA2 Text Level	F or NF	DRA2 Grade-Level Performance		
				Below	On	Above

Fiction and Nonfiction Records

DRA2, K–3, Fiction Texts

Date	Benchmark Assessment Book Title	DRA2 Text Level	Accuracy	Reading Engagement	Oral Reading Fluency	Printed Language Concepts	Comprehension

DRA2, K–3, Nonfiction Texts

Date	Benchmark Assessment Book Title	DRA2 Text Level	Accuracy	Reading Engagement	Oral Reading Fluency	Comprehension

DRA2, K–3, Student Book Graph

DRA2 Stage	Grade	DRA2 Level		Name
Extending	Third Grade	40	Advanced	
			Independent	
			Instructional	
		38	Advanced	
			Independent	
			Instructional	
		34	Advanced	
			Independent	
			Instructional	
		30	Advanced	
			Independent	
			Instructional	
	Second Grade	28	Advanced	
			Independent	
			Instructional	
Transitional		24	Advanced	
			Independent	
			Instructional	
		20	Advanced	
			Independent	
			Instructional	
		18	Advanced	
			Independent	
			Instructional	
	First Grade	16	Advanced	
			Independent	
			Instructional	
		14	Advanced	
			Independent	
			Instructional	
Early		12	Advanced	
			Independent	
			Developing	
		10	Advanced	
			Independent	
			Developing	
		8	Advanced	
			Independent	
			Developing	
		6	Advanced	
			Independent	
			Developing	
		4	Advanced	
			Independent	
			Developing	
Emergent	Kindergarten	3	Independent	
			Developing	
		2	Independent	
			Developing	
		1	Developing	
		A	Developing	
		Grade		Kindergarten	First	Second	Third
		Assessment Dates		

Advanced: Total score for Oral Reading Fluency <u>and</u> Comprehension must be within the Advanced range on the Continuum.
Independent: Total score for Oral Reading Fluency <u>and</u> Comprehension must be at least within the Independent range on the Continuum.
Instructional: Total score for either Oral Reading Fluency or Comprehension is within the Instructional range on the Continuum.

DRA2, *K–3*, Focus for Instruction: Class Profile for Emergent Readers

Levels A–3

Grade Level _____   Date _____

Names	Text Level	Reading Engagement			Oral Reading			Printed Language Concepts		
		Support Reading at Home	Favorite Book	Book-Handling Skills	Use of Cues	Monitoring/Self-Corrections	Accuracy	Directionality	One-to-One Correspondence	Letter/Word
1.										
2.										
3.										
4.										
5.										
6.										
7.										
8.										
9.										
10.										
11.										
12.										
13.										
14.										
15.										
16.										
17.										
18.										
19.										
20.										
21.										
22.										
23.										
24.										
25.										

Record students' names and check the areas selected as a focus for instruction.

Levels 4–12

Grade Level _____   Date _____

Names	Text Level	Reading Engagement		Oral Reading Fluency			Comprehension			
		Book Selection	Sustained Reading	Phrasing	Monitoring/Self-Corrections	Problem-Solving Unknown Words	Previewing	Retelling	Reflection	Making Connections
1.										
2.										
3.										
4.										
5.										
6.										
7.										
8.										
9.										
10.										
11.										
12.										
13.										
14.										
15.										
16.										
17.										
18.										
19.										
20.										
21.										
22.										
23.										
24.										
25.										

Record students' names and check the areas selected as a focus for instruction.

DRA2, K–3, Focus for Instruction: Class Profile for Transitional Readers

Levels 14–24

Grade Level _____   Date _____

Names	Text Level	Reading Engagement		Oral Reading Fluency			Comprehension					
		Book Selection	Sustained Reading	Expression and Phrasing	Rate	Accuracy: Word Analysis	Previewing/ Prediction	Retelling	Using Nonfiction Text Features	Reflection	Making Connections	Interpretation
1.												
2.												
3.												
4.												
5.												
6.												
7.												
8.												
9.												
10.												
11.												
12.												
13.												
14.												
15.												
16.												
17.												
18.												
19.												
20.												
21.												
22.												
23.												
24.												
25.												

Record students' names and check the areas selected as a focus for instruction. For students reading at Level 16, use *F* to indicate fiction and **NF** to indicate nonfiction next to the text level (e.g., 16F or 16NF).

DRA2, *K–3*, Focus for Instruction: Class Profile for Extending Readers

Levels 28–40

Grade Level _____

Date _____

Names	Text Level	Reading Engagement		Oral Reading Fluency			Comprehension						
		Wide Reading	Self-Assessment/ Goal Setting	Expression and Phrasing	Rate	Accuracy: Word Analysis	Use of Text Features	Nonfiction Text Features	Prediction	Summary	Literal Comprehension	Interpretation	Reflection
1.													
2.													
3.													
4.													
5.													
6.													
7.													
8.													
9.													
10.													
11.													
12.													
13.													
14.													
15.													
16.													
17.													
18.													
19.													
20.													
21.													
22.													
23.													
24.													
25.													

Record students' names and check the areas selected as a focus for instruction. For students reading at Levels 28 and 38, use *F* to indicate fiction and *NF* to indicate nonfiction next to the text level (e.g., 28F or 28NF). Place an asterisk after the text level if the student's score is below Independent.

DRA2, *K–3*, Class Reporting Form

Teacher _____ School _____ Grade _____ Date _____

Names	Text Level (F/NF)	Reading Engagement Score	Oral Reading Fluency Score	Printed Language Concepts/ Comprehension Score

Highlight the names of the students who are reading below the grade-level benchmark. For students reading Levels 28–40, place an asterisk after the text level if the Comprehension Score is below Independent.

Name _____   Date _____

Teacher _____   Grade _____

Complete the following sections to help you think about yourself as a reader.

Wide Reading

What books have you finished reading lately? You may use your record of books read.

1. _____

2. _____

3. _____

4. _____

5. _____

6. _____

7. _____

What are you reading at school now?

_____

_____

What are you reading at home now?

_____

_____

Self-Assessment and Goal Setting

What are 3 things you do well as a reader?

1. _____

_____

2. _____

_____

3. _____

_____

What are 3 things you would like to work on to become a better reader?

1. _____

_____

2. _____

_____

3. _____

_____

Teacher Notes